GENERAL RELATIVITY
AND COSMOLOGY

GENERAL RELATIVITY
AND COSMOLOGY

G. C. McVITTIE

O.B.E., Ph.D., M.A.

Professor of Astronomy
University of Illinois

1965

THE UNIVERSITY OF ILLINOIS PRESS

URBANA

First published 1956
Second edition 1965
Printed in Great Britain by
Butler & Tanner Ltd, Frome and London

Preface to the First Edition

The present volume originated in the various courses of lectures on relativity which I have delivered during the past ten years in the Universities of London, Harvard and Illinois. I have attempted to explore the possibilities of general relativity as a method in mathematical physics and astronomy and as a means of interpreting the data supplied by observation. This work therefore continues the tradition which was set by R. C. Tolman in his *Relativity, Thermodynamics and Cosmology* and developed by O. Heckmann in *Theorien der Kosmologie*. Investigations of a purely mathematical character, of which there are many in the field of general relativity, have therefore been omitted for the most part. The first five chapters contain an account of the basic principles of the theory and of its application to the gravitational field of the Sun. Readers who are chiefly interested in classical gas-dynamics will find in Chapters 6 and 7 a description of the way in which general relativity can help in the solution of the problems with which they are concerned. The subject of cosmology is treated in Chapters 8 and 9, and I have there endeavoured to throw the theoretical formulae into forms suitable for the numerical computation of the parameters they contain, as and when more complete observational data become available.

It remains for me to express my gratitude to Dr A. H. Taub for reading the manuscript and making many valuable suggestions and criticisms; to my colleagues at the Observatory, Dr Stanley P. Wyatt, Jr, and Dr M. H. Rogers, and to a graduate student, Mr Vernon Fowler, for checking the formulae in certain sections of the book; and to the Director and astronomers of the Mount Wilson and Palomar Observatories who so readily supplied me with data and described the observational programmes having cosmological bearing on which they were engaged or which they were planning. If errors and faults of exposition remain, it is not these friends and colleagues who gave so generously of their time and advice, but I alone who must bear the blame.

G. C. McVITTIE

University of Illinois Observatory,
Urbana, Ill.,
December 1954

Preface to the Second Edition

In preparing the second edition of this book, I have taken the opportunity to correct misprints and to make some minor re-arrangements in the contents of the first seven chapters. Chapter 5 has also been modified to take account of the laboratory verification of the gravitational displacement of spectral lines by means of the Mössbauer effect.

The last two chapters, on cosmology, have been entirely rewritten. This step was necessitated by the advances in observation largely produced by the development of radio astronomy. As a result, the approximate methods employed in the first edition are no longer entirely adequate though, of course, they can still be used to advantage on occasion. Exact formulae have therefore been developed in which the red-shift is employed as the parametric variable. The treatment has, I believe, gained in simplicity by this device. Moreover, if approximations in terms of the red-shift are desired, they are easily obtained from the exact formulae. An appendix has also been added which contains the essential formulae for those models of the universe whose properties are describable in terms of the elementary mathematical functions.

I would like to express my deep gratitude to the John Simon Guggenheim Memorial Foundation whose generous grant of a Fellowship gave me the time, free of other duties, in which to develop the theory contained in the new chapters on cosmology.

G. C. McVITTIE

University of Illinois Observatory,
  Urbana, Ill.,
    September 1964

Contents

GENERAL RELATIVITY
AND COSMOLOGY

CHAPTER 1

Introduction

1.1. Classical, Quantum and Relativity Mechanics

Today, in the middle of the twentieth century, three systems of mechanics are simultaneously in use: the classical, tracing its origin to Newton and now some two hundred and seventy years old; quantum mechanics, which dates from about 1925; and the theories of special and general relativity propounded by Einstein[1] in 1905 and in 1916 respectively. The historical development of the first two systems has been to a great extent similar. The successors of Newton gradually worked out the consequences of his three Laws of Motion by applying them to the elucidation of concrete physical situations; the motions of the planets were investigated theoretically to a greater and greater degree of accuracy; the theory of the motion of a rigid body was developed and applied to the problem of the rotation of the earth; and as new kinds of physical problems presented themselves, so new branches of classical mechanics (hydrodynamics, elasticity theory, etc.) were developed. It was not until this vast examination had taken place, and classical theory had been thoroughly tested as a tool in physics and astronomy, that any need to modify its basic postulates arose. And this did not happen until in the latter half of the nineteenth century optical experiments suggested that, when speeds comparable with that of light were in question, the Newtonian tool had lost its edge. A similar, though far more rapid, development characterized quantum mechanics. Its originators themselves, Schroedinger, Dirac, Heisenberg, and others, used it to investigate the motion, if such it can be called, of the electron in the hydrogen atom and their followers showed how quantum mechanics could elucidate the phenomena manifested by atoms of more complex structure. Now that the atomic nucleus has become a chief concern of physicists, it may well be that basic changes in the theory must be made; but if this is so, the possibility has arisen through, and as a consequence of, continued use of the theory in specific physical problems. Special relativity has also largely followed a development of this kind and, as its field of application has come to lie more and more in atomic physics, it has tended to drift away from general relativity to which at first sight it is so closely related.

When the history of general relativity is considered, however, a striking departure from precedent is noticed because in the fifty years that have

1

elapsed since its first enunciation by Einstein, the theory has been used to attack two problems only, both astronomical. The gravitational field of the Sun quickly yielded to treatment, leading to the elucidation of an outstanding discrepancy in the Newtonian theory of the motion of the perihelion of the planet Mercury, and to the phenomenon of the bending of light rays. Later, in the 1930's, came the second application, this time to the system of the galaxies considered as a whole, the so-called expanding universe theory. Apart from these instances, applications of general relativity are few indeed, a state of affairs that may perhaps be accounted for by its extreme mathematical complexity; investigators have found specific problems mathematically difficult and have soon turned away in discouragement. But this is not a sufficient explanation since mathematical intractability is not the perquisite of general relativity alone among the branches of mathematical physics. A more cogent reason is probably to be found in the diversion of effort produced by the search for a unified field theory of gravitation and electromagnetism[2] during which the 1916 theory has been repeatedly torn up by the roots and replaced by a formulation of kindred type. But each new variant has soon been discarded as unsatisfactory, even by its author, and the attempt at a solution from first principles has begun once more. Briefly, it has been argued that the concept of the field plays an important role in both classical gravitational, and classical electromagnetic, theory and since the four-dimensional space-times of the 1916 theory provide a more complete picture of the gravitational field than did Newton's scheme, therefore some analogous device should serve to describe both kinds of field. The argument was a strong one up to the time of the rise of quantum mechanics and the somewhat later 'discovery' of the neutron. Continuity is inherent in unified field theories, but quantum mechanics has shown that in the realm of atomic physics where electrical forces play the dominant role discontinuity is the fundamental characteristic, an observation itself constituting a warning against using the method of unified field theory in this context. Experimentally, moreover, a qualitative difference exists between gravitation and electromagnetism because there is no evidence that it is possible so to alter the properties of matter that a body will move in a gravitational field as if the field were absent. Yet, on the other hand, a body can be made electrically neutral and its motion is then unaffected by an electromagnetic field. So long, however, as matter was regarded as composed solely of protons and electrons, it could be argued that, ultimately at least, matter could not escape the influence of an electromagnetic field, but the validity of this argument was destroyed as soon as an electrically neutral ultimate particle – the neutron – had to be postulated. Of more importance perhaps is the fact that no unified field theory has up to now elucidated any phenomena nor suggested any new significant experiments.

It is true that in the 1916 theory – general relativity properly so called –

electromagnetism can be included in a half-hearted way, since the gravitational effect of electromagnetic energy can be incorporated into the scheme. But the generalized Maxwell's equations lie outside the system of field-equations and have to be postulated *ad hoc*. And again, no elucidation of phenomena has been achieved by this means. It is therefore reasonable to deduce from the experience of the past fifty years that the method of general relativity has nothing significant to say in the realm of electromagnetism where it would appear that quantum mechanics is the appropriate weapon. Instead, general relativity is best regarded as a generalization and, at the same time, an amalgamation, of Newtonian gravitation and hydrodynamics and therefore as a theory of mechanics dealing with the phenomena manifested by matter in bulk, not as a small-scale theory able to throw light on atomic phenomena.

1.2. The Nature of Scientific Law

In whichever of the three systems of mechanics a student's interest may lie, he must inevitably at some point come to grips with philosophical problems and be forced to answer as best he can such questions as: What is the nature of scientific knowledge? Are its conclusions certain and absolute fragments of a final truth, or are they inevitably temporary and evanescent constructs? An individual scientist may perhaps believe that he pursues his work without considering philosophical questions of this kind, but this belief is illusory, and arises simply because the scientist has unconsciously acquired some particular metaphysical outlook. Specific answers to philosophical questions are thus unconsciously supplied, the scientist regarding them as obvious and as incapable of being other than he has stated them to be. Though this philosophical method may lead to much self-confidence, it has its disadvantages, one of which will probably be that every new theory of mechanics takes on the appearance of a 'revolution in physics' though it is merely the scientist's philosophical prejudices, and not physics, that are being revolutionized. A more satisfactory outlook can be achieved by examining our customary modes of thought until we become aware of our own philosophical predilections. Whether these turn out to be profound or superficial is, in a sense, of minor consequence; the essence of the matter is that we should be aware of holding them.

The reader must therefore be apprised of the author's philosophical attitude, which must necessarily colour his work. A starting-point may be found in the proposition that sense-data, the data provided by observation and experiment, are alone given in the first instance. I know that I see the colour green, a spectral line, a pin-point of light in the sky which I call a star. In addition to such visual perceptions, there are auditory, tactual and other kinds, all of which together form an inchoate and disorderly conglomeration. As often as not, the first reaction of the human mind to this flood of sense-data is that which is expressed by the words 'alarm' or 'confusion': the child cries with fear when its senses are assailed by the visual, auditory and tactual experiences it suffers if it is caught out of doors in a thunderstorm. But the next reaction of the human mind is to make a rational picture of the sense-data that pour in on it from all sides, to arrange them in an orderly fashion, in short, to understand them. This is achieved by a process of selecting some, and excluding others, from amongst groups of sense-data all of which might be thought at first sight to be equally relevant. Consider, for example, the proposition 'The Sun rises above the horizon every morning', which makes sense of the changes from darkness to light that, in a general way, occur daily. To those who have lived in northern latitudes, this proposition is reached by excluding many very relevant experiences that contradict it. If Londoners wake up on a certain day and experience the sense-datum expressed by the statement 'there is a fog', it is certainly not the case that they also experience the sense-datum expressed by 'the Sun has risen above the horizon'. For all that their observations tell them, the Sun may have dissolved into nothing during the night, never to appear again. Indeed, the proposition is valid only in so far as the sense-data of scientists in foggy or cloudy regions, or in the Arctic circle in midwinter, are excluded from consideration. The value of the proposition lies in the fact that it co-ordinates and interprets a far larger group of sense-data than those associated with fog or Arctic darkness which, though obviously connected with the change from night into day on certain occasions, are excluded in establishing it.

A commonly held view of the end-result of the study of sense-data is that they reveal the existence of an External World called Nature whose properties are *rational* and are also *independent* of the scientific observer. The observer is engaged in discovering these properties through the indications given to him by his sense-data. For example, he tries to discover whether there are, or are not, entities called electrons, whether there is, or is not, an inverse square law of gravitation, and so on. More generally, the Laws of Nature are thought of as the principles on which this rational External World works. As an illustration of the independence of the observer and the properties of the External World, it is presumed that the proposition already given about the rising of the Sun would still be true even if human beings were insensitive to radiations of all kinds such as X-rays, light, heat, radio-waves and the rest. In this view of science the notions of 'cause and effect', of 'proof', of 'discovery' and of 'truth and falsehood' are employed. Thus it would be said that Newton *discovered* the inverse square law of gravitation, that Einstein *proved* that he was *wrong* and *discovered* that the *cause* of gravitation was the curvature of space. If, indeed, science is engaged in discovering the properties of an independently existing rational External World, then it must be admitted that the inquiry has been singularly unsuccessful. There are in fact many features of this World, which the scientists have purported to discover during the past, that have had to be modified or abandoned. The cycle and epicycle orbits of the planets, the phlogiston and caloric in the theory of combustion, the aether of the nineteenth century, the notion that matter was exclusively constituted of protons and electrons, to name a few instances, have all had their day and gone by the board. Even Newton's three Laws of Motion that for so long seemed to be the most certain and unalterable features of the External World have been replaced. The particular set of properties of the External World which, on this view, we believe ourselves to have discovered today, is in no better case, in spite of the fact that we attach to them the adjective 'modern'. We believe in these properties for precisely the same kind of reason that our predecessors believed in the features which they thought they had 'discovered', namely, because we need them in order to interpret the sense-data that are available to us at the present moment. They serve the purpose of ranging the sense-data into neat portmanteaux of theory, of rationalizing the confusion with which we are presented. In short, if the doctrine of a rational External World is accepted, past experience forces us to conclude that science is everlastingly in error, a Kepler, a Newton or an Einstein periodically 'proving' that his predecessors were mistaken.

A variant of this view is the Approximation Theory of the nature of scientific inquiry, the synthesis of sense-data achieved by each successive generation of scientists being now regarded as a new and better approximation to a final picture. But the term approximation is legitimately used only when it is known beforehand that the presumed goal exists. It is indeed possible to speak of an approximation to the sum of a convergent series because an independent proof can be established for the existence of the sum, but if the series is divergent, an approximation to its sum is meaningless. The Approximation Theory of science presupposes that a final and complete picture is attainable, a picture that presumably shares the rational character possessed by any scientific scheme, and thus the rational External World has again been introduced, though by the back door.

A preferable alternative to the doctrine of the rational External World is to regard science as a method of correlating sense-data, the standpoint of Herbert Dingle[3], amongst other philosophers of science. On this view, the corpus of sense-data may, or may not, form a rational whole, but the human mind by selecting classes of data succeeds in grouping them into rational systems. For example, Newtonian mechanics and gravitation theory groups into one rational system the multifarious phenomena of planetary motions, and into this same system there is integrated, surprisingly enough, the apparently quite independent phenomenon of the motion of the apple falling in Newton's garden. A logically different system of correlation – the quantum theory – serves to connect into another rational whole the sense-data we call atomic phenomena. Unobservables such as light, atoms, electromagnetic and gravitational fields, etc., are not constituents of an independently existing rational External World: they are but concepts useful in the manufacture of the systems of correlation. The properties of the unobservables are alterable as occasion demands; for example, in order to interpret certain sense-data, light is conceived of as a stream of particles; to interpret another group of data, it is thought of as a wave. The notions of truth and falsehood, of cause and effect, of discovery and explanation may now either be discarded or looked upon as arbitrary: the only important question is: How can we construct a rational scheme of thought – a theory – which shall include within its grasp as many apparently disconnected sense-data as possible? The vast correlation of astronomical and mechanical phenomena achieved by Newton did not, as it happens, include one phenomenon, the motion of the perihelion of the planet Mercury, which seems to belong to the same class. But the fact that this one phenomenon somehow escaped from the Newtonian net was not, and still is not, a reason for declaring that the whole structure is false. Indeed, the theoretical engineer can point to much evidence to the contrary, for most of our machines are constructed on strictly Newtonian principles. In other words, there is an immense range of mechanical phenomena, both in the engineering laboratory and in astronomy, which are correlated and interpreted to the nth place of decimals by Newton's theory of motion. On the other hand, Einstein's theory of general relativity is a different method of correlating phenomena: it can embrace both ordinary planetary motions *and* the phenomenon of the motion of the perihelion of Mercury. But whether it can also embrace the phenomena associated with the idea of rotation – the tides, for example – which presented little difficulty to Newtonian theory, is still an unsolved problem.

One consequence of this definition of a scientific theory is that there may well be two or more theories which adequately interpret a particular phenomenon. Thus, for example, the phenomenon of aberration, by which a star traces out a small closed path on the celestial sphere during each year, may equally well be interpreted in terms of Newtonian theory and in terms of Einstein's. Hence it cannot be said that there is a crucial experiment by which a theory stands or falls: it is not one experiment that makes a good theory but the wide scope of the experimental results which it can interconnect. Nor can a theory be true or false: it is in any case relevant to a highly selected group of data – usually with the recalcitrant ones ignored – and the theory can at best be said to be adequate or inadequate as a means of intercorrelating the members of the group.

On this view of science the Laws of Nature are simply the fundamental postulates lying at the base of a theory and are to be regarded as free creations of the human mind. These creations must be in agreement with observation, and the better they are the more observations they will serve to interpret and the more new kinds of observation they will suggest for investigation. But they are not unalterable: as data accumulate it may well happen that some particular scheme of Laws becomes inadequate and has to be abandoned in favour of a new set. This has occurred in the past and there is no guarantee that it will not occur again in the future. The Laws of Nature as enunciated in general relativity cannot therefore be defended by arguments based on logical simplicity or on mathematical elegance, nor by pointing to one or two crucial experiments, nor by speculations woven round the differential equations expressing the Laws. On the contrary, the criterion of validity is that of adequacy which can be discovered only by successively applying the Laws to as many concrete physical situations as the mathematical ability of the investigator permits. By this means the range of physical phenomena lying within the scope of the theory is revealed and, if eventually it has to be modified, modifications can be attempted with a full knowledge of its achievements.

1.3. Some Preliminary Remarks

If the fundamental laws of mechanics are in the main creations of the human mind, their *a priori* justification is of less importance than the careful tracing out of their implications and the comparison of the latter with experience. Therefore in the following pages an elaborate inductive derivation of the basic equations of general relativity is not attempted, analogy with Newtonian theory taking its place. However, in order to show how the analogies arise, the tensor calculus and certain results in the differential geometry of multi-dimensional manifolds are required. In its exact form general relativity will be applied to the gravitational field of the Sun and to the cosmological problem. But when the general relativity is regarded as a tool in mathematical physics, an approximate form of the theory may be equally useful so long as fruitful results are obtained. Under this aspect general relativity provides a method of reaching those solutions of the equations of classical gas-dynamics corresponding to motions under the control of the pressure-gradient and of the gravitational self-attraction of the gas.

It will be taken as axiomatic throughout the book that matter in bulk possesses a property called gravitation, and that where this attribute of matter is present in a physical situation some system of material bodies responsible for the gravitational effects must also be identifiable. To say instead that gravitation is a manifestation of the curvature of four-dimensional geometrical manifolds is to account for a mystery by means of an enigma and to endow with physical significance one of the mathematical functions useful in the description of the physical situation. Similarly, the gravitational field, whether in Newton's or in Einstein's theory, is regarded as a concept and, powerful as it may be, nothing more than an aid in the calculations that have to be performed. Admittedly, this interpretation is widely different from Einstein's, who has written, 'The field manifests itself in the motion of bodies', as if the field were the ultimate reality and the moving bodies casual accidents. It is, however, bodies, whether in motion or in equilibrium, that are the subject of observational exploration, and the notion of the field has been invented in order to interpret the phenomena which they display.

Many presentations of general relativity[4] make use of certain abstract units of mass, length and time in terms of which the constant of gravitation, G, and the velocity of light, c, are both assigned the value 1. This procedure has the advantage that the formulae of the theory can be written in the most compact form, but its disadvantages become apparent as soon as approximations have to be performed or expansions in powers of G/c^2 or of $1/c^2$ undertaken. It has indeed been well said by Harold Jeffreys[5] that an investigator undoubtedly uses the ordinary units of mass, length and time in his private calculations, and then, by converting his results to abstract units, succeeds in confusing the reader. Therefore the C.G.S. system will be employed throughout this book, except that certain multiples or sub-multiples of the centimetre, such as the parsec or the Ångström unit, may be introduced as occasion demands.

The two final chapters are devoted to the cosmology of general relativity and no systematic attempt is made to describe other cosmological theories[6] that are to be found in the literature. An exception is made with regard to the steady-state theory, however, in that a number of comparisons between general relativity and this theory are included. The emphasis throughout is on observational cosmology and, in thus comparing the predictions of theory with the data of observation, I have found it necessary to use a criterion of admissibility with respect to these data. I have been led to think that such a step is necessary by noticing that the temptation to substitute logic for observation is peculiarly hard to resist in astronomy and especially so in cosmology. This is because the relevant data are few in number and hard to come by. One alternative therefore is to supplement what is directly observed by additional items of information based on the *absence* of detectable phenomena. An extreme example will make this point clear. There are no known observations which reveal directly that the star Arcturus has a planet revolving around it. But calculations show that, if the planet had a mass less than a certain amount, none of the instruments available to astronomers could reveal its presence because measurements of infinite accuracy cannot be made. Therefore it is conceptually possible to assume that a planet of relatively small mass revolves about Arcturus since phenomena contradicting this assumption have not been detected. In contrast to this procedure, the method which will be adopted in this book is to lay emphasis on measurements which are positive and to treat with considerable reserve conclusions that depend on the absence of observable effects. In the Arcturus example, it would be said that the star had no planet so long as observation failed to reveal a phenomenon that could be attributed to the presence of such a body. This point of view is sometimes criticized on the ground that it assumes that cosmological data are of high accuracy. The criticism would be valid if the investigator claimed that he had arrived at a final solution of the problem of the nature of the universe by using them. Clearly this is an unjustified claim: the problem is solved in an interim fashion only and to the extent that it reveals a certain group of possible answers. Attempts to narrow down the list of alternatives, or to produce a unique model of the universe, by an appeal to conclusions based on the absence of phenomena will be treated as unacceptable. In this way it is possible to discover how much can be found out about the universe through measurements that yield non-null results rather than by the consideration of logical possibilities which might conceivably be the case.

CHAPTER 2

The Tensor Calculus and Riemannian Geometry

2.1. Manifold of Points. Tensors

The mathematical technique known as the tensor calculus[1] has many applications in mathematical physics, where, however, its use can often be avoided. But in relativity theory it is as essential a tool as is the ordinary calculus in Newtonian mechanics and no real understanding of the theory is possible without its aid. The fundamental notion is that of a geometrical point which is defined, as in elementary analytical geometry, by means of its coordinates. Thus in the geometry of the Euclidean plane a point is specified by giving its two Cartesian coordinates (X, Y) or its polar coordinates (r, θ). All the points which together constitute the plane are said to form a *two-dimensional manifold* of points, the number of dimensions of the manifold being equal to the number of independent coordinates required to specify a point in it. Ordinary three-dimensional Euclidean space forms a three-dimensional manifold of points, each point requiring three coordinates to specify it completely. Generalizing these ideas, an *n-dimensional manifold* of points is one for which n independent *real* numbers $(x^1, x^2, x^3, \ldots, x^n)$ are required to specify every point completely. These n numbers are denoted collectively by (x) and are called the coordinates of the point. The manifold is, for the moment, assumed to have no structure except that it is continuous in the sense that, in the neighbourhood of every point (x), there are other points whose coordinates differ infinitesimally from those of (x). Such a neighbouring point has coordinates $(x + dx)$, the small quantities $(dx^1, dx^2, dx^3, \ldots, dx^n)$ being called the differentials of the coordinates of (x).

The coordinates of a point are essentially a means of describing the point that is invented by the investigator. This description may be changed and one of the aims of the tensor calculus is to discover what consequential changes are produced by a simultaneous alteration of the coordinates of all the points of the manifold. The operation by which the coordinates (x) of every point in the manifold are altered to (x') is called a *coordinate transformation*, and two simple examples may be drawn from ordinary analytical geometry. In the two-dimensional manifold of the Euclidean plane, the trans-

10

formation from Cartesian coordinates $X = x^1$, $Y = x^2$ to polar coordinates $r = x'^1$, $\theta = x'^2$ is given by the equations

$$x^1 = x'^1 \cos x'^2, \qquad x^2 = x'^1 \sin x'^2, \tag{2.101}$$

whilst in the three-dimensional manifold of Euclidean space, the transformation from Cartesian coordinates $X = x^1$, $Y = x^2$, $Z = x^3$ to spherical-polar coordinates $r = x'^1$, $\theta = x'^2$, $\phi = x'^3$ is

$$\left.\begin{aligned}
x^1 &= x'^1 \sin x'^2 \cos x'^3, \\
x^2 &= x'^1 \sin x'^2 \sin x'^3, \\
x^3 &= x'^1 \cos x'^2.
\end{aligned}\right\} \tag{2.102}$$

These two sets of equations have the property of being soluble for the (x') in terms of the (x); for example, in the two-dimensional case, the equations (2.101) give

$$x'^1 = \{(x^1)^2 + (x^2)^2\}^{\frac{1}{2}},$$
$$x'^2 = \tan^{-1}(x^2/x^1),$$

with similar, but more complicated, relations for (2.102). In an n-dimensional manifold, a coordinate-transformation is expressed by n equations

$$x'^\lambda = f^\lambda(x^1, x^2, x^3, \ldots, x^n), \qquad (\lambda = 1, 2, 3, \ldots, n), \tag{2.103}$$

where the functions f^λ are soluble so that

$$x^\lambda = g^\lambda(x'^1, x'^2, x'^3, \ldots x'^n). \tag{2.104}$$

If the differentials of the equations (2.103) are taken, we have

$$dx'^\lambda = \sum_{\mu=1}^{n} \frac{\partial f^\lambda}{\partial x^\mu} dx^\mu = \sum_{\mu=1}^{n} \frac{\partial x'^\lambda}{\partial x^\mu} dx^\mu, \tag{2.105}$$

formulae that give the transformation of the differentials when the coordinates are altered. It is, however, not only the coordinates and their differentials that can be regarded as undergoing a change; for it is possible to imagine that certain functions, or groups of functions, of the coordinates have been defined at each point (x) and these also will be modified. In particular, suppose that the function $F(x)$ suffers no change of *value*—though its formal mathematical expression may be altered – when the coordinates are transformed by (2.103); then F will be said to be a *scalar* or a *tensor of rank zero*. An obvious example, drawn from the Euclidean geometry of three-dimensions, is $F(r)$ where $r^2 = X^2 + Y^2 + Z^2$, the transformations of the Cartesian coordinates being restricted to those corresponding to rotations of the coordinate-axes about the origin. Consider now a set of n functions $(V^1, V^2, V^3, \ldots V^n)$, each V^λ being a known function of the (x), and let the transformation (2.103) be performed on the coordinates. Then these n functions are said to be the components of a *contravariant vector*, or of a *contravariant tensor of rank one*, if they transform by the same rule as do the differentials, i.e. if the transformed functions V'^{λ} are connected with the V^{μ} by

$$V'^{\lambda} = \sum_{\mu=1}^{n} \frac{\partial x'^{\lambda}}{\partial x^{\mu}} V^{\mu}, \qquad (\lambda = 1, 2, 3, \ldots, n). \qquad (2.106)$$

From this definition it obviously follows that the differentials (dx) are themselves the components of a contravariant tensor of rank one. Another kind of vector whose components are $(U_1, U_2, U_3, \ldots, U_n)$ is called covariant (*covariant tensor of rank one*) if it transforms according to the law

$$U'_{\lambda} = \sum_{\mu=1}^{n} \frac{\partial x^{\mu}}{\partial x'^{\lambda}} U_{\mu}, \qquad (\lambda = 1, 2, 3, \ldots, n). \qquad (2.107)$$

The relationship between covariant and contravariant vectors depends on a theorem which states that the sum of products $\sum_{\lambda=1}^{n} V^{\lambda} U_{\lambda}$ is always a scalar, whatever pair of vectors be considered. To prove this, we have

$$\sum_{\mu=1}^{n} V'^{\mu} U'_{\mu} = \sum_{\mu=1}^{n} \left(\sum_{\lambda=1}^{n} \frac{\partial x'^{\mu}}{\partial x^{\lambda}} V^{\lambda} \right) \left(\sum_{\nu=1}^{n} \frac{\partial x^{\nu}}{\partial x'^{\mu}} U_{\nu} \right)$$

$$= \sum_{\lambda=1}^{n} \sum_{\nu=1}^{n} \frac{\partial x^{\nu}}{\partial x^{\lambda}} V^{\lambda} U_{\nu}.$$

But the coordinates x^{ν}, x^{λ} are independent and therefore

$$\frac{\partial x^{\nu}}{\partial x^{\lambda}} = \left\{ \begin{matrix} 0 \text{ if } \nu \neq \lambda, \\ 1 \text{ if } \nu = \lambda. \end{matrix} \right\}. \qquad (2.108)$$

From this it follows that

$$\sum_{\mu=1}^{n} V'^{\mu} U'_{\mu} = \sum_{\lambda=1}^{n} V^{\lambda} U_{\lambda},$$

so that the value of the sum of products is unaltered by the coordinate-transformation and is therefore a scalar. The sum of products of corresponding components of a covariant and a contravariant vector is called the *inner product* of the two vectors.

A noteworthy feature of the preceding formulae is that any term in which an index occurs twice, once in the 'upper', or contravariant, and once in the 'lower', or covariant position, is invariably prefixed by a summation sign covering the values 1 to n of the repeated index. This is illustrated by the index μ in formulae (2.105), (2.106) and (2.107). For the sake of brevity it is therefore customary to omit the summation signs in such cases and to introduce the *summation convention* which consists in asserting that the double presence of an index in a term is to imply summation of that term over all values of 1 to n of the index. Thus, for example, formulae (2.106), (2.107) will be written

$$V'^{\lambda} = \frac{\partial x'^{\lambda}}{\partial x^{\mu}} V^{\mu}, \qquad U'_{\lambda} = \frac{\partial x^{\mu}}{\partial x'^{\lambda}} U_{\mu}.$$

The definitions of scalars and vectors which have been given depend essentially on the laws of transformation of the functions of the coordinates involved. It is not difficult to extend this notion to entities that have laws of transformation similar to, but more complicated than, those of scalars or vectors. Consider for instance the n^2 functions of the coordinates, $T^{\mu\nu}$, $(\mu, \nu = 1, 2, 3, \ldots, n)$ whose law of transformation is

$$T'^{\mu\nu} = \frac{\partial x'^{\mu}}{\partial x^{\alpha}} \frac{\partial x'^{\nu}}{\partial x^{\beta}} T^{\alpha\beta}, \qquad (\mu, \nu = 1, 2, 3, \ldots, n). \tag{2.109}$$

These n^2 functions $T^{\mu\nu}$ are said to form a *contravariant tensor of rank two*, an individual function $T^{\mu\nu}$ being called a component of the tensor. Comparing (2.109) and (2.106), it is evident that the law of transformation of a contravariant vector has been, in a sense, duplicated, but the reader must not jump to the (erroneous) conclusion that every contravariant tensor of rank two can be expressed as a combination of contravariant vectors. Again, by analogy with (2.107), the n^2 functions of the coordinates $K_{\mu\nu}$, $(\mu, \nu = 1, 2, 3, \ldots, n)$ with the transformation law

$$K'_{\mu\nu} = \frac{\partial x^{\alpha}}{\partial x'^{\mu}} \frac{\partial x^{\beta}}{\partial x'^{\nu}} K_{\alpha\beta}, \tag{2.110}$$

together form a *covariant tensor of rank two*. Finally, it is possible to define n^2 functions of the coordinates P^{μ}_{ν}, $(\mu, \nu = 1, 2, 3, \ldots, n)$ which have a law of transformation that partakes partly of the contravariant, and partly of the covariant, character, viz.

$$P'^{\mu}_{\nu} = \frac{\partial x'^{\mu}}{\partial x^{\alpha}} \frac{\partial x^{\beta}}{\partial x'^{\nu}} P^{\alpha}_{\beta}. \tag{2.111}$$

These n^2 functions are said to form a *mixed tensor of rank two*.

The rank of a tensor indicates only the number of its indices per component, not the covariant or contravariant character of these indices. It is possible to define tensors of rank higher than the second by the rule that each contravariant index is associated with a law of transformation similar to that of a contravariant vector, and that a covariant index follows the rule of transformation of a covariant vector. Thus the n^4 functions of the coordinates, $R^{\rho}_{\lambda\mu\nu}$, together form a tensor of rank four with three covariant indices and one contravariant index. The law of transformation is here

$$R'^{\rho}_{\lambda\mu\nu} = \frac{\partial x'^{\rho}}{\partial x^{\alpha}} \frac{\partial x^{\beta}}{\partial x'^{\lambda}} \frac{\partial x^{\gamma}}{\partial x'^{\mu}} \frac{\partial x^{\delta}}{\partial x'^{\nu}} R^{\alpha}_{\beta\gamma\delta}.$$

It is customary to denote a vector or a tensor by a single one of its components, so that, for example, the tensor whose law of transformation is (2.109) will be referred to as 'the tensor $T^{\mu\nu}$'.

Inspection of the laws of transformation of tensors shows that, if a tensor is a *null-tensor*, i.e. if it has all its components equal to zero in one coordinate-system, its components will all be zero in any other coordinate-system. It is therefore impossible to destroy the null character of a tensor by simply changing the coordinate-system.

There are operations that can be performed on tensors through which a given tensor gives rise to other tensors. One such operation is that of *contraction* which produces from a given tensor of rank λ ($\lambda \geq 2$), a new tensor of rank $\lambda - 2$. A particular covariant and a particular contravariant index of the tensor having been selected, all the components for which these two indices have equal numerical values are summed. The result is a component of a new tensor called the contracted form of the original one. For example, suppose that the given tensor is the fourth rank tensor $R^{\rho}_{\lambda\mu\nu}$, and suppose that the contravariant index ρ and the third covariant index ν are selected for the contraction operation. The contracted form is

$$R_{\lambda\mu} = R^{\rho}_{\lambda\mu\rho}$$

and the verification that $R_{\lambda\mu}$ is indeed a covariant tensor of rank two follows thus: Transforming the coordinate-system,

$$R'_{\lambda\mu} = R'^{\rho}_{\lambda\mu\rho} = \frac{\partial x'^{\rho}}{\partial x^{\alpha}} \frac{\partial x^{\beta}}{\partial x'^{\lambda}} \frac{\partial x^{\gamma}}{\partial x'^{\mu}} \frac{\partial x^{\delta}}{\partial x'^{\rho}} R^{\alpha}_{\beta\gamma\delta},$$

and therefore by (2.108),

$$R'_{\lambda\mu} = \frac{\partial x^{\beta}}{\partial x'^{\lambda}} \frac{\partial x^{\gamma}}{\partial x'^{\mu}} R_{\beta\gamma},$$

which shows that the functions $R_{\lambda\mu}$ have the transformation law (2.110) and hence are the components of a covariant tensor of rank two. The contraction operation can be applied to $R^{\rho}_{\lambda\mu\nu}$ in other ways, for instance, by selecting the index ρ and the second covariant index μ. The result is a new contracted tensor

$$S_{\lambda\nu} = R^{\rho}_{\lambda\rho\nu}$$

and it is not the case, in general, that $R_{\lambda\mu} = S_{\lambda\mu}$.

If the contraction operation is applied to a mixed tensor of rank two, say T^{λ}_{μ}, the result is a tensor of rank zero, i.e. a scalar. Thus to every mixed tensor of rank two there is associated a unique scalar obtained by contraction.

Another operation which can be performed on two tensors is that of forming their *inner product*; one of the tensors must have at least one contravariant, and the other at least one covariant, index. Components with the same numerical values of the two indices are multiplied together and the sum of all such products taken. The result is the component of a tensor with rank two lower than the combined ranks of the original tensors. For example, let the tensors be $T^{\lambda\mu}$ and $S^{\alpha}_{\beta\gamma}$, whose combined ranks are five; then four inner product tensors can be formed from them, viz. $T^{\lambda\mu}S^{\alpha}_{\lambda\gamma}$, $T^{\lambda\mu}S^{\alpha}_{\beta\lambda}$, $T^{\lambda\mu}S^{\alpha}_{\mu\gamma}$, and $T^{\lambda\mu}S^{\alpha}_{\beta\mu}$, each of these tensors being of rank three. To show that these inner products are indeed tensors, consider the transformation law of $T'^{\lambda\mu}S'^{\alpha}_{\lambda\gamma}$, for example; it is

$$T'^{\lambda\mu}S'^{\alpha}_{\lambda\gamma} = \frac{\partial x'^{\lambda}}{\partial x^{\rho}}\frac{\partial x'^{\mu}}{\partial x^{\sigma}}\frac{\partial x'^{\alpha}}{\partial x^{\tau}}\frac{\partial x^{\eta}}{\partial x'^{\lambda}}\frac{\partial x^{\zeta}}{\partial x'^{\gamma}}T^{\rho\sigma}S^{\tau}_{\eta\zeta}$$

$$= \frac{\partial x'^{\mu}}{\partial x^{\sigma}}\frac{\partial x'^{\alpha}}{\partial x^{\tau}}\frac{\partial x^{\zeta}}{\partial x'^{\gamma}}T^{\rho\sigma}S^{\tau}_{\rho\zeta},$$

which is the transformation law of a tensor of rank three with two contravariant and one covariant index. Thus the operations of contraction and of forming inner products have the effect of suppressing two of the indices, one contravariant and one covariant, of the symbols with which we start.

The process of forming inner products is useful in determining the tensor character of a set of functions of the coordinates by means of the *quotient theorem*, which states:

Any set of functions of the coordinates whose inner product with an arbitrary covariant (or contravariant) vector is a tensor, are themselves the components of a tensor.

The proof of this theorem is sufficiently illustrated by applying it to a set of n^2 functions that may be denoted by $T(\lambda\mu)$, $(\lambda, \mu = 1, 2, 3, \ldots, n)$. Suppose that it is known that the inner product $\sum\limits_{\lambda=1}^{n} U_{\lambda}T(\lambda\mu)$ of these functions with an arbitrary covariant vector U_{λ} always gives a contravariant vector V^{μ}. When the coordinates are transformed

$$\sum_{\lambda=1}^{n} U'_{\lambda}T'(\lambda\mu) = V'^{\mu} = \frac{\partial x'^{\mu}}{\partial x^{\nu}}V^{\nu}$$

$$= \sum_{\nu=1}^{n}\frac{\partial x'^{\mu}}{\partial x^{\nu}}\left\{\sum_{\lambda=1}^{n} U_{\lambda}T(\lambda\nu)\right\}.$$

But if primed and unprimed symbols are interchanged in (2.107), it follows that

$$U_{\lambda} = \frac{\partial x'^{\rho}}{\partial x^{\lambda}}U'_{\rho}$$

and therefore

$$\sum_{\lambda=1}^{n} U'_{\lambda}T'(\lambda\mu) = \sum_{\nu=1}^{n}\frac{\partial x'^{\mu}}{\partial x^{\nu}}\left\{\sum_{\lambda=1}^{n}\frac{\partial x'^{\rho}}{\partial x^{\lambda}}U'_{\rho}T(\lambda\nu)\right\}$$

or

$$\sum_{\rho=1}^{n} U'_{\rho}\left\{T'(\rho\mu) - \sum_{\nu=1}^{n}\sum_{\lambda=1}^{n}\frac{\partial x'^{\mu}}{\partial x^{\nu}}\frac{\partial x'^{\rho}}{\partial x^{\lambda}}T(\lambda\nu)\right\} = 0.$$

The vector U_{λ} is, however, arbitrary and therefore

$$T'(\rho\mu) = \sum_{\nu=1}^{n}\sum_{\lambda=1}^{n}\frac{\partial x'^{\mu}}{\partial x^{\nu}}\frac{\partial x'^{\rho}}{\partial x^{\lambda}}T(\lambda\nu),$$

which shows that the n^2 functions $T(\rho\mu)$ transform by the law of transformation (2.109) and so are the components of a contravariant tensor of rank two.

An important mixed tensor of rank two may be found by application of the quotient theorem. Consider the n^2 quantities δ_μ^λ where

$$\delta_\mu^\lambda = \begin{cases} 0 \text{ if } \lambda \neq \mu, \\ 1 \text{ if } \lambda = \mu, \end{cases} \quad (\lambda, \mu = 1, 2, 3, \ldots, n) \tag{2.112}$$

then, if U_ν is an arbitrary covariant vector, it obviously follows that $\delta_\mu^\nu U_\nu = U_\mu$ and therefore that the inner product of the δ_μ^λ with an arbitrary covariant vector is a covariant vector. Hence the δ_μ^λ must be the components of a mixed tensor of rank two. Moreover, the components of this tensor have the same value in all coordinate-systems because, on transforming to a new system,

$$\delta'^\lambda_\mu = \frac{\partial x'^\lambda}{\partial x^\alpha} \frac{\partial x^\beta}{\partial x'^\mu} \delta^\alpha_\beta = \frac{\partial x'^\lambda}{\partial x^\alpha} \frac{\partial x^\alpha}{\partial x'^\mu} = \frac{\partial x'^\lambda}{\partial x'^\mu}$$

$$= \begin{cases} 0 \text{ if } \lambda \neq \mu, \\ 1 \text{ if } \lambda = \mu. \end{cases}$$

Hence

$$\delta'^\lambda_\mu = \delta^\lambda_\mu, \quad (\lambda, \mu = 1, 2, 3, \ldots, n).$$

2.2. Riemannian Space

The manifold of points so far considered has had no structure and, in particular, no definition of the 'distance' between a pair of its points has been given. In arriving at such a definition, the case of a surface, or two-dimensional manifold, may serve as a guide. The simplest example of a surface is the Euclidean plane in which rectangular Cartesian coordinates exist; if (X, Y) and $(X + dX, Y + dY)$ are two neighbouring points in this plane, then Pythagoras' theorem states that the distance, ds, between this pair of points is given by

$$ds^2 = dX^2 + dY^2. \tag{2.201}$$

This formula is called the expression for the *metric* of the manifold, and it can be shown that it contains within itself the essentials of the geometry of the plane, in particular that the straight line is the shortest distance between two points, that parallel lines are of infinite length and do not intersect in any finite part of the plane, and so on. In (2.201) it is important to notice that the coefficients of the squares of dX and dY are both equal to unity and that, since no term in $dXdY$ occurs, the metric is said to be orthogonal. These properties are, however, due to the use of Cartesian coordinates and disappear if other types of coordinate-systems are employed. For example, in terms of polar coordinates (r, θ) where $X = r \cos \theta$, $Y = r \sin \theta$ the metric becomes

$$ds^2 = dr^2 + r^2 d\theta^2,$$

and the coefficients of the squares of dr and $d\theta$ are 1 and r^2, respectively, whilst orthogonality is still preserved. But if the coordinate-system is (u, v), where $X = uv$, $Y = \frac{1}{2}(u^2 + v^2)$, the metric is

$$ds^2 = (u^2 + v^2)du^2 + 4uvdudv + (u^2 + v^2)dv^2,$$

the coefficients of the quadratic terms in du and dv now being $(u^2 + v^2)$, $4uv$ and $(u^2 + v^2)$, respectively, the orthogonality property also being masked by the use of this coordinate-system. Thus the expression for the metric of a manifold with a particular geometry – in this case the Euclidean plane – may take many forms, according to the coordinate-system which is employed, and the reduction of one form to another, when the coordinate-transformation is not known *a priori*, is a problem of considerable difficulty.

In three-dimensional Euclidean space, when Cartesian coordinates (X, Y, Z) are used, the metric has the form

$$ds^2 = dX^2 + dY^2 + dZ^2, \tag{2.202}$$

which is again the statement of Pythagoras' theorem. If the coordinates are transformed by (2.102) with the identifications

$$x^1 = X, \qquad x^2 = Y, \qquad x^3 = Z,$$
$$x'^1 = r, \qquad x'^2 = \theta, \qquad x'^3 = \phi,$$

the metric becomes

$$ds^2 = dr^2 + r^2d\theta^2 + r^2 \sin^2 \theta d\phi^2.$$

Hence the metric of the two-dimensional surface formed by the points lying on the surface of a sphere of radius a is

$$ds^2 = a^2(d\theta^2 + \sin^2 \theta \, d\phi^2). \tag{2.203}$$

The geometry of the surface of a sphere is intrinsically different from that of the Euclidean plane: straight lines are replaced by great circles which are of finite length, and necessarily intersect, so that there are no parallels in the Euclidean sense, and so on. This difference in geometry is mirrored in the non-existence of real coordinate-transformations which will transform (2.203) into (2.201), or vice versa. Thus, not only may the metric of a given two-dimensional manifold take on many forms according to the coordinate-system in use, but there are manifolds with intrinsically different geometries whose metrics cannot be transformed into one another by any coordinate-transformation. It will be shown later how such geometries may be distinguished from one another.

There is a transformation of (2.203) which will be needed in the sequel and which is obtained by writing

$$\sin \theta = r/(1 + r^2/4), \tag{2.204}$$

where r is a dimensionless variable that is to be distinguished from the radius-vector of polar coordinates in the Euclidean plane. The metric (2.203) becomes

$$ds^2 = a^2\frac{dr^2 + r^2d\phi^2}{(1 + r^2/4)^2}. \tag{2.205}$$

As θ increases from zero to π, r increases from zero to 2 at $\theta = \frac{1}{2}\pi$ and thence to infinity at $\theta = \pi$.

The foregoing expressions for the metrics of two- and three-dimensional manifolds have one feature in common: when expressed in orthogonal form, their terms are all positive. But this need not be so, and the introduction of negative terms is one way of producing manifolds that do not have Euclidean geometries. As an example, consider a three-dimensional manifold which differs from three-dimensional Euclidean space in that its metric has the expression

$$ds^2 = dX^2 + dY^2 - dZ^2. \tag{2.206}$$

If the coordinates are altered to (r_1, θ, ϕ), where

$$X = r_1 \sinh \theta \cos \phi, \qquad Y = r_1 \sinh \theta \sin \phi, \qquad Z = r_1 \cosh \theta,$$

the metric becomes

$$ds^2 = - dr_1{}^2 + r_1{}^2 d\theta^2 + r_1{}^2 \sinh^2 \theta \, d\phi^2,$$

and the metric of the surface $r_1 = a$, where a is a constant, is

$$ds^2 = a^2(d\theta^2 + \sinh^2 \theta \, d\phi^2).$$

If in this formula we write $\sinh \theta = r/(1 - r^2/4)$ there comes

$$ds^2 = a^2 \frac{dr^2 + r^2 d\phi^2}{(1 - r^2/4)^2}, \tag{2.207}$$

a form analogous to (2.205). Clearly $r = 0$ when $\theta = 0$, and increases to $r = 2$ when θ is infinite.

With these preliminaries on two-dimensional manifolds, we may pass to the general case of an n-dimensional manifold. A *Riemannian space* is a manifold of points in which the 'distance' between any neighbouring pair of points (x) and $(x + dx)$ is a *scalar*, ds, whose expression in terms of the coordinates is called the *metric* and is defined by the formula

$$ds^2 = g_{\mu\nu} dx^\mu dx^\nu, \tag{2.208}$$

where the $g_{\mu\nu}$ are functions of the coordinates (x). They are called the *coefficients of the metric* and are assumed to be symmetrical in their indices, i.e.

$$g_{\mu\nu} = g_{\nu\mu};$$

there are therefore $\frac{1}{2}n(n + 1)$ independent coefficients of the metric. It is also assumed that the determinant g, whose elements are the $g_{\mu\nu}$, viz.:

$$g = \begin{vmatrix} g_{11} \, g_{12} \, g_{13} \cdots g_{1n} \\ g_{21} \, g_{22} \, g_{23} \cdots g_{2n} \\ g_{31} \, g_{32} \, g_{33} \cdots g_{3n} \\ \cdot \quad \cdot \quad \cdot \quad \cdot \quad \cdot \\ \cdot \quad \cdot \quad \cdot \quad \cdot \quad \cdot \\ \cdot \quad \cdot \quad \cdot \quad \cdot \quad \cdot \\ g_{n1} \, g_{n2} \, g_{n3} \cdots g_{nn} \end{vmatrix}, \tag{2.209}$$

is not identically zero. Finally ds will be called the *interval*, rather than the distance, between (x) and $(x + dx)$.

In most of the applications of Riemannian spaces to general relativity, special types of spaces are considered in which $g_{\mu\nu} = 0$ if $\mu \neq \nu$ and they are said to be orthogonal. All of the surviving $g_{\mu\nu}$ are not necessarily positive: the difference between the number of positive, and the number of negative, $g_{\mu\nu}$ being called the *signature* of the metric. In the most general Riemannian space it is not possible to find any coordinate-system which expresses the metric orthogonally, but it is the case that special coordinate-systems can be set up at a pre-assigned point of the space in terms of which the metric is orthogonal. At the point, the metric has again a definite signature that cannot be changed by transforming from one special coordinate-system to another.

It will now be proved that the functions $g_{\mu\nu}$ are the components of a co-variant tensor of rank two called the *metrical tensor*. Since ds is a scalar,

$$ds^2 = g'_{\lambda\mu}dx'^{\lambda}dx'^{\mu} = g_{\lambda\mu}dx^{\lambda}dx^{\mu},$$

and therefore by (2.105)

$$g'_{\lambda\mu}\frac{\partial x'^{\lambda}}{\partial x^{\alpha}}\frac{\partial x'^{\mu}}{\partial x^{\beta}}dx^{\alpha}dx^{\beta} = g_{\lambda\mu}dx^{\lambda}dx^{\mu}.$$

Since the differentials of the coordinates are independent, the last equation can only be true if

$$g'_{\lambda\mu}\frac{\partial x'^{\lambda}}{\partial x^{\alpha}}\frac{\partial x'^{\mu}}{\partial x^{\beta}} = g_{\alpha\beta}.$$

Interchanging primed and unprimed letters, there comes

$$g'_{\alpha\beta} = g_{\lambda\mu}\frac{\partial x^{\lambda}}{\partial x'^{\alpha}}\frac{\partial x^{\mu}}{\partial x'^{\beta}},$$

which is the law (2.110) of transformation of a covariant tensor of rank two.

The metrical tensor serves to define a second symmetrical fundamental tensor, the *contravariant metrical tensor*, in the following way: Consider the n^2 functions $g^{\lambda\mu}$ defined by

$$g^{\lambda\mu} = (\text{co-factor of } g_{\lambda\mu} \text{ in } g)/g, \qquad (2.210)$$

which, by the law of multiplication of determinants, satisfy

$$g^{\lambda\mu}g_{\lambda\nu} = \delta^{\mu}_{\nu}. \qquad (2.211)$$

Then the functions $g^{\lambda\mu}$ define a contravariant tensor of rank two, a statement whose truth can be verified through the quotient theorem; if, indeed, V^{ν} is an arbitrary contravariant vector, then the inner product $U_{\lambda} = g_{\lambda\nu}V^{\nu}$ is an arbitrary covariant vector. But

$$g^{\lambda\mu}U_{\lambda} = g^{\lambda\mu}g_{\lambda\nu}V^{\nu} = \delta^{\mu}_{\nu}V^{\nu} = V^{\mu},$$

and therefore the inner product of the $g^{\lambda\mu}$ with an arbitrary covariant vector U_{λ} yields a contravariant vector. Thus the $g^{\lambda\mu}$ must be the components of a contravariant tensor of rank two.

The foregoing formulae may be exemplified by the metric (2.205) for the surface of a sphere. The metrical tensor, the determinant g, and the contravariant metrical tensor are, writing $r = x^1$, $\phi = x^2$,

$$g_{11} = a^2(1 + r^2/4)^{-2}, \qquad g_{12} = g_{21} = 0, \qquad g_{22} = a^2r^2(1 + r^2/4)^{-2},$$
$$g = a^4r^2(1 + r^2/4)^{-4},$$
$$g^{11} = a^{-2}(1 + r^2/4)^2, \qquad g^{21} = g^{12} = 0, \qquad g^{22} = a^{-2}r^{-2}(1 + r^2/4)^2.$$

It is also worth observing that, in three-dimensional Euclidean geometry, when Cartesian coordinates are used and the metric is (2.202), we have

$$\left.\begin{array}{l} g_{11} = g_{22} = g_{33} = 1, \qquad g_{\mu\nu} = 0 \ (\mu \neq \nu), \\ g = 1, \\ g^{11} = g^{22} = g^{33} = 1, \qquad g^{\mu\nu} = 0 \ (\mu \neq \nu), \end{array}\right\} \qquad (2.212)$$

so that the metrical tensor and its contravariant form have components whose values are either unity or zero.

The metrical tensors enable us to perform the operations of 'raising' and 'lowering' the indices of a tensor, which change a covariant index into a contravariant one, and vice versa. This process consists of forming the inner product of the given tensor with one or other of the metrical tensors, and the resulting tensor is not regarded as a new one but merely as a new form of the old tensor. The same letter is therefore employed to denote the tensor. Thus in the case of vectors V^λ, U_λ the process gives, respectively,

$$V_\mu = g_{\lambda\mu}V^\lambda, \qquad U^\mu = g^{\lambda\mu}U_\lambda.$$

Again, from a tensor of rank two, $T^{\lambda\mu}$, there is obtained

$$T^\lambda_\mu = g_{\mu\nu}T^{\lambda\nu}, \qquad T_{\lambda\mu} = g_{\lambda\sigma}T^\sigma_\mu = g_{\lambda\sigma}g_{\mu\nu}T^{\sigma\nu}.$$

It is not difficult to prove that the results of these operations are, in fact, tensors of the types indicated. Consider, for example, the law of transformation of V^μ, which is

$$V'_\mu = g'_{\lambda\mu}V'^\lambda = \left(\frac{\partial x^\alpha}{\partial x'^\lambda}\frac{\partial x^\beta}{\partial x'^\mu}g_{\alpha\beta}\right)\left(\frac{\partial x'^\lambda}{\partial x^\gamma}V^\gamma\right) = \frac{\partial x^\alpha}{\partial x'^\gamma}\frac{\partial x^\beta}{\partial x'^\mu}g_{\alpha\beta}V^\gamma$$
$$= \delta^\alpha_\gamma\frac{\partial x^\beta}{\partial x'^\mu}g_{\alpha\beta}V^\gamma = \frac{\partial x^\beta}{\partial x'^\mu}g_{\alpha\beta}V^\alpha = \frac{\partial x^\beta}{\partial x'^\mu}V_\beta,$$

and thus turns out to be the law of transformation of a covariant vector.

Tensors obtained from one another by the process of raising or lowering indices are known as *associated tensors*. In Euclidean geometry, when Cartesians are used, there is no difference in value between the components of tensors after raising or lowering of indices, as may be seen from (2.212). This is one of the reasons why, in elementary vector algebra, it is not usually necessary to differentiate between covariant and contravariant vectors.

By raising a covariant index if necessary, a vector can always be expressed in its contravariant form V^λ, say; taking the inner product of the covariant and contravariant forms of the vector, a scalar is obtained, which is called the *length* of the vector, whose square may be expressed in any one of the following forms

$$V^2 = V^\lambda V_\lambda = g^{\lambda\mu}V_\mu V_\lambda = g_{\lambda\mu}V^\lambda V^\mu. \qquad (2.213)$$

2.3. Geodesics

Attention has hitherto been confined to the changes that tensors undergo when the coordinates of the points of a Riemannian space are transformed. It is now necessary to consider changes of a different kind that arise when, the coordinate-system being kept fixed, the value of a tensor at one point is compared with its value at another. Such changes may be usefully regarded as due to the 'motion' of the tensor from one point to the other and it is therefore necessary to define some kind of path through the Riemannian space along which the tensor may be imagined to travel. The fundamental paths are called *geodesics* of the space and they have properties analogous to those of straight lines in Euclidean space. The geodesics are particular kinds of curves in the space and a curve is defined by n equations

$$x^\lambda = F^\lambda(\mu), \qquad (\lambda = 1, 2, 3, \ldots, n), \qquad (2.301)$$

where μ is a parameter varying from point to point of the curve. By substituting from these equations into (2.208) and then integrating with respect to μ, it is possible to express the interval s measured along the curve in terms of μ. The geodesic joining two points P_0 and P_1 is then defined to be a curve for which the interval between P_0 and P_1 has a stationary value compared with the interval measured along any other neighbouring curve joining the two points. This property certainly holds good for a straight line in Euclidean geometry though, in that case, it is also true that the straight line gives the *shortest* interval from one point to the other. It will not, however, be necessary for the present purpose to inquire whether or not the geodesic in a Riemannian space gives the minimum or maximum value of the interval between any two of its points.

The differential equations of a geodesic can be found as follows, the finite equations of this curve being unattainable without a precise knowledge of the functions $g_{\mu\nu}$. Suppose that (2.301) represents the finite equations of the geodesic joining P_0 and P_1, so that the interval s is

$$s = \int_{\mu_0}^{\mu_1} \left\{ g_{\lambda\nu}(x) \frac{dx^\lambda}{d\mu} \frac{dx^\nu}{d\mu} \right\}^{\frac{1}{2}} d\mu \qquad (2.302)$$

where μ_0, μ_1 are the values of μ at P_0 and P_1 respectively. Any other curve joining P_0 and P_1, and always lying close to the geodesic, will have equations of the form

$$\bar{x}^\lambda = x^\lambda + \varepsilon\omega^\lambda = F^\lambda(\mu) + \varepsilon\omega^\lambda(\mu),$$

where $\omega^\lambda = 0$ at $\mu = \mu_0$ and $\mu = \mu_1$, and ε is a small quantity whose square and higher powers may be neglected. If $\bar{s}$ is the interval along the neighbouring curve joining P_0 and P_1, then

$$\bar{s} = \int_{\mu_0}^{\mu_1} \left\{ g_{\lambda\nu}(\bar{x}) \frac{d\bar{x}^\lambda}{d\mu} \frac{d\bar{x}^\nu}{d\mu} \right\}^{\frac{1}{2}} d\mu,$$

and therefore, neglecting all powers of ε above the first,

$$\bar{s} - s = \int_{\mu_0}^{\mu_1} \left\{ g_{\lambda\nu} \frac{dx^\lambda}{d\mu} \frac{dx^\nu}{d\mu} + \varepsilon \left(\frac{\partial g_{\lambda\nu}}{\partial x^\sigma} \frac{dx^\lambda}{d\mu} \omega^\sigma + 2 g_{\lambda\nu} \frac{d\omega^\lambda}{d\mu} \frac{dx^\nu}{d\mu} \right) \right\}^{\frac{1}{2}} d\mu$$

$$- \int_{\mu_0}^{\mu_1} \left\{ g_{\lambda\nu} \frac{dx^\lambda}{d\mu} \frac{dx^\nu}{d\mu} \right\}^{\frac{1}{2}} d\mu.$$

But since $ds = \{ g_{\lambda\nu} dx^\lambda dx^\nu \}^{\frac{1}{2}}$, the last equation can be written

$$\bar{s} - s = \tfrac{1}{2} \varepsilon \int_{\mu_0}^{\mu_1} \left\{ \left(\omega^\sigma \frac{\partial g_{\lambda\nu}}{\partial x^\sigma} \frac{dx^\lambda}{d\mu} + 2 g_{\lambda\nu} \frac{d\omega^\lambda}{d\mu} \right) \frac{dx^\nu}{d\mu} \frac{d\mu}{ds} \right\} d\mu.$$

It is now possible to simplify the calculation, if $s \neq 0$, by assuming that the parameter μ is identical with s itself measured along the geodesic. For in this case $d\mu/ds = 1$ and

$$\bar{s} - s = \tfrac{1}{2} \varepsilon \int_{s_0}^{s_1} \left\{ \left(\omega^\sigma \frac{\partial g_{\lambda\nu}}{\partial x^\sigma} \frac{dx^\lambda}{ds} + 2 g_{\lambda\nu} \frac{d\omega^\lambda}{ds} \right) \frac{dx^\nu}{ds} \right\} ds,$$

the x^λ, ω^λ now being regarded as functions of s. Integration by parts of the second term in the last equation gives

$$\bar{s} - s = \tfrac{1}{2} \varepsilon \int_{s_0}^{s_1} \left\{ \frac{\partial g_{\lambda\nu}}{\partial x^\sigma} \frac{dx^\lambda}{ds} \frac{dx^\nu}{ds} - 2 \frac{d}{ds} \left(g_{\sigma\nu} \frac{dx^\nu}{ds} \right) \right\} \omega^\sigma ds + \varepsilon \left[g_{\lambda\nu} \frac{dx^\nu}{ds} \omega^\lambda \right]_{s_0}^{s_1}.$$

But the functions ω^λ vanish at $s = s_0$ and $s = s_1$, and therefore the integrated term is zero. If therefore the interval is to have a stationary value for the geodesic compared with neighbouring curves, $\bar{s} - s$ must be zero for any choice of the functions ω^λ. This is possible only if the coefficient of each ω^σ in the integrand is separately zero, and therefore the differential equations of a geodesic are the n equations

$$\frac{d}{ds} \left(g_{\sigma\nu} \frac{dx^\nu}{ds} \right) - \tfrac{1}{2} \frac{\partial g_{\lambda\nu}}{\partial x^\sigma} \frac{dx^\lambda}{ds} \frac{dx^\nu}{ds} = 0, \; (\sigma = 1, 2, 3, \ldots, n). \qquad (2.303)$$

The form (2.303) of the equations of a geodesic is of great use in practice and will be repeatedly employed in the sequel. But for theoretical purposes, there is another form which involves the *Christoffel symbols* of the first and second kinds, that are defined respectively as follows:

$$\left. \begin{aligned} (\lambda\mu, \nu) = (\mu\lambda, \nu) &= \tfrac{1}{2} \left(\frac{\partial g_{\lambda\nu}}{\partial x^\mu} + \frac{\partial g_{\mu\nu}}{\partial x^\lambda} - \frac{\partial g_{\lambda\mu}}{\partial x^\nu} \right), \\ \begin{Bmatrix} \nu \\ \lambda\mu \end{Bmatrix} = \begin{Bmatrix} \nu \\ \mu\lambda \end{Bmatrix} &= \tfrac{1}{2} g^{\nu\sigma} \left(\frac{\partial g_{\lambda\sigma}}{\partial x^\mu} + \frac{\partial g_{\mu\sigma}}{\partial x^\lambda} - \frac{\partial g_{\lambda\mu}}{\partial x^\sigma} \right). \end{aligned} \right\} \qquad (2.304)$$

These symbols are symmetrical with respect to the two indices that are written together, but they are not components of tensors as may be verified by using the transformation laws for the tensors $g_{\mu\nu}$, $g^{\mu\nu}$. It is also easily proved that the two kinds of Cristoffel symbols are related by

$$\begin{Bmatrix} \nu \\ \lambda\mu \end{Bmatrix} = g^{\nu\sigma}(\lambda\mu, \sigma), \qquad (\lambda\mu, \nu) = g_{\nu\sigma} \begin{Bmatrix} \sigma \\ \lambda\mu \end{Bmatrix}.$$

The equations (2.303) may be written

$$g_{\sigma\nu}\frac{d^2x^\nu}{ds^2} + \tfrac{1}{2}\left(\frac{\partial g_{\sigma\lambda}}{\partial x^\nu} + \frac{\partial g_{\sigma\nu}}{\partial x^\lambda} - \frac{\partial g_{\lambda\nu}}{\partial x^\sigma}\right)\frac{dx^\lambda}{ds}\frac{dx^\nu}{ds} = 0,$$

and, if these equations be multiplied by $g^{\tau\sigma}$ and the summation indicated by the doubly occurring index σ be performed, the result is

$$\frac{d^2x^\tau}{ds^2} + \left\{{\tau \atop \lambda\nu}\right\}\frac{dx^\lambda}{ds}\frac{dx^\nu}{ds} = 0, \qquad (\tau = 1, 2, 3, \ldots, n), \qquad (2.305)$$

which are the standard forms of the equations of the geodesics of the Riemannian space, excluding, however, those geodesics for which $s = 0$ along the curve.

The equations (2.305) may be used to find the transformation law for the Christoffel symbols. When the coordinate system is changed from (x) to (x') the equations preserve their form and become

$$\frac{d^2x'^\tau}{ds^2} + \left\{{\tau \atop \lambda\nu}\right\}'\frac{dx'^\lambda}{ds}\frac{dx'^\nu}{ds} = 0.$$

These reduce to

$$\frac{d^2x^\alpha}{ds^2} + \left\{{\alpha \atop \beta\gamma}\right\}\frac{dx^\beta}{ds}\frac{dx^\gamma}{ds} = 0,$$

if the Christoffel symbols of the second kind transform so that

$$\left\{{\alpha \atop \beta\gamma}\right\} = \frac{\partial x^\alpha}{\partial x'^\tau}\frac{\partial^2 x'^\tau}{\partial x^\beta \partial x^\gamma} + \left\{{\tau \atop \lambda\nu}\right\}'\frac{\partial x^\alpha}{\partial x'^\tau}\frac{\partial x'^\lambda}{\partial x^\beta}\frac{\partial x'^\nu}{\partial x^\gamma}.$$

This is not a tensor transformation and so the Christoffel symbols are not components of a tensor. The last equation may be thrown into a useful equivalent form by carrying out the following three operations: firstly, interchange primed and unprimed symbols; secondly, multiply the result by $\partial x'^\beta/\partial x^\mu$; thirdly, make use of the relation obtained by differentiating partially with respect to x'^γ the equations

$$\frac{\partial x'^\alpha}{\partial x^\tau}\frac{\partial x^\tau}{\partial x'^\beta} = \delta^\alpha_\beta,$$

noting that the partial derivatives of the right-hand side are zero. The final result is

$$\left\{{\alpha \atop \beta\gamma}\right\}'\frac{\partial x'^\beta}{\partial x^\mu} = -\frac{\partial x^\lambda}{\partial x'^\gamma}\frac{\partial^2 x'^\alpha}{\partial x^\lambda \partial x^\mu} + \left\{{\tau \atop \mu\nu}\right\}\frac{\partial x'^\alpha}{\partial x^\tau}\frac{\partial x^\nu}{\partial x'^\gamma}. \qquad (2.306)$$

If the dx^μ correspond to an infinitesimal displacement along the geodesic for a change ds of interval, the vector dx^μ/ds $(\mu = 1, 2, 3, \ldots, n)$ is called the unit tangent vector to the geodesic. By dividing (2.208) throughout by ds^2, it follows that the tangent vector satisfies

$$g_{\mu\nu}\frac{dx^\mu}{ds}\frac{dx^\nu}{ds} = 1, \qquad (2.307)$$

an equation which also shows by (2.213) that this vector is of unit length.

Another important conclusion is that (2.307) is an integral of the n equations of the geodesic (2.305).

Another kind of geodesic, called a *null-geodesic*, is obtained by assuming that the interval between any two points on the curve is zero. If μ is a non-zero scalar parameter varying along the null-geodesic, then a curve of this kind is characterized by possessing an integral of its defining equations expressed by

$$h = g_{\lambda\nu}\frac{dx^\lambda}{d\mu}\frac{dx^\nu}{d\mu} = 0, \qquad (2.308)$$

in place of (2.307). The differential equations of a null-geodesic are obtained by noticing that, if P_0 and P_1 are two points on it, then the integral

$$I = \int_{\mu_0}^{\mu_1} h\,d\mu$$

must be zero along the curve. Along a neighbouring curve, the approximate value of this integral is

$$\bar{I} = \int_{\mu_0}^{\mu_1} \bar{h}\,d\mu = \int_{\mu_0}^{\mu_1}\left\{\bar{g}_{\nu\sigma}(\mu)\frac{d\bar{x}^\nu}{d\mu}\frac{d\bar{x}^\sigma}{d\mu}\right\}d\mu$$

$$= \int_{\mu_0}^{\mu_1}\left\{g_{\nu\sigma}\frac{dx^\nu}{d\mu}\frac{dx^\sigma}{d\mu} + \varepsilon\left(\frac{\partial g_{\nu\sigma}}{\partial x^\lambda}\frac{dx^\nu}{d\mu}\frac{dx^\sigma}{d\mu}\omega^\lambda + 2g_{\nu\sigma}\frac{dx^\nu}{d\mu}\frac{d\omega^\sigma}{d\mu}\right)\right\}d\mu.$$

The first term in the integrand vanishes because $h = 0$ and therefore

$$\bar{I} = \varepsilon\int_{\mu_0}^{\mu_1}\left\{\frac{\partial g_{\nu\sigma}}{\partial x^\lambda}\frac{dx^\nu}{d\mu}\frac{dx^\sigma}{d\mu} - 2\frac{d}{d\mu}\left(g_{\lambda\sigma}\frac{dx^\sigma}{d\mu}\right)\right\}\omega^\lambda d\mu + \varepsilon\left[g_{\lambda\sigma}\frac{dx^\sigma}{d\mu}\omega^\lambda\right]_{\mu_0}^{\mu_1},$$

in which the integrated term also vanishes as before. Thus if the property $h = 0$ holds to the first order for all curves in the neighbourhood of the null-geodesic joining P_0 and P_1, it follows that $\bar{I} = I = 0$. Hence

$$\frac{d}{d\mu}\left(g_{\lambda\sigma}\frac{dx^\sigma}{d\mu}\right) - \frac{1}{2}\frac{\partial g_{\nu\sigma}}{dx^\lambda}\frac{dx^\nu}{d\mu}\frac{dx^\sigma}{d\mu} = 0, \qquad (\lambda = 1, 2, 3, \ldots, n), \qquad (2.309)$$

and, as before, these equations can be transformed into

$$\frac{d^2x^\sigma}{d\mu^2} + \left\{\begin{matrix}\sigma\\\lambda\nu\end{matrix}\right\}\frac{dx^\lambda}{d\mu}\frac{dx^\nu}{d\mu} = 0, \qquad (\sigma = 1, 2, 3, \ldots, n), \qquad (2.310)$$

which are the standard forms of the equations of the null-geodesics, a first integral of which is (2.307).

As a simple illustration of geodesics, consider the three-dimensional Euclidean space whose metric is (2.202). Since the components of the metrical tensor are constants, the differential equations of the geodesics, (2.303), are

$$\frac{d^2X}{ds^2} = 0, \qquad \frac{d^2Y}{ds^2} = 0, \qquad \frac{d^2Z}{ds^2} = 0,$$

which are immediately integrable to give the equations of a straight line, passing through the point (X_0, Y_0, Z_0), viz.

$$\frac{X - X_0}{l} = \frac{Y - Y_0}{m} = \frac{Z - Z_0}{n} = s.$$

The direction-cosines of the line are (l, m, n) and, as is well known, they satisfy

$$l^2 + m^2 + n^2 = 1.$$

But they are also the components of the unit tangent vector to the geodesic, the last equation being equivalent to (2.307) when the metric is (2.202).

By way of another example on geodesics, consider the verification of the statement that great circles drawn on the surface of a sphere are curves of this type. The point $\theta = 0$ in (2.203) may be chosen arbitrarily on the surface of the sphere; the curves $\phi = $ constant are then the great circle 'meridians' corresponding to this 'pole', the curves $\theta = $ constant being the (small) 'circles of latitude', only the curve $\theta = \frac{1}{2}\pi$ being a great circle. If in (2.303) the identification $x^1 = \theta$, $x^2 = \phi$ be made, these equations reduce to the pair

$$\frac{d}{ds}\left(a^2\frac{d\theta}{ds}\right) - a^2 \sin \theta \cos \theta\left(\frac{d\phi}{ds}\right)^2 = 0,$$

$$\frac{d}{ds}\left(a^2 \sin^2 \theta\frac{d\phi}{ds}\right) = 0.$$

Particular solutions of these are obviously $\phi = $ constant, $a\theta = s$, or $\theta = \frac{1}{2}\pi$, $a\phi = s$, corresponding to the 'meridians' and the 'equator', respectively, of the point chosen as 'pole'. A 'circle of latitude' on which θ has a constant value not equal to $\frac{1}{2}\pi$ will not satisfy the geodesic equations. Thus great circles are geodesics and small circles are not, though, of course, it has not been proved that the *only* curves on the sphere that are geodesics are great circles.

The null-geodesics of three-dimensional Euclidean space with metric (2.202) are, by (2.309) and (2.308), the straight lines

$$\frac{X - X_0}{l} = \frac{Y - Y_0}{m} = \frac{Z - Z_0}{n} = \mu, \tag{2.311}$$

whose direction-cosines, however, satisfy the relation

$$l^2 + m^2 + n^2 = 0,$$

and so cannot all be real. Thus the null-geodesics are, in this case, imaginary straight lines. But the situation is different for a space such as (2.206), where one of the coefficients of the metric is negative, because the null-geodesics are now still of the form (2.311) but with (l, m, n) satisfying

$$l^2 + m^2 - n^2 = 0.$$

Thus real values of (l, m, n) are possible, and both the geodesics and the null-geodesics of the space (2.206) are real straight lines.

2.4. Covariant Differentiation

The geodesics of a Riemannian space constitute a set of paths defined in an invariant manner by the stationary property of the scalar interval measured along any one of them. These curves therefore do not depend on any particular coordinate-system and provide an intrinsic way of proceeding from one point of the space to another. They can thus be used for calculating the change in a vector or a tensor from one point to another, this entity being imagined 'transported' along the geodesic joining the two points. Let (x) be a point on a geodesic and $(x + dx)$ a neighbouring point on it, and let $\lambda^\mu = dx^\mu/ds$ be the unit tangent vector to the geodesic. Let V^μ be a contravariant vector whose covariant form is V_μ; then $V_\mu \lambda^\mu$ is, of course, a scalar. The vector $V^\mu(x + dx)$ is *defined* to be the result of transporting V^μ from the point (x) to the point $(x + dx)$ by noticing that

$$\frac{d}{ds}(V_\mu \lambda^\mu) = \frac{d}{ds}(g_{\mu\nu} V^\nu \lambda^\mu)$$

is a scalar, whatever pair of nearby points on the geodesic are considered. This definition gives rise to a mixed tensor of rank two called the *covariant derivative* of V^μ in the following way: By (2.305), (2.304)

$$\frac{d}{ds}(g_{\mu\nu} V^\nu \lambda^\mu) = \left\{ g_{\mu\nu} \frac{\partial V^\nu}{\partial x^\sigma} + V^\nu \frac{\partial g_{\mu\nu}}{\partial x^\sigma} - \begin{Bmatrix} \tau \\ \sigma\mu \end{Bmatrix} g_{\nu\tau} V^\nu \right\} \lambda^\sigma \lambda^\mu$$

$$= \left\{ g_{\mu\nu} \frac{\partial V^\nu}{\partial x^\sigma} + \left(\frac{\partial g_{\mu\nu}}{\partial x^\sigma} - (\sigma\mu, \nu) \right) V^\nu \right\} \lambda^\sigma \lambda^\mu$$

$$= \left\{ \frac{\partial V^\nu}{\partial x^\sigma} + \begin{Bmatrix} \nu \\ \sigma\mu \end{Bmatrix} V^\mu \right\} \lambda_\nu \lambda^\sigma.$$

These operations can also be carried out in the coordinate system (x'). Transforming from (x') to (x), one finds with the aid of (2.306) that

$$\frac{\partial V'^\alpha}{\partial x'^\gamma} + \begin{Bmatrix} \alpha \\ \beta\gamma \end{Bmatrix}' V'^\beta = \frac{\partial x'^\alpha}{\partial x^\mu} \frac{\partial x^\lambda}{\partial x'^\gamma} \left\{ \frac{\partial V^\mu}{\partial x^\lambda} + \begin{Bmatrix} \mu \\ \lambda\nu \end{Bmatrix} V^\nu \right\},$$

which shows that a mixed tensor of rank two is involved.

This tensor is called the *covariant derivative* of the original vector V^μ and is denoted by $V^\mu_{,\nu}$, using the comma to indicate that the tensor is a covariant derivative, so that

$$V^\mu_{,\nu} = \frac{\partial V^\mu}{\partial x^\nu} + \begin{Bmatrix} \mu \\ \nu\sigma \end{Bmatrix} V^\sigma. \qquad (2.401)$$

The inner product of the covariant derivative of V^μ with the unit tangent vector, λ^ν, to the geodesic is itself a contravariant vector which may be written

$$V^\mu_{,\nu} \lambda^\nu = \frac{dV^\mu}{ds} + \begin{Bmatrix} \mu \\ \sigma\tau \end{Bmatrix} V^\sigma \lambda^\tau. \qquad (2.402)$$

This vector is called the *total covariant derivative* of the original vector V^μ. If

V^μ is chosen to be the unit tangent vector itself, it follows from (2.305) that the total covariant derivative of the unit tangent vector is zero. Thus the geodesics are curves whose unit tangent vectors have zero total covariant derivatives.

The invariance along a geodesic of the inner product of a covariant vector U_μ and the unit tangent vector defines the covariant derivative $U_{\mu,\nu}$ of U_μ. We have

$$\frac{d}{ds}(U_\mu \lambda^\mu) = \left\{\frac{\partial U_\mu}{\partial x^\nu} - \left\{{\sigma \atop \mu\nu}\right\}U_\sigma\right\}\lambda^\mu \lambda^\nu,$$

so that

$$U_{\mu,\nu} = \frac{\partial U_\mu}{\partial x^\nu} - \left\{{\sigma \atop \mu\nu}\right\}U_\sigma, \qquad (2.403)$$

is a covariant tensor of rank two, by direct transformation from (x') to (x).

The procedure for finding the covariant derivatives of tensors of rank higher than the first is to form scalars from them by continued inner multiplication with the unit tangent vector to a geodesic and then to apply the operation d/ds to the scalars. Thus, if $Y_{\mu\nu}$ is a covariant tensor of rank two, the quantity $Y_{\mu\nu}\lambda^\mu\lambda^\nu$ is a scalar and, with the help of (2.305), it follows that

$$\frac{d}{ds}(Y_{\mu\nu}\lambda^\mu\lambda^\nu) = \left\{\frac{\partial Y_{\mu\nu}}{\partial x^\sigma} - \left\{{\tau \atop \mu\sigma}\right\}Y_{\tau\nu} - \left\{{\tau \atop \nu\sigma}\right\}Y_{\mu\tau}\right\}\lambda^\sigma\lambda^\mu\lambda^\nu.$$

By direct transformation from (x') to (x), it can be proved that the set of quantities

$$Y_{\mu\nu,\sigma} = \frac{\partial Y_{\mu\nu}}{\partial x^\sigma} - \left\{{\tau \atop \mu\sigma}\right\}Y_{\tau\nu} - \left\{{\tau \atop \nu\sigma}\right\}Y_{\mu\tau}, \qquad (2.404)$$

are the components of a covariant tensor of rank three, which is the covariant derivative of $Y_{\mu\nu}$. The covariant derivative of a mixed tensor of rank two, X^λ_ν, is

$$X^\lambda_{\nu,\mu} = \frac{\partial X^\lambda_\nu}{\partial x^\mu} + \left\{{\lambda \atop \mu\sigma}\right\}X^\sigma_\nu - \left\{{\sigma \atop \nu\mu}\right\}X^\lambda_\sigma, \qquad (2.405)$$

and of a contravariant tensor of rank two, $Z^{\lambda\nu}$ is

$$Z^{\lambda\nu}_{,\mu} = \frac{\partial Z^{\lambda\nu}}{\partial x^\mu} + \left\{{\lambda \atop \mu\sigma}\right\}Z^{\sigma\nu} + \left\{{\nu \atop \mu\sigma}\right\}Z^{\lambda\sigma}. \qquad (2.406)$$

It will be observed on comparing (2.404), (2.405) and (2.406) with (2.401) and (2.403) that the terms involving the Christoffel symbols in the first three formulae obey the following rule: Each covariant index of the original tensor gives rise to a 'Christoffel symbol' term which is of the same form as the corresponding term in the covariant derivative of a covariant vector, while each contravariant index produces a term similar to that in the covariant derivative of a contravariant vector. This rule is found to hold good for tensors of all ranks, as the reader may verify for himself.

The process of covariant differentiation may be applied to the metrical tensors $g_{\mu\nu}$ and $g^{\mu\nu}$ and to δ^μ_ν. Using (2.304) and (2.404) there comes

$$g_{\mu\nu,\lambda} = \frac{\partial g_{\mu\nu}}{\partial x^\lambda} - \begin{Bmatrix} \sigma \\ \mu\lambda \end{Bmatrix} g_{\sigma\nu} - \begin{Bmatrix} \sigma \\ \lambda\nu \end{Bmatrix} g_{\mu\sigma}$$

$$= \frac{\partial g_{\mu\nu}}{\partial x^\lambda} - (\mu\lambda,\nu) - (\nu\lambda,\mu)$$

$$= \frac{\partial g_{\mu\nu}}{\partial x^\lambda} - \tfrac{1}{2}\left(\frac{\partial g_{\mu\nu}}{\partial x^\lambda} + \frac{\partial g_{\lambda\nu}}{\partial x^\mu} - \frac{\partial g_{\mu\lambda}}{\partial x^\nu}\right) - \tfrac{1}{2}\left(\frac{\partial g_{\nu\mu}}{\partial x^\lambda} + \frac{\partial g_{\lambda\mu}}{\partial x^\nu} - \frac{\partial g_{\nu\lambda}}{\partial x^\mu}\right)$$

$$= 0,$$

and therefore *the covariant derivative of the metrical tensor is zero*. Again,

$$\delta^\mu_{\nu,\lambda} = \frac{\partial \delta^\mu_\nu}{\partial x^\lambda} + \begin{Bmatrix} \mu \\ \sigma\lambda \end{Bmatrix} \delta^\sigma_\nu - \begin{Bmatrix} \sigma \\ \lambda\nu \end{Bmatrix} \delta^\mu_\sigma$$

$$= \begin{Bmatrix} \mu \\ \nu\lambda \end{Bmatrix} - \begin{Bmatrix} \mu \\ \lambda\nu \end{Bmatrix}$$

$$= 0,$$

and, since $g_{\mu\nu}g^{\lambda\nu} = \delta^\lambda_\mu$ it also follows that the covariant derivative of $g^{\lambda\nu}$ is zero. Thus the three fundamental tensors may be treated as constants in covariant differentiation.

There is an important tensor that can be deduced from the covariant derivative of a given tensor of rank two, which is called the *vectorial divergence* of the latter. In order to show how vectorial divergences are obtained, the following result on the sum of Christoffel symbols is required: If g is the determinant of the coefficients of the metric then, by the rule of differentiation of determinants,

$$\frac{\partial g}{\partial x^\nu} = \sum_{\lambda,\mu} (\text{co-factor of } g_{\lambda\mu} \text{ in } g) \times \frac{\partial g_{\lambda\mu}}{\partial x^\nu}$$

$$= g\, g^{\lambda\mu} \frac{\partial g_{\lambda\mu}}{\partial x^\nu}.$$

But

$$\begin{Bmatrix} \lambda \\ \lambda\nu \end{Bmatrix} = \tfrac{1}{2} g^{\lambda\sigma}\left(\frac{\partial g_{\lambda\sigma}}{\partial x^\nu} + \frac{\partial g_{\nu\sigma}}{\partial x^\lambda} - \frac{\partial g_{\lambda\nu}}{\partial x^\sigma}\right)$$

$$= \tfrac{1}{2} g^{\lambda\sigma} \frac{\partial g_{\lambda\sigma}}{\partial x^\nu}.$$

Hence

$$\begin{Bmatrix} \lambda \\ \lambda\nu \end{Bmatrix} = \tfrac{1}{2}\frac{1}{g}\frac{\partial g}{\partial x^\nu} = \frac{1}{\sqrt{(g)}}\frac{\partial \sqrt{(g)}}{\partial x^\nu} = \frac{\partial \log \sqrt{(g)}}{\partial x^\nu}. \tag{2.407}$$

Now consider a contravariant vector V^λ and let $V^\lambda_{,\mu}$ be its covariant derivative; then $V^\lambda_{,\lambda}$ is a unique scalar called the *divergence* of V^λ. Moreover

$$V^\lambda_{,\lambda} = \frac{\partial V^\lambda}{\partial x^\lambda} + \begin{Bmatrix} \lambda \\ \nu\lambda \end{Bmatrix} V^\nu = \frac{\partial V^\lambda}{\partial x^\lambda} + \frac{1}{\sqrt{(g)}}\frac{\partial \sqrt{(g)}}{\partial x^\nu} V^\nu$$

$$= \frac{1}{\sqrt{(g)}}\frac{\partial \sqrt{(g)}V^\lambda}{\partial x^\lambda}. \tag{2.408}$$

Again let $T^{\mu\nu}$ be a contravariant tensor of rank two and let $T_{,\lambda}^{\mu\nu}$ be its covariant derivative; then $T_{,\lambda}^{\mu\lambda}$ is a vector associated with $T^{\mu\nu}$ and is called its *vectorial divergence*. The formula for the vectorial divergence is

$$T_{,\lambda}^{\mu\lambda} = \frac{\partial T^{\mu\lambda}}{\partial x^{\lambda}} + \left\{\begin{matrix}\mu\\\lambda\sigma\end{matrix}\right\}T^{\sigma\lambda} + \left\{\begin{matrix}\lambda\\\lambda\sigma\end{matrix}\right\}T^{\mu\sigma}$$

$$= \frac{1}{\sqrt{(g)}}\frac{\partial \sqrt{(g)}T^{\mu\lambda}}{\partial x^{\lambda}} + \left\{\begin{matrix}\mu\\\lambda\sigma\end{matrix}\right\}T^{\sigma\lambda}. \tag{2.409}$$

There is, however, a second vectorial divergence which is obtained by contracting with respect to the first contravariant index of $T^{\mu\nu}$, viz.

$$T_{,\lambda}^{\lambda\nu} = \frac{1}{\sqrt{(g)}}\frac{\partial \sqrt{(g)}T^{\lambda\nu}}{\partial x^{\lambda}} + \left\{\begin{matrix}\nu\\\lambda\sigma\end{matrix}\right\}T^{\lambda\sigma}.$$

These two vectorial divergences are equal if the tensor $T^{\mu\nu}$ is *symmetric*, i.e. if its components are such that $T^{\mu\nu} = T^{\nu\mu}$. In other cases, the two vectorial divergences obtained from the given tensor of rank two are not identical.

2.5. The Riemann-Christoffel and Ricci Tensors

There are two important tensors, one of rank four, $R_{\lambda\mu\nu}^{\sigma}$, and one of rank two, $R_{\lambda\mu}$, which involve the first and second partial derivatives of the coefficients of the metric and which arise by repeated application of the process of covariant differentiation to tensors. In the ordinary calculus, if $F(x)$ is a function of the n variables x^{λ}, the process of partial differentiation applied to the first partial derivative $\partial F/\partial x^{\mu}$ yields a second partial derivative $\partial^2 F/\partial x^{\mu}\partial x^{\nu}$ which, unless the function F is selected so as to have special properties, is equal to $\partial^2 F/\partial x^{\nu}\partial x^{\mu}$. Repetition of the process of covariant differentiation will certainly lead to a second covariant derivative (a tensor), but this will not, in general, have the symmetry property of an ordinary second partial derivative. Thus let $V_{\lambda,\mu}$ be the first covariant derivative of a covariant vector V_{λ} and let λ^{ν} as usual stand for the unit tangent vector to a geodesic. Then by (2.404)

$$V_{\lambda,\mu\nu} = \frac{\partial V_{\lambda,\mu}}{\partial x^{\nu}} - \left\{\begin{matrix}\tau\\\lambda\nu\end{matrix}\right\}V_{\tau,\mu} - \left\{\begin{matrix}\tau\\\mu\nu\end{matrix}\right\}V_{\lambda,\tau}$$

$$= \frac{\partial^2 V_{\lambda}}{\partial x^{\mu}\partial x^{\nu}} - \left\{\begin{matrix}\tau\\\lambda\nu\end{matrix}\right\}\frac{\partial V_{\tau}}{\partial x^{\mu}} - \left\{\begin{matrix}\tau\\\mu\nu\end{matrix}\right\}\frac{\partial V_{\lambda}}{\partial x^{\tau}} - \left\{\begin{matrix}\tau\\\lambda\mu\end{matrix}\right\}\frac{\partial V_{\tau}}{\partial x^{\nu}}$$

$$- V_{\tau}\frac{\partial}{\partial x^{\nu}}\left\{\begin{matrix}\tau\\\lambda\mu\end{matrix}\right\} + \left\{\begin{matrix}\tau\\\mu\nu\end{matrix}\right\}\left\{\begin{matrix}\sigma\\\tau\lambda\end{matrix}\right\}V_{\sigma} + \left\{\begin{matrix}\tau\\\lambda\nu\end{matrix}\right\}\left\{\begin{matrix}\sigma\\\mu\tau\end{matrix}\right\}V_{\sigma},$$

which is the component $V_{\lambda,\mu\nu}$ of the second covariant derivative of the vector V_{λ}, obtained by first differentiating covariantly with respect to x^{μ} and then with respect to x^{ν}. If the order of these two covariant differentiations is reversed the component $V_{\lambda,\nu\mu}$ of the second covariant derivative is obtained.

Since the difference of two tensors is a tensor, the quantities $V_{\lambda,\mu\nu} - V_{\lambda,\nu\mu}$ are components of a covariant tensor of rank three, and

$$V_{\lambda,\mu\nu} - V_{\lambda,\nu\mu} = \left[-\frac{\partial}{\partial x^\nu}\begin{Bmatrix}\sigma\\\lambda\mu\end{Bmatrix} + \frac{\partial}{\partial x^\mu}\begin{Bmatrix}\sigma\\\lambda\nu\end{Bmatrix} - \begin{Bmatrix}\tau\\\lambda\mu\end{Bmatrix}\begin{Bmatrix}\sigma\\\tau\nu\end{Bmatrix} + \begin{Bmatrix}\tau\\\lambda\nu\end{Bmatrix}\begin{Bmatrix}\sigma\\\mu\tau\end{Bmatrix} \right] V_\sigma.$$

By the quotient theorem, the expression in the square bracket must be the component of a tensor of rank four, contravariant as to the index σ and covariant as to λ, μ and ν. This tensor, called the *Riemann-Christoffel tensor*, is denoted by

$$R^\sigma_{\lambda\mu\nu} = \frac{\partial}{\partial x^\mu}\begin{Bmatrix}\sigma\\\lambda\nu\end{Bmatrix} - \frac{\partial}{\partial x^\nu}\begin{Bmatrix}\sigma\\\lambda\mu\end{Bmatrix} + \begin{Bmatrix}\tau\\\lambda\nu\end{Bmatrix}\begin{Bmatrix}\sigma\\\mu\tau\end{Bmatrix} - \begin{Bmatrix}\tau\\\lambda\mu\end{Bmatrix}\begin{Bmatrix}\sigma\\\tau\nu\end{Bmatrix}, \qquad (2.501)$$

and is constructed entirely out of the components of the metrical tensor $g_{\mu\nu}$ and their first and second partial derivatives. Its importance lies in the fact that it is the next most complicated tensor of a Riemannian space, after the metrical tensor itself, and it is intrinsically associated with the metric of the space. The covariant form of the Riemann-Christoffel tensor is

$$R_{\kappa\lambda\mu\nu} = g_{\sigma\kappa}R^\sigma_{\lambda\mu\nu} = g_{\sigma\kappa}\frac{\partial}{\partial x^\mu}[g^{\varepsilon\sigma}(\lambda\nu,\varepsilon)] - g_{\sigma\kappa}\frac{\partial}{\partial x^\nu}[g^{\varepsilon\sigma}(\lambda\mu,\varepsilon)] + \begin{Bmatrix}\tau\\\lambda\nu\end{Bmatrix}(\mu\tau,\kappa) - \begin{Bmatrix}\tau\\\lambda\mu\end{Bmatrix}(\tau\nu,\kappa)$$

$$= \frac{\partial}{\partial x^\mu}(\lambda\nu,\kappa) - \frac{\partial}{\partial x^\nu}(\lambda\mu,\kappa) + (\lambda\nu,\varepsilon)g_{\sigma\kappa}\frac{\partial g^{\varepsilon\sigma}}{\partial x^\mu} - (\lambda\mu,\varepsilon)g_{\sigma\kappa}\frac{\partial g^{\varepsilon\sigma}}{\partial x^\nu}$$

$$+ g^{\tau\sigma}[(\lambda\nu,\sigma)(\mu\tau,\kappa) - (\lambda\mu,\sigma)(\tau\nu,\kappa)].$$

But

$$g_{\sigma\kappa}\frac{\partial g^{\varepsilon\sigma}}{\partial x^\mu} = \frac{\partial}{\partial x^\mu}(g_{\sigma\kappa}g^{\varepsilon\sigma}) - g^{\varepsilon\sigma}\frac{\partial g_{\sigma\kappa}}{\partial x^\mu}$$

$$= \frac{\partial \delta^\sigma_\kappa}{\partial x^\mu} - g^{\varepsilon\sigma}\frac{\partial g_{\sigma\kappa}}{\partial x^\mu}$$

$$= -g^{\varepsilon\sigma}\frac{\partial g_{\sigma\kappa}}{\partial x^\mu}, \qquad (2.502)$$

and, since $g_{\sigma\kappa,\mu} = 0$,

$$\frac{\partial g_{\sigma\kappa}}{\partial x^\mu} = (\sigma\mu,\kappa) + (\kappa\mu,\sigma). \qquad (2.503)$$

Hence

$$R_{\kappa\lambda\mu\nu} = \frac{\partial}{\partial x^\mu}(\lambda\nu,\kappa) - \frac{\partial}{\partial x^\nu}(\lambda\mu,\kappa)$$

$$- g^{\varepsilon\sigma}\left[(\lambda\nu,\varepsilon)\frac{\partial g_{\sigma\kappa}}{\partial x^\mu} - (\lambda\mu,\varepsilon)\frac{\partial g_{\sigma\kappa}}{\partial x^\nu}\right]$$

$$+ g^{\varepsilon\sigma}[(\lambda\nu,\sigma)(\mu\varepsilon,\kappa) - (\lambda\mu,\sigma)(\varepsilon\nu,\kappa)];$$

thus interchanging summation suffixes ε, σ in the last square bracket and using (2.503), we find

$$R_{\kappa\lambda\mu\nu} = \frac{\partial}{\partial x^\mu}(\lambda\nu,\kappa) - \frac{\partial}{\partial x^\nu}(\lambda\mu,\kappa) + g^{\varepsilon\sigma}[(\lambda\mu,\varepsilon)(\kappa\nu,\sigma) - (\lambda\nu,\varepsilon)(\mu\kappa,\sigma)].$$

Substitution of the full expressions (2.304) for the Christoffel symbols of the first kind that occur in the first two terms leads to the covariant form of the Riemann-Christoffel tensor

$$R_{\kappa\lambda\mu\nu} = \tfrac{1}{2}\left[\frac{\partial^2 g_{\nu\kappa}}{\partial x^\lambda \partial x^\mu} + \frac{\partial^2 g_{\lambda\mu}}{\partial x^\nu \partial x^\kappa} - \frac{\partial^2 g_{\lambda\nu}}{\partial x^\mu \partial x^\kappa} - \frac{\partial^2 g_{\mu\kappa}}{\partial x^\nu \partial x^\lambda}\right]$$
$$+ g^{\varepsilon\sigma}[(\lambda\mu,\varepsilon)(\kappa\nu,\sigma) - (\lambda\nu,\varepsilon)(\kappa\mu,\sigma)]. \qquad (2.504)$$

It will be observed that the 'lowered' index in the covariant form of the Riemann-Christoffel tensor has been written as the first of the four covariant indices. With this convention as to the position of the indices the following symmetry and antisymmetry properties of the tensor may be noticed:

Interchange of the last pair of covariant indices changes the sign of a component, i.e.

$$R^\sigma_{\lambda\mu\nu} = -R^\sigma_{\lambda\nu\mu}, \qquad R_{\kappa\lambda\mu\nu} = -R_{\kappa\lambda\nu\mu}. \qquad (2.505)$$

The tensor is therefore said to be antisymmetrical with respect to these two indices. From formula (2.504) it is evident that the tensor is also antisymmetrical with respect to the first pair of indices and that it is symmetrical with respect to a double interchange of the indices in both the first and second pairs, i.e.

$$R_{\kappa\lambda\mu\nu} = -R_{\lambda\kappa\mu\nu}, \qquad R_{\kappa\lambda\mu\nu} = R_{\lambda\kappa\nu\mu}. \qquad (2.505)$$

Furthermore, the tensor is symmetrical with respect to an interchange of the pairs of indices, without change of order of the indices within each pair, i.e.

$$R_{\kappa\lambda\mu\nu} = R_{\mu\nu\kappa\lambda}. \qquad (2.505)$$

Lastly, the components of the tensor satisfy a *cyclical relation* which may be established thus: Let F be a scalar function of position, then

$$\frac{dF}{ds} = \frac{\partial F}{\partial x^\mu}\lambda^\mu$$

is a scalar for 'transportation' along a geodesic. Thus, by the quotient theorem,

$$X_\mu = \frac{\partial F}{\partial x_\mu}$$

is a covariant vector whose covariant derivative $X_{\mu,\nu}$ is such that

$$X_{\mu,\nu} = \frac{\partial X_\mu}{\partial x^\nu} - \left\{\begin{matrix}\sigma\\\mu\nu\end{matrix}\right\}X_\sigma = \frac{\partial^2 F}{\partial x^\mu \partial x^\nu} - \left\{\begin{matrix}\sigma\\\mu\nu\end{matrix}\right\}\frac{\partial F}{\partial x^\sigma} = X_{\nu,\mu}.$$

Hence $X_{\mu,\nu\lambda} = X_{\nu,\mu\lambda}$ and the following algebraic identity is true:

$$X_{\mu,\nu\lambda} - X_{\mu,\lambda\nu} + X_{\nu,\lambda\mu} - X_{\nu,\mu\lambda} + X_{\lambda,\mu\nu} - X_{\lambda,\nu\mu} = 0.$$

But by definition of the Riemann-Christoffel tensor

$$X_{\mu,\nu\lambda} - X_{\mu,\lambda\nu} = R^\sigma_{\mu\nu\lambda}X_\sigma$$

and the identity given above becomes

$$X_\sigma(R^\sigma_{\mu\nu\lambda} + R^\sigma_{\nu\lambda\mu} + R^\sigma_{\lambda\mu\nu}) = 0.$$

However, the scalar function F is arbitrary and therefore

$$R^\sigma_{\lambda\mu\nu} + R^\sigma_{\mu\nu\lambda} + R^\sigma_{\nu\lambda\mu} = 0. \qquad (2.506)$$

The upshot of this discussion of symmetry and antisymmetry properties is that the number of *independent* components of the Riemann-Christoffel tensor is not n^4 but a far more limited number. It can indeed be proved [2] that, in an n-dimensional Riemannian space, the independent covariant components are $n^2(n^2 - 1)/12$ in number.

In relativity theory applications of the tensor calculus a very important part is played by a symmetrical tensor of rank two, called the *Ricci tensor*, which is obtained by contraction from the Riemann-Christoffel tensor. Contracting in (2.501) the contravariant index with the last of the three covariant indices, a typical component of the Ricci tensor is

$$R_{\lambda\mu} = \frac{\partial}{\partial x^\mu}\left\{\begin{matrix}\sigma\\\lambda\sigma\end{matrix}\right\} - \frac{\partial}{\partial x^\sigma}\left\{\begin{matrix}\sigma\\\lambda\mu\end{matrix}\right\} + \left\{\begin{matrix}\tau\\\lambda\sigma\end{matrix}\right\}\left\{\begin{matrix}\sigma\\\mu\tau\end{matrix}\right\} - \left\{\begin{matrix}\tau\\\lambda\mu\end{matrix}\right\}\left\{\begin{matrix}\sigma\\\tau\sigma\end{matrix}\right\}$$

$$= \frac{\partial^2 \log \sqrt{g}}{\partial x^\mu \partial x^\lambda} - \frac{\partial}{\partial x^\sigma}\left\{\begin{matrix}\sigma\\\lambda\mu\end{matrix}\right\} + \left\{\begin{matrix}\tau\\\lambda\sigma\end{matrix}\right\}\left\{\begin{matrix}\sigma\\\mu\tau\end{matrix}\right\} - \left\{\begin{matrix}\tau\\\lambda\mu\end{matrix}\right\}\frac{\partial \log \sqrt{g}}{\partial x^\tau}. \tag{2.507}$$

The mixed form of this tensor is, of course, $R_\mu^\lambda = g^{\lambda\sigma}R_{\sigma\mu}$ from which a scalar, called the *curvature invariant*,[3] may be obtained by contraction, viz.

$$R_\lambda^\lambda = g^{\lambda\sigma}R_{\sigma\lambda}. \tag{2.508}$$

The Riemann-Christoffel tensor is also known as the *curvature tensor* because it does measure a property of the Riemannian space that is analogous to the curvature of a two-dimensional surface. This aspect of the tensor is, however, in the present author's view, of more value to those who are interested in geometrical applications of the tensor calculus than to those who intend to work in relativity theory. But it is nevertheless of interest to show, by considering the case of a spherical surface, how the association of the Riemann-Christoffel tensor with the concept of curvature comes into being. If the sphere is of radius a, the metric of its spherical surface is, by (2.203),

$$ds^2 = a^2(d\theta^2 + \sin^2 \theta \, d\phi^2),$$

and, with the identification $\theta = x^1$, $\phi = x^2$, the non-vanishing coefficients of the metric and their associated functions are

$$g_{11} = a^2, \qquad g_{22} = a^2 \sin^2 \theta,$$
$$g = a^4 \sin^2 \theta,$$
$$g^{11} = a^{-2}, \qquad g^{22} = a^{-2} \sin^{-2} \theta.$$

The non-vanishing Christoffel symbols are

$$(12,2) = (21,2) = -(22,1) = a^2 \sin \theta \cos \theta,$$
$$\{^1_{22}\} = -\tfrac{1}{2}\sin 2\theta, \qquad \{^2_{21}\} = \{^2_{12}\} = \cot \theta.$$

The relations (2.505), (2.506) show that there is but one independent component of the covariant Riemann-Christoffel tensor which, by (2.504), may be taken to be

$$R_{1221} = -a^2 \sin^2 \theta. \tag{2.509}$$

From formula (2.507) it follows that the Ricci tensor has two non-zero components, viz.

$$R_{11} = -1, \qquad R_{22} = -\sin^2 \theta,$$

while the curvature invariant is

$$R_\lambda^\lambda = g^{11} R_{11} + g^{22} R_{22} = -2/a^2.$$

Now the Gaussian curvature of a sphere of radius a is known to be $1/a^2$ and the last result shows that the curvature invariant is proportional to the Gaussian curvature. But even in this simplest possible case, neither the Riemann-Christoffel, nor the Ricci tensor, nor even the curvature invariant can simply be written down from a knowledge of the Gaussian curvature of the Riemannian space. When the space is of more than two dimensions, the relationship of these tensors to the 'curvature' of the space is even more remote [4] and, for this reason, the matter will not be discussed further here, except for the following remark. In certain Riemannian spaces of n dimensions it is possible to find a coordinate-system (X) covering all the points of the space, in terms of which the metric becomes

$$ds^2 = \sum_{\lambda=1}^{n} \varepsilon_\lambda (dX^\lambda)^2, \tag{2.510}$$

where the ε_λ are positive or negative *constants*. From (2.304) it then follows that all the Christoffel symbols are identically zero and consequently from (2.504), (2.507) and (2.508), that the Riemann-Christoffel and Ricci tensors, and the curvature invariant, are also all identically zero. Such spaces are called *flat* by analogy with the Euclidean plane whose metric (2.201) is of type (2.510) when Cartesian coordinates are used. It will now also be seen that the Riemann-Christoffel tensor is an indicator of the flatness or otherwise of a Riemannian space [5]: if the space is flat this tensor is identically zero and this null-character cannot be destroyed by a coordinate-transformation. Thus non-flatness is a property of the Riemannian space that is intrinsic and does not depend on the particular coordinate-system in terms of which the metric has been expressed. Examples of flat three-dimensional spaces are the ordinary Euclidean space with metric (2.202) and the space whose metric is (2.206). A Riemannian space that is not flat will be called a *curved* space; the reader need not, however, strive to imagine what this term means with respect to the 'amount of bending' of the space. A curved space, for the purposes of this book, is simply one whose Riemann-Christoffel tensor does not vanish identically at one, at least, of the points of the space.

2.6. Local Cartesian and Riemannian Coordinates

In a Riemannian space of n dimensions there are certain types of special coordinate-systems which are useful for describing the points lying in the neighbourhood of a given point O. The first system of this kind which will be discussed is the *local Cartesian* which exists at any point of a Riemannian space of any type. However, we give the proof only for a Riemannian space which admits coordinate-systems in terms of which the metric is orthogonal, i.e.

$$ds^2 = \sum_{\lambda=1}^{n} \varepsilon_\lambda \gamma_{\lambda\lambda}(x)(dx^\lambda)^2, \tag{2.601}$$

where $g_{\lambda\lambda} = \varepsilon_\lambda \gamma_{\lambda\lambda}$ and the ε_λ are equal to either $+1$ or -1. Let the point O have coordinates (x_0) and consider the coordinates

$$X^\lambda = \gamma_{\lambda\lambda}^{\frac{1}{2}}(x_0)(x^\lambda - x_0^\lambda), \qquad (\lambda = 1, 2, 3, \ldots, n), \tag{2.602}$$

the summation convention being suspended. The differentials of these coordinates are

$$dX^\lambda = \gamma_{\lambda\lambda}^{\frac{1}{2}}(x_0)dx^\lambda, \tag{2.603}$$

and therefore on substitution into (2.601), the metric becomes

$$ds^2 = \sum_{\lambda=1}^{n} \varepsilon_\lambda (dX^\lambda)^2, \tag{2.604}$$

which is identical with the metric (2.510) of a flat space. The coordinates X^λ are called *local Cartesians* and are valid for those points near enough to O for the differences $\gamma_{\lambda\lambda}^{\frac{1}{2}}(x) - \gamma_{\lambda\lambda}^{\frac{1}{2}}(x_0)$ to be of order not exceeding $x^\lambda - x_0^\lambda$. If the space were indeed flat, then it would be possible to integrate the differential equations

$$\frac{dX^\lambda}{dx^\lambda} = \gamma_{\lambda\lambda}^{\frac{1}{2}}(x),$$

a process that cannot be performed in a curved Riemannian space.

The second important type of local coordinates is called *Riemannian coordinates* and it will be shown that *at the origin of Riemannian coordinates, the Christoffel symbols of both kinds, and the first order partial derivatives of the $g_{\mu\nu}$, all vanish*. The proof of this theorem is the following: Let O be the preassigned point with coordinates (x_0) and consider the family of geodesics that pass through O, each geodesic being specified by its unit tangent vector λ_0^σ at O. Using the suffix zero to denote values calculated at O, it follows from (2.305) that

$$\left(\frac{d\lambda^\sigma}{ds}\right)_0 = -\begin{Bmatrix} \sigma \\ \mu\nu \end{Bmatrix} \lambda_0^\mu \lambda_0^\nu, \tag{2.605}$$

and, by differentiating (2.305) once with respect to s, that

$$\left(\frac{d^2\lambda^\sigma}{ds^2}\right)_0 = A_{\mu\nu\tau}^\sigma \lambda_0^\mu \lambda_0^\nu \lambda_0^\tau, \tag{2.606}$$

where

$$A_{\mu\nu\tau}^\sigma = \left[-\frac{\partial}{\partial x^\tau}\begin{Bmatrix} \sigma \\ \mu\nu \end{Bmatrix} + 2\begin{Bmatrix} \sigma \\ \tau\alpha \end{Bmatrix}\begin{Bmatrix} \alpha \\ \mu\nu \end{Bmatrix} \right]_0.$$

Further differentiations of (2.305) with respect to s would provide the values of higher derivatives of λ_0^σ, but these are not needed for the present purpose. Consider now a point P on one of the geodesics passing through O, the interval being reckoned to have the value zero at O and s at P. Then the coordinates of P can be expressed in terms of those of O by means of Taylor series, viz.

$$x^\sigma = x_0^\sigma + \lambda_0^\sigma s + \tfrac{1}{2}\left(\frac{d\lambda^\sigma}{ds}\right)_0 s^2 + \tfrac{1}{6}\left(\frac{d^2\lambda^\sigma}{ds^2}\right)_0 s^3 + \dots, \ (\sigma = 1, 2, 3, \dots, n),$$

which, by (2.605) and (2.606), are

$$x^\sigma = x_0^\sigma + \lambda_0^\sigma s - \tfrac{1}{2}\left\{{\sigma \atop \mu\nu}\right\}_0 \lambda_0^\mu \lambda_0^\nu s^2 + \tfrac{1}{6}A_{\mu\nu\tau}^\sigma \lambda_0^\mu \lambda_0^\nu \lambda_0^\tau s^3 + \dots \qquad (2.607)$$

Suppose that a new coordinate-system, with origin at O, is defined, in which the coordinates of P are

$$y^\sigma = \lambda_0^\sigma s, \qquad (\sigma = 1, 2, 3, \dots, n), \qquad (2.608)$$

then (2.607) becomes

$$x^\sigma - x_0^\sigma = y_0^\sigma - \tfrac{1}{2}\left\{{\sigma \atop \mu\nu}\right\}_0 y^\mu y^\nu + \tfrac{1}{6}A_{\mu\nu\tau}^\sigma y^\mu y^\nu y^\tau + \dots, \qquad (2.609)$$

which are the transformation formulae from the system (x) to the system (y) and are valid within the domain of convergence of the series on the right-hand side. The metric of the space is

$$ds^2 = g_{\mu\nu}(x)dx^\mu dx^\nu$$

and becomes

$$ds^2 = g'_{\mu\nu}(y)dy^\mu dy^\nu$$

when the coordinate-system is transformed by (2.609). In terms of the (y) system, the equations of the geodesics are

$$\frac{d^2 y^\sigma}{ds^2} + \left\{{\sigma \atop \mu\nu}\right\}' \frac{dy^\mu}{ds}\frac{dy^\nu}{ds} = 0, \qquad (2.610)$$

where the prime indicates that the Christoffel symbols are calculated for $g'_{\mu\nu}(y)$. But the finite equations of the geodesics in the (y) system are (2.608), which must be solutions of the differential equations (2.610). Substitution therefore gives, at O,

$$\left\{{\sigma \atop \mu\nu}\right\}_0' \lambda_0^\mu \lambda_0^\nu = 0$$

and, since the λ_0^μ may refer to any one of the geodesics through O, it follows that

$$\left\{{\sigma \atop \mu\nu}\right\}_0' = 0, \qquad (\sigma, \mu, \nu = 1, 2, 3, \dots, n).$$

Hence, by (2.304), all the Christoffel symbols of the first kind are also zero at O and from (2.304), (2.503) it follows that

$$\left(\frac{\partial g'_{\mu\nu}}{\partial y^\sigma}\right)_0 = 0, \qquad (\sigma, \mu, \nu = 1, 2, 3, \dots, n),$$

which completes the proof of the theorem. A corollary is that, at the origin of Riemannian coordinates, covariant derivatives reduce to ordinary partial derivatives.

2.7. The Bianchi Identity and the Einstein Tensor

With the aid of Riemannian coordinates, it is possible to establish an identity, called the Bianchi identity, which is fundamental to relativity theory. If O is any point of the Riemannian space at which the Riemannian coordinates are (y) then, by (2.501) and the results of the previous section, the expression for the mixed Riemann-Christoffel tensor evaluated at O is

$$R^{\sigma}_{\lambda\mu\nu} = \frac{\partial}{\partial y^{\mu}}\left\{{\sigma \atop \lambda\nu}\right\} - \frac{\partial}{\partial y^{\nu}}\left\{{\sigma \atop \lambda\mu}\right\},$$

and the covariant derivative of this tensor is

$$R^{\sigma}_{\lambda\mu\nu,\tau} = \frac{\partial^2}{\partial y^{\mu}\partial y^{\tau}}\left\{{\sigma \atop \lambda\nu}\right\} - \frac{\partial^2}{\partial y^{\nu}\partial y^{\tau}}\left\{{\sigma \atop \lambda\mu}\right\}.$$

Permuting cyclically the indices μ, ν, τ and adding the resulting equations, we obtain the *Bianchi identity*

$$R^{\sigma}_{\lambda\mu\nu,\tau} + R^{\sigma}_{\lambda\nu\tau,\mu} + R^{\sigma}_{\lambda\tau\mu,\nu} = 0. \tag{2.701}$$

Though this identity has been established by the use of a special coordinate-system, it is a tensor equation and therefore holds good in any coordinate-system. Suppose therefore that (x) is an arbitrarily selected coordinate-system in the Riemannian space. Contraction of (2.701) with respect to σ and ν yields

$$R_{\lambda\mu,\tau} + R^{\sigma}_{\lambda\sigma\tau,\mu} + R^{\sigma}_{\lambda\tau\mu,\sigma} = 0,$$

and, remembering that the $g_{\mu\nu}$ may be treated as constants in covariant differentiation,

$$R^{\rho}_{\mu,\tau} + (g^{\lambda\rho}R^{\sigma}_{\lambda\sigma\tau})_{,\mu} + (g^{\lambda\rho}R^{\sigma}_{\lambda\tau\mu})_{,\sigma} = 0.$$

But, by the symmetry properties (2.505) of the Riemann-Christoffel tensor,

$$g^{\lambda\rho}R^{\sigma}_{\lambda\sigma\tau} = -g^{\lambda\rho}R^{\sigma}_{\lambda\tau\sigma} = -R^{\rho}_{\tau},$$
$$g^{\lambda\rho}R^{\sigma}_{\lambda\tau\mu} = g^{\lambda\rho}g^{\sigma\kappa}R_{\kappa\lambda\tau\mu} = g^{\sigma\kappa}g^{\lambda\rho}R_{\lambda\kappa\mu\tau}$$
$$= g^{\sigma\kappa}R^{\rho}_{\kappa\mu\tau}.$$

Hence

$$R^{\rho}_{\mu,\tau} - R^{\rho}_{\tau,\mu} + (g^{\sigma\kappa}R^{\rho}_{\kappa\mu\tau})_{,\sigma} = 0,$$

or, contracting again with respect to ρ and τ

$$R^{\rho}_{\mu,\rho} - R^{\rho}_{\rho,\mu} + (g^{\sigma\kappa}R_{\kappa\mu})_{,\sigma} = 0.$$

Changing the summation index σ in the last term to ρ, the last equation is

$$2R^{\rho}_{\mu,\rho} - R^{\rho}_{\rho,\mu} = 0. \tag{2.702}$$

But, if $2\varLambda$ is an arbitrary constant

$$R^{\rho}_{\rho,\mu} = \frac{\partial R^{\rho}_{\rho}}{\partial x^{\mu}} = \frac{\partial(R^{\rho}_{\rho} - 2\varLambda)}{\partial x^{\mu}} = \frac{\partial}{\partial x^{\sigma}}\{\delta^{\sigma}_{\mu}(R^{\rho}_{\rho} - 2\varLambda)\},$$

and therefore (2.702) may be written in its final form

$$\{R_\mu^\sigma - \tfrac{1}{2}\delta_\mu^\sigma(R_\rho^\rho - 2\Lambda)\}_{,\sigma} = 0. \tag{2.703}$$

This equation states that *the vectorial divergence of the Einstein tensor*, $R_\mu^\sigma - \tfrac{1}{2}\delta_\mu^\sigma(R_\rho^\rho - 2\Lambda)$, *vanishes identically*, a result of fundamental importance in the applications of tensor calculus to relativity theory. By raising or lowering indices, the Einstein tensor may take any one of the following three forms:

$$\left.\begin{array}{ll} \text{Covariant} & R_{\mu\nu} - \tfrac{1}{2}g_{\mu\nu}(R_\rho^\rho - 2\Lambda), \\ \text{Mixed} & R_\nu^\mu - \tfrac{1}{2}\delta_\nu^\mu (R_\rho^\rho - 2\Lambda), \\ \text{Contravariant} & R^{\mu\nu} - \tfrac{1}{2}g^{\mu\nu}(R_\rho^\rho - 2\Lambda), \end{array}\right\} \tag{2.704}$$

and, since the Ricci tensor, $R_{\mu\nu}$, and the metrical tensor, $g_{\mu\nu}$, are symmetrical tensors, so also is the Einstein tensor.

2.8. Tensor Calculus in Relativity Theory

The Riemannian spaces employed in relativity theory are of four dimensions, each point in them therefore being specified by four real coordinates (x^4, x^1, x^2, x^3). The metrics of these Riemannian spaces are

$$ds^2 = g_{\mu\nu}dx^\mu dx^\nu, \qquad (\mu,\nu = 1, 2, 3, 4), \tag{2.801}$$

and the spaces are restricted to those which have the following property: If local Cartesian coordinates are introduced at any point, so that the metric becomes

$$ds^2 = \sum_{\lambda=1}^{4} \varepsilon_\lambda(dX^\lambda)^2,$$

then *one of the four ε_λ is of opposite sign to the other three*. The sub-class of such Riemannian spaces whose metrics are orthogonal plays an important role in relativity theory; in these

$$ds^2 = \gamma_{44}(dx^4)^2 - \gamma_{11}(dx^1)^2 - \gamma_{22}(dx^2)^2 - \gamma_{33}(dx^3)^2, \tag{2.802}$$

where γ_{44}, γ_{11}, γ_{22}, γ_{33} are positive functions of the four coordinates. The non-zero components of the metrical tensor are

$$g_{44} = \gamma_{44}, \qquad g_{11} = -\gamma_{11}, \qquad g_{22} = -\gamma_{22}, \qquad g_{33} = -\gamma_{33}. \tag{2.803}$$

It is now convenient to introduce the convention that a *latin* index can take the values 1, 2, 3 only, whereas a *greek* index takes on all four values 1, 2, 3, 4. The indices *lmn* will be reserved to stand for any cyclic permutation of the numbers 123. The determinant of the coefficients of the metric is

$$g = g_{44}g_{11}g_{22}g_{33} = -\gamma_{44}\gamma_{11}\gamma_{22}\gamma_{33}, \tag{2.804}$$

and therefore has a negative value. This is inconvenient in practice but the difficulty can be overcome by noticing that, wherever g enters into a formula that has to be calculated in detail, its presence is ultimately due to the use of

D

(2.407). Examples will be found in (2.408), (2.409) or (2.507). But (2.407) may be written

$$\begin{Bmatrix} \lambda \\ \lambda\nu \end{Bmatrix} = \tfrac{1}{2}\frac{1}{g}\frac{\partial g}{\partial x^\nu} = \tfrac{1}{2}\frac{1}{(-g)}\frac{\partial(-g)}{\partial x^\nu} = \frac{\partial \log \sqrt{(-g)}}{\partial x^\nu},$$

and therefore $\sqrt{(g)}$ may be replaced by $\sqrt{(-g)}$ in the formulae quoted.

The contravariant components of the metrical tensor for the metric (2.802) are, by (2.210) and (2.803), (2.804),

$$g^{44} = \frac{1}{g_{44}} = \frac{1}{\gamma_{44}}, \qquad g^{ii} = \frac{1}{g_{ii}} = -\frac{1}{\gamma_{ii}}, \qquad (i = 1, 2, 3), \tag{2.805}$$

while the non-zero Christoffel symbols are ($\lambda \neq \mu$)

$$\left. \begin{aligned}
(\lambda\mu,\lambda) &= -(\lambda\lambda,\mu) = \tfrac{1}{2}\frac{\partial g_{\lambda\lambda}}{\partial x^\mu}, \qquad (\lambda\lambda,\lambda) = \tfrac{1}{2}\frac{\partial g_{\lambda\lambda}}{\partial x^\lambda}, \\
\begin{Bmatrix} \lambda \\ \mu\mu \end{Bmatrix} = -\tfrac{1}{2}\frac{1}{g_{\lambda\lambda}}\frac{\partial g_{\mu\mu}}{\partial x^\lambda}, \quad \begin{Bmatrix} \lambda \\ \lambda\mu \end{Bmatrix} = \tfrac{1}{2}\frac{\partial \log g_{\lambda\lambda}}{\partial x^\mu}, \quad \begin{Bmatrix} \lambda \\ \lambda\lambda \end{Bmatrix} = \tfrac{1}{2}\frac{\partial \log g_{\lambda\lambda}}{\partial x^\lambda},
\end{aligned} \right\} \tag{2.806}$$

the summation convention being suspended. Finally the equations (2.303) of the geodesics become

$$\frac{d}{ds}\left(g_{\lambda\lambda}\frac{dx^\lambda}{ds}\right) - \tfrac{1}{2}\sum_{\nu=1}^{4}\frac{\partial g_{\nu\nu}}{\partial x^\lambda}\left(\frac{dx^\nu}{ds}\right)^2 = 0, \qquad (\lambda = 1, 2, 3, 4), \tag{2.807}$$

with a similar form for the null-geodesic equations (2.310), and the integrals (2.307) and (2.308) now read, respectively,

$$\sum_{\nu=1}^{4} g_{\nu\nu}\left(\frac{dx^\nu}{ds}\right)^2 = 1, \tag{2.808}$$

$$\sum_{\nu=1}^{4} g_{\nu\nu}\left(\frac{dx^\nu}{d\mu}\right)^2 = 0. \tag{2.809}$$

CHAPTER 3

Newtonian Mechanics and Special Relativity

3.1. Newtonian Mechanics of a Particle

In order to have a clear understanding of general relativity it is also necessary to know something about the two theories of mechanics which preceded it, the Newtonian theory and the theory of special relativity. An exhaustive account of these disciplines will not here be, attempted, but certain important points must be emphasized.

It is a truism that the position and motion of one body cannot be assigned and described except with reference to some other body. The genius of Newton avoided this complication by introducing into his system of mechanics two postulates that underlie his three Laws of Motion. The first postulate was that there exists a universal absolute time in terms of which every event that is observed can be unequivocally dated; and the second postulate was that there is an absolute Euclidean three-dimensional space wherein every body can be located, at any instant of absolute time, in a unique manner. The metric of the space, in terms of rectangular Cartesian coordinates, is of the form (2.202), a formula that it is now convenient to write as

$$ds^2 = dX_1^2 + dX_2^2 + dX_3^2, \tag{3.101}$$

using (X_1, X_2, X_3) for the three Cartesian coordinates. Newtonian theory does not, however, contain any rules as to how the absolute time and the absolute coordinate-system are to be identified. In practice, absolute time is identified with a time defined by the motions of the bodies of the solar system. But clearly this is a pragmatic definition, without logical necessity, its justification lying in the fact that it enables predictions to be made that are in conformity with observation. Apart from this difficulty, there is also the question of deciding how two events, widely separated in space, can be identified as being simultaneous. Suppose that at one place, A, on the Earth's surface there occurs an event which purports to be simultaneous with another event occurring at a distant point B on the Earth. One way of deciding whether or not the two events are simultaneous would be to transport the clock at A to the point B and compare its reading with the clock at the latter place. But this assumes that the transportation of the clock at A does not in any way affect its rate of working. Alternatively, radio time-signals might be used, but this again implies that the motion of electromagnetic waves is known. In either case, the establishment of the simultaneity of two events, so widely separated in space that no one observer can experience both, is a matter of carrying out some specified procedure and performing certain calculations. And it is not self-evident that simultaneity defined by one procedure and one kind of calculation will also give rise to simultaneity when another procedure and type of calculation are used. The question of identifying absolute space is still more difficult, even if the problem is reduced to identifying some fundamental Cartesian coordinate-system, so to speak 'anchored' in this space. Is the origin of this coordinate-system to be in the Earth, in the Sun, in the so-called fixed stars, or elsewhere? Again, there is no difficulty in practice: the Gordian knot is cut by simply asserting that a particular coordinate-system is the fundamental one, continuing to use it until a contradiction with observation is reached, and then identifying some other system in its place. Thus in engineering experiments in the laboratory, a coordinate-system with origin at a point on the Earth's surface can secure complete agreement with observation. But if this system is used in meteorological theory or in long-range ballistics, contradictions with the observed facts arise that can, however, be removed by identifying the fundamental system with one whose origin is at the centre of the Earth. With respect to this new system, the original one is no longer regarded as being 'anchored' in the absolute Euclidean space but in some unspecified sense 'in motion' relative to it.

The simplest kind of body contemplated in Newtonian mechanics is the 'particle' which is envisaged as having no extension in space but as possessing an absolute scalar attribute called 'mass'. It is thus in theory describable as occupying at any instant a mathematical point. But the notion of a particle is conceptual: there is no upper limit to the size of a body which can be regarded as a particle. For example, in elementary planetary theory, the Earth, the Sun and the other planets of the solar system are all 'particles'; in elementary ballistics the Earth becomes a body of effectively infinite extension in space while the 'particle' is now, for instance, a rifle bullet. Thus it is impossible to identify a particle in any absolute sense: the meaning of the concept changes according to the phenomena which are under discussion.

Newton's First Law of Motion may be stated mathematically by saying that the equations of motion of a free particle in terms of the absolute Cartesian coordinate-system, are

$$\frac{d^2 X_i}{dT^2} = 0, \qquad (i = 1, 2, 3), \tag{3.102}$$

where (X_1, X_2, X_3) are the coordinates of the particle at absolute time T. These equations control the motion of the particle and are independent of its mass, shape, temperature and other physical attributes. The Second Law of Motion may be stated as

$$m\frac{d^2 X_i}{dT^2} = F_i, \qquad (i = 1, 2, 3), \tag{3.103}$$

where m is the mass of the particle and (F_1, F_2, F_3) is the force acting on it. The Third Law of Motion is most easily expressed in words and asserts that, if there are two interacting bodies, the forces which each exerts on the other are equal and opposite. It is worthy of note that the acceleration of a particle varies inversely as its mass for the application of a given force, as is obvious by inspection of equations (3.103).

The equations (3.102) and (3.103) may be used to show that there is not one but an infinity of absolute Cartesian coordinate-systems in the following way: Since we have not been able to give a definition of an absolute system, let us assume that an absolute system is one in which the First and Second Laws for the motion of a particle are expressible by equations (3.102) and (3.103). Consider then a transformation from a coordinate-system (X) to a system (X') given by the equations

$$T' = T, \qquad X'_1 = X_1 - uT, \qquad X'_2 = X_2, \qquad X'_3 = X_3, \tag{3.104}$$

where u is a constant. This means that the two systems have parallel directions for their coordinate-axes, that their origins coincided at $T = 0$ and that the origin of one of them moves with uniform speed along the common axes. It is assumed in Newtonian mechanics that the components of a force depend only on the directions of the coordinate-axes of a Cartesian system and not on whether this system is in motion relative to some other system. Hence the transformed equations (3.102) and (3.103) are

$$\frac{d^2 X'_i}{(dT')^2} = 0, \qquad m\frac{d^2 X'_i}{(dT')^2} = F_i, \tag{3.105}$$

and their mathematical form has therefore not been changed by passage from one of the systems (3.104) to the other. Both these systems may therefore be regarded as being 'fundamental' or, to give them their technical name, both are *Newtonian inertial systems*. This equivalence of Newtonian inertial systems, which are in uniform relative motion with respect to one another, only serves to make yet more nebulous the notion that they are somehow 'anchored' in the absolute Euclidean space of Newtonian theory.

The velocity of a moving particle is dX_i/dT, $(i = 1, 2, 3)$ in one of the two inertial systems (3.104) but is

$$\frac{dX'_1}{dT} = \frac{dX_1}{dT} - u, \qquad \frac{dX'_2}{dT} = \frac{dX_2}{dT}, \qquad \frac{dX'_3}{dT} = \frac{dX_3}{dT} \tag{3.106}$$

in the other. Thus although the acceleration of the particle has the same value in the two systems, this is not true, with one exception, for its velocity. The exception occurs when the magnitude of the velocity of the particle is infinitely large relative to one inertial system provided, of course, that u is finite. Denoting by $\mathscr{C}$ a velocity of infinite magnitude, then

$$\mathscr{C}^2 = \sum_{i=1}^{3} \left(\frac{dX'_i}{dT}\right)^2$$

$$= \left(\frac{dX_1}{dT} - u\right)^2 + \left(\frac{dX_2}{dT}\right)^2 + \left(\frac{dX_3}{dT}\right)^2$$

$$= \sum_{i=1}^{3} \left(\frac{dX_i}{dT}\right)^2,$$

because u is negligibly small compared with one at least of the velocity-components dX_i/dT. Hence in Newtonian mechanics the infinitely large velocity $\mathscr{C}$ is an absolute velocity in the sense that a particle possesses it in all Newtonian inertial systems, the transformation from one system to another making no change in the magnitude of this velocity.

3.2. Newtonian Mechanics of Extended Bodies

The reader will be aware that Newtonian mechanics can be extended to deal with bodies that are not point-masses but are of finite size. One way of doing this is to define the so-called rigid body which is conceived of as a set of particles whose mutual distances apart remain invariant during the motion of the body. This concept is a definite one because of the assumed existence of an absolute space and an absolute time. At any given instant of absolute time each constituent particle of the body can be described unambiguously as occupying a point of absolute space, and the notion of the invariance of the mutual distances apart of the particles is clear and meaningful. The motion of a rigid body entails, for its complete description, the notions of moments and products of inertia, of centres of mass, of angular momentum, etc., and of all the concepts associated with rotation. It might be thought that, when the Newtonian theory comes to be modified in special and general relativity, these modifications would incorporate some analogue of Newtonian rigid-body dynamics, since they certainly will include particle dynamics. But this is not the case: the path of development has started instead from a different aspect of Newtonian theory, the hydrodynamics of non-rigid continuous media.

In general relativity, the continuous medium that plays the most important role is the perfect fluid, whose Newtonian dynamics we shall now briefly describe. For our present purpose the fluid need not be conceived of as consisting of particles but as a continuous distribution of matter possessing a density, i.e. a mass per unit volume. If any imaginary surface is drawn in the fluid, the fluid on either side of this surface exerts a force on the fluid on the other side which is normal to the surface. It may then be deduced that at each point of the fluid, this force, or stress, is independent of direction. It is called the isotropic pressure in the fluid. Consider, then, a perfect fluid of density ρ and pressure p whose motion is to be described in terms of a Newtonian inertial system with Cartesian coordinates X_i, $(i = 1, 2, 3)$. At the point (X_1, X_2, X_3) the fluid is assumed to have a velocity whose components are (U_1, U_2, U_3), these three quantities being functions of the three X_i and of T. By considering the conservation of linear momentum of the material in an infinitesimal volume of absolute space, it can be proved that the equations of motion of the fluid are

$$\frac{\partial U_i}{\partial T} + \sum_{j=1}^{3} U_j \frac{\partial U_i}{\partial X_j} = -\frac{1}{\rho} \frac{\partial p}{\partial X_i} + F_i, \qquad (i = 1, 2, 3), \qquad (3.201)$$

where the three quantities $-\partial p/\partial X_i$ are the components of the pressure-gradient force and the three F_i are the components of the force per unit mass due to all other causes. In addition to the equations of motion, there is in Newtonian hydrodynamics an additional equation which expresses the conservation of mass within the unit volume. It is called the equation of continuity and reads

$$\frac{\partial \rho}{\partial T} + \sum_{j=1}^{3} \frac{\partial \rho U_j}{\partial X_j} = 0. \qquad (3.202)$$

If the equations (3.201) are multiplied throughout by ρ they may also be written, using the notation of Sec. (2.8), the definition (2.112) of δ_μ^λ and the fact that the distinction between covariance and contravariance disappears in Euclidean space when Cartesians are used,

$$\frac{\partial \rho U_i}{\partial T} + \frac{\partial}{\partial X_j}(\rho U_i U_j + \delta_{ij} p) - U_i \left(\frac{\partial \rho}{\partial T} + \frac{\partial \rho U_j}{\partial X_j} \right) = \rho F_i.$$

Hence, by (3.202), an equivalent form for the equations of motion is

$$\frac{\partial \rho U_i}{\partial T} + \frac{\partial}{\partial X_j}(\rho U_i U_j + \delta_{ij} p) = \rho F_i, \qquad (i = 1, 2, 3). \qquad (3.203)$$

Thus the motion of a perfect fluid in Newtonian hydrodynamics is described by the four equations (3.202) and (3.203) which contain the partial derivatives of the ten functions ρ, ρU_i and $(\rho U_i U_j + \delta_{ij} p)$ on their left-hand sides and either zero, or the external force-components F_i on their right-hand sides. An important characteristic of these equations is that, even if the force F_i is given as a function of the coordinates, there are only four equations for the five unknowns ρ, p and the three U_i. Hence by themselves the equations are indeterminate and it is necessary to introduce some further relation between the density, pressure and/or the velocity of the fluid before a solution of the equations can be obtained. This additional relation may be found in the principle of the conservation of energy, one form of which will be discussed below[1].

The indeterminateness of the hydrodynamical equations is also easily over-come when the fluid is a liquid, because a liquid is to all intents and purposes incompressible. The *constant* ρ = constant is therefore applicable and is basic to the massive theory of hydrodynamics, properly so called, that was largely developed in the nineteenth and early twentieth centuries. In more recent times, however, attention has turned to another aspect of hydro-dynamics, called gas-dynamics, in which gases, which are compressible fluids, are in question. A perfect gas, of unit effective molecular weight, is a fluid which possesses an *equation of state*, relating its pressure, density and tem-perature, that may be written

$$p = \mathscr{R}\rho\mathscr{T}, \tag{3.204}$$

where $\mathscr{T}$ is the temperature on the absolute scale and $\mathscr{R}$ (= $8\cdot314 \times 10^7$ erg/deg.) is the gas constant. Because of the introduction of the temperature, equations (3.202) to (3.204) still form an indeterminate set, but it is now poss-ible to appeal to thermodynamics for additional equations. Heat is a form of energy, the amount of heat required to raise the temperature of 1 gram of water from $14\cdot5°$ C. to $15\cdot5°$ C., when the pressure is 760 mm. of Hg, being equivalent to a mechanical energy of amount $\mathscr{J} = 4\cdot185 \times 10^7$ ergs/cal. In the case of gases, different amounts of heat are required to raise unit mass of the substance through one degree of temperature according as the unit mass is confined within rigid boundaries or is free to expand against the pressure of the surrounding gas, the pressure remaining constant. This gives rise to the notions of the specific heat at constant volume, c_v, and to that at constant pressure, c_p, whose ratio is $\gamma = c_p/c_v$. It is proved in treatises on thermo-dynamics that if dQ is the amount of heat added to unit specific volume of the gas, with a consequent increase of temperature $d\mathscr{T}$ and increase of volume $d(1/\rho)$, then

$$\mathscr{J}dQ = \mathscr{J}c_v d\mathscr{T} + pd(1/\rho)$$

or, if the unit mass be regarded as being in motion,

$$\mathscr{J}\frac{dQ}{dT} = \mathscr{J}c_v\frac{d\mathscr{T}}{dT} + p\frac{d}{dT}\left(\frac{1}{\rho}\right), \tag{3.205}$$

where d/dT is the operator, 'following the motion',

$$\frac{d}{dT} = \frac{\partial}{\partial T} + U_j\frac{\partial}{\partial X_j}. \tag{3.206}$$

The density ρ may be eliminated from (3.205) with the help of (3.204); with the aid of the known relationship

$$\mathscr{R} = \mathscr{J}c_v(\gamma - 1), \tag{3.207}$$

equation (3.205) becomes

$$\frac{1}{c_v\mathscr{T}}\frac{dQ}{dT} = \frac{d}{dT}(\log p - \gamma \log \rho).$$

In thermodynamics, there is a quantity called the *entropy* that is defined by $dQ/\mathscr{T}$ for the unit mass under consideration. For our present purpose it is more convenient to assume that the specific heat at constant volume is constant for a given gas, and to define the entropy as

$$dS = \frac{dQ}{c_v \mathscr{T}}.$$

Thus the first and second laws of thermodynamics finally give rise to

$$\frac{dS}{dT} = \frac{d}{dT}(\log p - \gamma \log \rho), \tag{3.208}$$

or, on integration following the motion of a unit mass of gas, to

$$S = \log \bar{\eta} + \log p - \gamma \log \rho, \tag{3.209}$$

where $\bar{\eta}$ is a constant that may differ from unit mass to unit mass in a certain distribution of gas. But if the entropy of every unit mass is constant and has the same value, it follows that

$$p = \eta \rho^{\gamma}, \tag{3.210}$$

where η is now an absolute constant.

The indeterminacy of the five equations (3.202) to (3.204) for the six unknowns $\rho, p, \mathscr{T}$ and the three U_i, may now be resolved by imposing conditions on the entropy S. An *adiabatic* flow is one in which each unit mass of the gas preserves its entropy, but each mass need not have the same entropy. By (3.208) this condition is

$$0 = \frac{d}{dT}(\log p - \gamma \log \rho). \tag{3.211}$$

When all unit masses have one and the same constant entropy, the pressure and density are related by the *isentropic* equation (3.210). In gas-dynamics this equation is often loosely referred to as the 'equation of state' of the gas, but this is a misnomer; the equation of state is the defining relation (3.204), while equations (3.211) and (3.210) are merely special possibilities arising from particular assumptions as to the thermodynamic behaviour of the gas.

3.3. Newtonian Gravitational Theory

The phenomenon of gravitation presents itself in the first instance to the scientist in the observation that all bodies released near the surface of the Earth fall towards it with the same constant acceleration g. In saying this, of course, abstraction is made of accidental features of the motion, such as the friction of the air. The acceleration appears to be independent of all physical characteristics of the moving body, its shape, mass, temperature, presumed internal constitution, and so forth. In this respect, the body moves like one obeying Newton's First Law of Motion, when again none of the physical attributes come into play, *except* that the body's velocity is not now uniform. The presence of the acceleration g, in Newtonian gravitational theory, is regarded as evidence of the operation of a force in the sense of Newton's Second Law, which is called the Force of Gravity. This force, however, has a very peculiar characteristic when it is compared with the other forces that occur in nature, for example, that exerted by a stretched elastic string. A given elastic string, stretched by a given amount and allowed to accelerate in turn bodies of different masses that are free to move, will produce different accelerations in the various bodies. Unlike this elastic force, the force of gravity has a self-adjusting character: it 'knows' exactly how to operate so as to produce the same acceleration g in bodies of different masses. This remarkable pheno-menon is usually expressed in a manner that conceals the fundamental experi-mental fact, by saying that the inertial and the gravitational masses of a body are equal. This statement may be elucidated as follows: if m is the mass of the body, the force of gravity on it is $W = mg$, by Newton's law. This force of gravity is, of course, also known as the weight of the body. But now suppose that all accelerations are expressed as fractions of the acceleration of gravity g. Then in (3.103) we may write

$$Wa_i = F_i, \qquad (i = 1, 2, 3),$$

where the three a_i are the components of acceleration divided by g, i.e.

$$a_i = \frac{d^2 X_i}{dT^2} \bigg/ g.$$

Thus, in this form of Newton's Second Law, the weight, or gravitational mass, of the body plays the same part as the inertial mass did in the original enunciation. Again, suppose that a standard mass m_0 be selected, whose gravitational mass is therefore $W_0 = m_0 g$. Hence

$$\frac{W}{W_0} = \frac{m}{m_0}$$

because g is the common acceleration produced in both m and m_0 by the force of gravity. Thus if m_0 is chosen to be the unit of inertial mass and W_0 to be the unit of gravitational mass, it follows that, in these units, $W = m$, or, in other words, that the inertial mass is equal to the gravitational. The whole argument, however, turns on the observed common value g for the acceler-ation produced by the force of gravity, which we have called the self-adjusting character of this peculiar force.

In Newtonian gravitational theory this characteristic of the force of gravity is allowed for by the ingenious device of assuming that the gravitational force between two particles is proportional, amongst other things, to the product of the inertial masses of the particles. If m, M are the masses of the particles, one of which is at (x_1, x_2, x_3) and the other at (X_1, X_1, X_3) at the same instant of absolute time, then the equations of motion of m are

$$m\frac{d^2 x_i}{dT^2} = -\frac{GmM}{r^2}\frac{(x_i - X_i)}{r}, \qquad (i = 1, 2, 3), \tag{3.301}$$

where r, the distance between the particles in absolute space, is given by

$$r^2 = \sum_{j=1}^{3} (x_j - X_j)^2, \qquad (3.302)$$

and G is the gravitational constant whose value in c.g.s. units is

$$G = 6 \cdot 668 \times 10^{-8} \text{ cm}^3\text{gr}^{-1}\text{sec}^{-2}. \qquad (3.303)$$

Since the mass m disappears from the equations of motion (3.301), particles of all masses will have equations of motion of the same mathematical form, provided M is kept fixed, and therefore the motions of these particles will be essentially independent of their masses. Another important feature of equations (3.301) is that their mathematical form is preserved under transformations from one Newtonian inertial coordinate-system to another. For, by (3.104), the acceleration-components preserve their form under such a transformation, while the force components depend on the differences $(x_j - X_j)$ which again maintain their mathematical form by the cancellation of the terms in uT. These results thus depend on the postulates of the existence of an absolute space in which the particles are uniquely located and of an absolute time, in terms of which the positions of the particles can be dated.

Where there is a continuous distribution of gravitating matter, whose density is ρ, the corresponding gravitational potential, V, is related to ρ by Poisson's equation.

$$\nabla^2 V = \sum_{j=1}^{3} \frac{\partial^2 V}{\partial X_j{}^2} = -4\pi G\rho. \qquad (3.304)$$

This means that the gravitational force which would be exerted by the distribution on a particle of unit mass inserted into the distribution, but whose own gravitational effect is regarded as negligibly small, is

$$F_i = \frac{\partial V}{\partial X_i}, \qquad (i = 1, 2, 3). \qquad (3.305)$$

This force is therefore the gravitational self-attraction of the distribution of matter, i.e. the gravitational force per unit mass which one part of the material exerts on another part. It will be convenient in the sequel to modify the definition of the potential which, in (3.304) has the physical dimensions of (length)^2/(time)^2, and to replace V by a function ψ with the physical dimensions of (mass)/(length). The relation between V and ψ is

$$V = 4\pi G\psi \qquad (3.306)$$

and the equations (3.304), (3.305) then become, respectively,

$$\nabla^2 \psi = -\rho \qquad (3.307)$$

$$F_i = 4\pi G \frac{\partial \psi}{\partial X_i}, \qquad (i = 1, 2, 3). \qquad (3.308)$$

All the equations in Secs. 3.1 to 3.3 have been written in terms of Cartesian coordinates but, as is well known, this is not essential in Newtonian mechanics. Curvilinear coordinates may also be employed, the transformation from Cartesians to curvilinears (Y_1, Y_2, Y_3) being

$$X_i = f_i(Y_1, Y_2, Y_3), \qquad (i = 1, 2, 3),$$

where the f_i are certain functions of the coordinates (Y). Spherical and cylindrical polar coordinates, the generalized coordinates of Lagrange's equations, and the various systems employed in hydrodynamics and Newtonian potential theory provide illustrations which can be found in the standard treatises on classical mechanics. It is worth remarking, however, that whereas the transformation equations may be extended to include the time, the time itself is transformed by the identity transformation, so that we have

$$T = T',$$
$$X_i = f_i(Y_1, Y_2, Y_3, T'), \qquad (i = 1, 2, 3),$$

as the most general time and space transformation envisaged in Newtonian mechanics.

3.4. Special Relativity [2]

From the point of view of mechanics properly so called, as distinct from electromagnetic theory, the critical distinction between special relativity and Newtonian mechanics lies in a new definition of an inertial coordinate-system in which the infinite absolute velocity $\mathscr{C}$ is replaced by a finite absolute velocity c. The usefulness of this change will be explained in the next section, where a physical identification of c is given; for the moment the mathematical nature of the modification will be described.

The obvious and overwhelming success of Newtonian mechanics in the interpretation and correlation of the data of observation leads us to conclude that, if this theory must be modified, it should be modified as little as possible. To this end the hypothesis of an underlying Euclidean three-dimensional space will be retained as will Newton's First Law of Motion. The first modification in the Newtonian scheme which will be made is an obvious one, namely, that completely to specify any happening or occurrence it is necessary to state, not only *where*, but also *when* the occurrence took place. Thus an occurrence, technically known as an *event*, needs four numbers to specify it completely, three of which are coordinates fixing its location in space, whilst the fourth, which may be called a time-coordinate, fixes it in time. In Newtonian mechanics, this obvious characteristic of events is masked by the assumption of an underlying absolute time, two observers of a given event being presumed able to fix its absolute time by some procedure or other. In special relativity inertial systems may be defined as follows: since space is Euclidean, Cartesian coordinate-systems may be used, and a given event E may be described as occurring at the instant x^4 at the position (x^1, x^2, x^3) relative to one of the inertial systems, S. Now let S' be a second inertial system moving with uniform speed u with respect to S and suppose that the same event E is described in S' by its Cartesian coordinates (x'^1, x'^2, x'^3) and time of occurrence, x'^4. In contrast to Newtonian theory, it will not be assumed *a priori* that $x'^4 \equiv x^4$. Consider then the transformation, known as the Lorentz transformation.

$$
\left.
\begin{aligned}
x'^4 &= \beta\left(x^4 - \frac{u}{c^2}x^1\right), \\
x'^1 &= \beta(x^1 - ux^4), \\
x'^2 &= x^2, \\
x'^3 &= x^3, \\
\beta &= \left(1 - \frac{u^2}{c^2}\right)^{-\frac{1}{2}},
\end{aligned}
\right\}
\tag{3.401}
$$

where u is a constant with the dimensions of velocity and c is the (finite) absolute velocity. This transformation has the following properties: Firstly, if c is large compared with u and can be regarded as effectively equal to $\mathscr{C}$, the transformation becomes identical with (3.104), the two times x'^4 and x^4 becoming identical. Secondly, the directions of the x^2-, x^3- axes are the same as those of x'^2 and x'^3, the origins thus lying on the common x'^1- and x^1-axis. The origins obviously coincide at the instant, common to the two time-systems, $x'^4 = x^4 = 0$. Thirdly, the transformation is a linear one between the space and time-coordinates of the two systems. Hence, since the finite equations of motion of a particle moving under Newton's First Law of Motion are linear equations connecting (x^1, x^2, x^3) with x^4, they will remain linear equations when (x'^1, x'^2, x'^3) and x'^4 are employed. Finally, the velocity components of a moving point are

$$
q_i = \frac{dx^i}{dx^4}, \qquad (i = 1, 2, 3),
\tag{3.402}
$$

and transform to

$$
\left.
\begin{aligned}
q'_1 &= \frac{dx'^1}{dx'^4} = \frac{q_1 - u}{1 - uq_1/c^2}, \\
q'_2 = \frac{dx'^2}{dx'^4} = \frac{q_2}{\beta(1 - uq_1/c^2)}, \qquad q'_3 &= \frac{dx'^3}{dx'^4} = \frac{q_3}{\beta(1 - uq_1/c^2)},
\end{aligned}
\right\}
\tag{3.403}
$$

under (3.401). Thus a point at rest relative to the (x) coordinate system $(q_1 = 0, q_2 = 0, q_3 = 0)$ has velocity $-u$ relative to the (x') system, while a point at rest relative to the second system has velocity $+u$ relative to the first. Moreover, the absolute velocity is c because, if $q_1^2 + q_2^2 + q_3^2 = c^2$, it follows from (3.403) that

$$
\begin{aligned}
q_1'^2 + q_2'^2 + q_3'^2 &= \left\{(q_1 - u)^2 + \left(1 - \frac{u^2}{c^2}\right)(q_2^2 + q_3^2)\right\}\left(1 - \frac{uq_1}{c^2}\right)^{-2} \\
&= \left\{c^2 - 2q_1 u + u^2 - \frac{u^2}{c^2}(c^2 - q_1^2)\right\}\left(1 - \frac{uq_1}{c^2}\right)^{-2} \\
&= c^2.
\end{aligned}
\tag{3.404}
$$

The combination of time and space coordinates (x^4, x^1, x^2, x^3) and (x'^4, x'^1, x'^2, x'^3) connected by the Lorentz transformation (3.401), are called *inertial systems* in special relativity. The relative speed of either system with respect to the other has the constant value u. Newton's First Law of Motion has the same mathematical form in both systems, and there is a finite absolute velocity c common to both. The principle of special relativity extends these ideas and states that *all the equations of mathematical physics should be unchanged in mathematical form on transformation from the coordinates of one inertial system to those of another.* This statement is to be regarded as expressing an end to be achieved, rather than as something which has been accomplished since Einstein enunciated the principle in 1905.

3.5. The Velocity of Light

A physical interpretation for the absolute velocity c is obtained through a famous optical experiment, first performed in 1881 and repeated many times since, known as the Michelson-Morley experiment. The principle of the experiment is as follows: two rigid arms, $O'A$ and $O'B$, of equal length are rigidly fastened together at right angles. At A and B are mirrors, normal to each arm, while at O' there is a half-silvered mirror inclined at forty-five degrees to $O'A$. If a ray of light is sent in the direction $O'A$, it will be divided by the mirror at O' so that one part will travel to A and back to O', while the other part travels to B and back to O'. The returning parts of the beam will

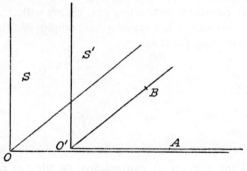

Fig. 1.

recombine at O' and can be observed by an appropriate apparatus directed along the line $O'B$. If the times of travel of the two portions of the beam are not exactly equal, the reunited beam will be slightly out of phase, and interference fringes will be seen. The purpose of this device, as it was used by Michelson and Morley, was to determine the speed of the Earth in its orbit round the Sun, which is roughly 30 km.sec^{-1}, in terms of the velocity of light, which is 3×10^5 km.sec^{-1}. They argued as follows, in purely Newtonian terms and making use of the relative-velocity formulae (3.106). Let $O'A$ be directed along the direction of motion of the Earth at the moment in question and $O'B$ at right angles to this direction, and let the X'_1- and X'_2-axes be taken along $O'A$ and $O'B$, respectively. If u is the speed of the Earth in its orbit, let the coordinate system (X_1, X_2, X_3) with origin at O be that relative to which the Earth has this speed and let the X_1- and X_2-axes be parallel, respectively, to $O'A$ and $O'B$. Then if the velocity of light is C relative to the (X_1, X_2, X_3) system, it follows from the Newtonian formulae (3.106), that the portion of the ray travelling from O' to A travels at the speed $C - u$ on its outgoing journey and returns with the speed $C + u$. Hence the time for the double journey from O' to A and back to O', is $(2l/C)/(1 - u^2/C^2)$, where l is the length of $O'A$ or of $O'B$. A corresponding calculation for the double journey O' to B and back to O' gives a time of $(2l/C)/\left(\dfrac{1 - u^2}{C^2}\right)^{1/2}$. Hence, neglecting the cube, and higher powers, of the small quantity u/C, it follows that, even if the apparatus were constructed in an ideally perfect manner, there would still be a difference in the times amounting to $(l/C)(u^2/C^2)$ and therefore interference fringes in the reunited beam should be seen. The wave-theory of light then allows us, by methods that need not concern us here, to calculate the speed u in terms of C from measurements made on the interference fringes. The experimental methods employed were sufficiently accurate to detect a speed of 6 to 10 km.sec^{-1} but, to the surprise of the investigators, the orbital speed of the Earth was found to be zero, within the errors of the observations.

This contradiction between the astronomical and optical determinations of the speed of the Earth is resolved in special relativity by rejecting the Newtonian relative-velocity formulae (3.106) and by identifying the velocity of light with the finite absolute velocity c of the Lorentz transformation formulae (3.401). The inertial systems S and S' of Sec. 3.4 may be defined as follows: S is the system with origin at O relative to which the Earth has the velocity of 30 km.sec^{-1} ($= u$), with its x^1-axis directed along the Earth's motion; while S' is attached to the Earth, its x'^1-axis along $O'A$ and coincident with the x^1-axis of S, the other spatial axes of S and S' being parallel. By means of the Lorentz transformation, with O' at the spatial origin of the system S', it can be proved that the times of the double journeys to A and B, respectively, are both $2l/c$ in time x'^4 used in S' and so no interference fringes are to be expected. On the other hand, in the time x^4 used in S, both times are $2l\beta/c$ and therefore again no interference fringes should occur. Thus, if the velocity of light is equal to the absolute velocity c in both S and S', the travel times along $O'A$ and $O'B$ are equal to one another in either S or S', but these times do not have the same values in S and in S'.

The identification of c with the absolute velocity is a special case of the application of the principle of special relativity, light being regarded as an electromagnetic phenomenon propagated as a wave. For it can be proved that

Maxwell's equations of the electromagnetic field are unchanged in mathematical form under a Lorentz transformation (3.401); and so is the wave equation for any quantity F, viz.

$$\frac{1}{c^2}\frac{\partial^2 F}{(\partial x^4)^2} = \frac{\partial^2 F}{(\partial x^1)^2} + \frac{\partial^2 F}{(\partial x^2)^2} + \frac{\partial^2 F}{(\partial x^3)^2}.$$

3.6. Minkowski Space-time

Having thus identified the finite absolute velocity of special relativity with the velocity of light, we return again to physical events regarded as entities specified by four coordinates of which a time-specification is one. To fix ideas, consider the system S in which the coordinates of an event are (x^4, x^1, x^2, x^3) and let it be supposed that all the events under contemplation are plotted as points in a four-dimensional Riemannian space whose metric is

$$ds^2 = (dx^4)^2 - \frac{1}{c^2}\{(dx^1)^2 + (dx^2)^2 + (dx^3)^2\}. \qquad (3.601)$$

The Lorentz transformation equations (3.401) may be solved for the unprimed in terms of the primed coordinates to give

$$\left.\begin{array}{ll} x^4 = \beta\left(x'^4 + \dfrac{ux'^1}{c^2}\right), & x^1 = \beta(x'^1 + ux'^4), \\[2mm] x^2 = x'^2, & x^3 = x'^3, \\[2mm] & \beta = \left(1 - \dfrac{u^2}{c^2}\right)^{-\frac{1}{2}}, \end{array}\right\} \qquad (3.602)$$

and the differentials of these equations, with u and c constant, turn the metric (3.601) into

$$ds^2 = (dx'^4)^2 - \frac{1}{c^2}\{(dx'^1)^2 + (dx'^2)^2 + (dx'^3)^2\}.$$

Thus the mathematical form of the metric is unchanged by passing to the coordinates of S' from those of S and we may therefore regard the system S as a typical system. The Riemannian four-dimensional space whose metric is (3.601) will be called the *Minkowski space-time*, after one of the mathematicians who first employed it, and in order to emphasize that one coordinate is a time, the other three referring to spatial position. The interval, s, in (3.601) obviously has the physical dimensions of time.

It is sometimes said that special relativity has 'abolished the distinction between space and time' because it employs the device of mapping, or representing, events as points in the four-dimensional Minkowski space-time. But it may equally well be argued that our intuitive perception of a distinction between space and time is carefully preserved in this method of representation. Suppose that two events (x) and $(x + dx)$ are spatially coincident, but temporally separated, in the system S. This means that

$$dx^4 \neq 0, \qquad dx^i = 0, \qquad (i = 1, 2, 3),$$

and hence the interval that separates them is, by (3.601),

$$ds = \pm \, dx^4,$$

and therefore is a *real number*. On the other hand, suppose that the two events are simultaneous in S but spatially distinct, so that

$$dx^4 = 0, \qquad dx^i \neq 0, \qquad (i = 1, 2, 3).$$

If $dl^2 = \sum_{j=1}^{3} (dx^j)^2$, formula (3.601) shows that the interval separating these two events is

$$ds = \pm \left\{ - \frac{\sum\limits_{j=1}^{3} (dx^j)^2}{c^2} \right\}^{\frac{1}{2}} = \pm \, idl/c,$$

which is an *imaginary number* since dl is necessarily real. Thus two events that are temporally separated have an interval that is a real number, and two events that are spatially separated have an interval that is an imaginary number. In more complicated cases, all four coordinate-differences may differ from zero: if the interval between the two events turns out to be a (non-zero) real number, the separation of the two events is said to be *time-like*, if an imaginary number, it is said to be *space-like*. It is also easy to show by means of the Lorentz transformation (3.401) that these properties of pairs of events cannot be altered by passing from the coordinates of one inertial system to those of another. The device of employing real and imaginary numbers for the values of the intervals between different kinds of events is thus the expression in special relativity of man's intuitive notion that space and time are essentially distinct. There are, however, pairs of events of a special kind, namely, those for which the interval is zero. For these, by (3.601)

$$c^2(dx^4)^2 = \sum_{j=1}^{3} (dx^j)^2,$$

or, on passing to the coordinates of another inertial system S',

$$c^2(dx'^4)^2 = \sum_{j=1}^{3} (dx'^j)^2.$$

Thus once again the property of zero interval cannot be destroyed by a coordinate-transformation.

The relativity of the concepts of simultaneity and of length are well illustrated by the Lorentz transformation formulae. Consider the two events E_1 and E_2, whose coordinates in the system S are $(x_1^4, x_1^1, 0, 0)$ and $(x_2^4, x_2^1, 0, 0)$ respectively. Taking differences of these coordinates and using (3.401), we have for the non-vanishing differences in terms of the coordinates of S'

$$x'_2 - x'_1 = \beta \left[(x_2^4 - x_1^4) - \frac{u}{c^2}(x_2^1 - x_1^1) \right],$$

$$x'^1_2 - x'^1_1 = \beta[(x_2^1 - x_1^1) - u(x_2^4 - x_1^4)].$$

E

If E_1 and E_2 are simultaneous, but not spatially coincident, in S, we have $x_2^4 = x_1^4$, $x_2^1 \neq x_1^1$ and therefore $x_2'^4 \neq x_1'^4$ as well as $x_2'^1 \neq x_1'^1$; hence E_1 and E_2 are neither simultaneous nor spatially coincident when the coordinates of S' are used. This is not surprising in view of what has been said in Sec. 3.1: simultaneity of two widely separated events is always a matter of calculation and the passage from S to S' constitutes a change in the method of calculating. Moreover

$$x_2'^4 - x_1'^4 = -\frac{\beta u}{c^2}(x_2^1 - x_1^1) \neq 0,$$

$$x_2'^1 - x_1'^1 = \beta(x_2^1 - x_1^1),$$

and therefore the *length* $x_2^1 - x_1^1$ in S has become $\left(1 - \frac{u^2}{c^2}\right)^{\frac{1}{2}} (x_2'^1 - x_1'^1)$ in

S'. This relativity of length has sometimes been regarded as a physical property of rigid measuring rods – the so-called Fitzgerald contraction – but it is in fact a property of coordinate-systems in the Minkowski space-time, i.e. a property of the method of so labelling events that the absolute velocity is expressible by a finite, and not an infinite, number.

3.7. The Geodesics and Null-geodesics of the Minkowski Space-time

The metric (3.601) of the Minkowski space-time indicates that it is a Riemannian space of four dimensions for which, in terms of the notation introduced in Sec. 2.8,

$$\left.\begin{array}{l} g_{44} = 1, \quad g_{ii} = -\dfrac{1}{c^2}, \quad g_{ij} = 0, \quad (i \neq j = 1, 2, 3), \\[2mm] g = -\dfrac{1}{c^6}, \\[2mm] g^{44} = 1, \quad g^{ii} = -c^2, \quad g^{ij} = 0, \quad (i \neq j = 1, 2, 3). \end{array}\right\} \tag{3.701}$$

Since S is a typical inertial coordinate system, the metric is orthogonal in any such system. All the components of the metrical tensor are constants and therefore the Minkowski space-time is flat. The equations of the geodesics, by (2.806) and (2.807), become

$$\frac{d^2x^\sigma}{ds^2} = 0, \quad (\sigma = 1, 2, 3, 4), \tag{3.702}$$

and are therefore immediately integrable to give

$$\left.\begin{array}{l} \dfrac{dx^\sigma}{ds} = v^\sigma, \\[2mm] x^\sigma - x_0^\sigma = v^\sigma s, \end{array}\right\} \tag{3.703}$$

where the four v^σ and the four x_0^σ are constants of integration. The first four constants satisfy, by (2.808),

$$1 = (v^4)^2 - \frac{1}{c^2}\sum_{j=1}^{3}(v^j)^2. \tag{3.704}$$

When the three new constants q_i are introduced by

$$q_i = \frac{v^i}{v^4} = \frac{dx^i}{dx^4}, \tag{3.705}$$

the integrals of the equations (3.702) may be written

$$\left. \begin{array}{l} x^i - x_0^i = q_i(x^4 - x_0^4), \\ x^4 - x_0^4 = v^4 s, \end{array} \right\} \tag{3.706}$$

while (3.704) becomes

$$\left(\frac{ds}{dx^4}\right)^2 = \frac{1}{(v^4)^2} = 1 - \frac{1}{c^2} \sum_{j=1}^{3} (q_j)^2 = 1 - \frac{q^2}{c^2}. \tag{3.707}$$

These results have been obtained by the mathematical process of solving the equations of the geodesics, the coordinates of S having been used. If the coordinates of any other inertial system S' had been employed instead, entirely parallel formulae would have resulted which can, indeed, be obtained by attaching a prime to every symbol except s and c in formulae (3.702) to (3.707). But now these formulae are capable of a physical interpretation, viz. the three q_i are the (constant) components of velocity of a moving particle and the equations (3.706) are the integrals of its equations of motion provided that it moves in accordance with Newton's First Law of Motion. It will, however, be shown below that the velocity of the particle must be less than c, and, therefore, the quantity ds in (3.707) must be a real number, since the time differential dx^4 is necessarily real. Hence we conclude that: *the time-like geodesics of the Minkowski space-time are curves in four dimensions that represent the history of the motion of a particle moving under Newton's First Law.* By the 'history of the motion' is meant the sequence of positions in space with their associated times, as plotted in the system S. But since these conclusions are based on the theory of geodesics, they are true with reference to the co-ordinates of any inertial system.

The four constants v^σ are the components of a contravariant vector in the four-dimensional Minkowski space-time – the unit tangent vector to a geodesic. The three velocity-components q_i do not, however, form part of a four-dimensional vector, since they are formed by taking the ratios of three components of v^σ to the fourth, v^4. Now the principle of special relativity states that the equations of mathematical physics must retain their mathematical form under the transformation (3.401) and this may be secured by expressing all relations by means of tensors. For a particle, the history of whose motion is represented by a geodesic of the Minkowski space-time, a tensor definition of velocity and of acceleration is obtained by asserting that the velocity is to be represented by the unit tangent vector, v^σ, to the geodesic, called the *velocity 4-vector*, while the acceleration is represented by the *acceleration 4-vector* d^2x^σ/ds^2, ($\sigma = 1, 2, 3, 4$). In virtue of (3.702), the acceleration 4-vector for a particle obeying Newton's First Law is a null-vector.

The null-geodesics of the Minkowski space-time may be dealt with by replacing s by a non-vanishing parameter μ in (3.702), (3.703) and (3.706) and by replacing (3.704) and (3.707) by the following two equations,

$$
\left.\begin{array}{l}
0 = (v^4)^2 - \dfrac{1}{c^2} \sum_{j=1}^{3} (v^j)^2, \\[2mm]
q^2 = c^2.
\end{array}\right\}
\tag{3.708}
$$

These results, like the previous ones, are also independent in mathematical form of the coordinates of the particular inertial system used. In view of what has been said in Sec. 3.5, *a null-geodesic may be interpreted physically as the representation in the Minkowski space-time of the history of the motion of a light-ray.*

An important result of special relativity may be stated here without proof. Expressed in four-dimensional form the momentum of a particle is described by the three spatial components of a 4-vector whose fourth component is the relative mass-energy

$$
Mc^2 = mc^2 \left(1 - \frac{q^2}{c^2} \right)^{-\frac{1}{2}}.
$$

Here m is called the rest-mass or proper-mass of the particle and is therefore the mass of the particle in an inertial coordinate-system in which its velocity, q, happens to be zero at the instant in question. Since $M \longrightarrow \infty$ as $q \longrightarrow c$, it is said that a particle cannot attain a speed equal to that of light. If powers of q^2/c^2 greater than the first are neglected, we have

$$
Mc^2 = mc^2 + \tfrac{1}{2}mq^2,
$$

so that the mass-energy is the sum of the kinetic energy of the particle and of the quantity mc^2, a result which can be interpreted by saying that the mass m of a particle is equivalent to an amount of energy mc^2. The proof of these results, however, pre-supposes that Lorentz transformations exist amongst coordinate-systems, a statement which is not valid – except in a limited 'local' sense – in the more complicated space-times that will be employed in general relativity.

3.8. Special Relativity Mechanics of Extended Bodies

The recasting of the equations of mathematical physics in a form invariant under Lorentz transformations meets with a difficulty when a generalization of the inverse square law of gravitation is attempted or when a revised definition of a rigid body is in question. The difficulty stems from the fact that, in both cases, it is necessary to find an analogue of the Newtonian absolute distance between two particles in space which shall be invariant under a Lorentz transformation. Consider the inertial system S and let the two particles be the simultaneous events

$$
(x^4, x_1^1, x_1^2, x_1^3) \text{ and } (x^4, x_2^1, x_2^2, x_2^3).
$$

Then the spatial distance between the two particles is l where

$$l^2 = (x_2^1 - x_1^1)^2 + (x_2^2 - x_1^2)^2 + (x_2^3 - x_1^3)^2.$$

But now the two events are described in S' as $(x_1'^4, x_1'^1, x_1'^2, x_1'^3)$ and $(x_2'^4, x_2'^1, x_2'^2, x_2'^3)$; they are no longer simultaneous and, by (3.602)

$$l^2 = \beta^2(x_2'^1 - x_1'^1 + ux_2'^4 - ux_1'^4)^2 + (x_2'^2 - x_1'^2)^2 + (x_2'^3 - x_1'^3)^2$$

$$= \left(1 - \frac{u^2}{c^2}\right)(x_2'^1 - x_1'^1)^2 + (x_2'^2 - x_1'^2)^2 + (x_2'^3 - x_1'^3)^2$$

$$= (l')^2 - \frac{u^2}{c^2}(x_2'^1 - x_1'^1)^2.$$

Hence l, which depended only on the spatial separation of the particles when the coordinates of S were used, involves the relative velocity of the two inertial systems when those of S' are employed. Thus if l were to be used in a special relativity formulation of the inverse square law of gravitation, it would be necessary to state which inertial system was the 'correct' one, in contradiction to the principle of special relativity. Similarly a particular inertial system would have to be specified in terms of which the particles of a rigid body remained at constant distances apart. While this obstacle has been overcome for the gravitational problem through the theory of general relativity, a satisfactory relativistic form of rigid-body dynamics is still largely to seek[3].

The problem of generalization is much more easily solved for the case of a perfect fluid. Consider the Newtonian equations (3.202) and (3.203) when the only force acting on the fluid is its pressure-gradient, viz.

$$\left.\begin{array}{l} \dfrac{\partial \rho}{\partial T} + \dfrac{\partial \rho U_j}{\partial X_j} = 0, \\[2ex] \dfrac{\partial \rho U_i}{\partial T} + \dfrac{\partial}{\partial X_j}(\rho U_i U_j + \delta_{ij}p) = 0. \end{array}\right\} \tag{3.801}$$

Let it be assumed that, in an inertial system of special relativity, the velocity of the fluid at the four-dimensional point (x^4, x^1, x^2, x^3) is represented by a unit velocity 4-vector u^μ which must therefore satisfy

$$1 = g_{\mu\sigma}u^\mu u^\sigma = u^\mu u_\mu = (u^4)^2 - \frac{1}{c^2}\sum_{j=1}^{3}(u^j)^2, \tag{3.802}$$

the velocity-components of the fluid being the three quantities

$$q_i = u^i/u^4, \qquad (i = 1, 2, 3).$$

Since it is again assumed that $q^2 = \displaystyle\sum_{j=1}^{3}(q_j)^2 < c^2$ it follows from (3.802) that

$$\frac{1}{(u^4)^2} = 1 - \frac{q^2}{c^2} > 0. \tag{3.803}$$

The four functions u^μ are, in general, functions of all four coordinates (x) and therefore the motion of the fluid is unsteady. Suppose also that the fluid is characterized by two scalars, its density ρ, expressed in gr.cm^{-3}, and its istropic pressure p, expressed in dynes cm^{-2}, and consider the ten functions of position

$$T^{\mu\nu} = \left(\rho + \frac{p}{c^2}\right)u^\mu u^\nu - g^{\mu\nu}\frac{p}{c^2}, \qquad (3.804)$$

satisfying the four differential equations

$$\frac{\partial T^{\mu\nu}}{\partial x^\nu} = 0. \qquad (3.805)$$

Since u^μ is a contravariant 4-vector and ρ and p are scalars it follows that $T^{\mu\nu}$ is a contravariant tensor of rank 2 in the Minkowski space-time, and it is obviously a symmetrical tensor. The name given to this tensor is the *energy-tensor* of the perfect fluid. Using (3.701) in (3.804) and then identifying the absolute velocity c with the infinite absolute velocity $\mathscr{C}$ of Newtonian theory, the components of $T^{\mu\nu}$ reduce to the ten quantities ρ, ρU_j and $(\rho U_i U_j + \delta_{ij}p)$ that occur in the Newtonian equations (3.801). Again the Lorentz transformation (3.401) shows that, if c is identified with $\mathscr{C}$, the coordinate x^4 (or x'^4) is identifiable with the absolute time T, and the three x^i (or x'^i) with the absolute Cartesian coordinates X_i, X'_i employed in (3.104). Hence the four equations (3.805) reduce to the Newtonian equations (3.801) and may be regarded as their generalizations in special relativity. Moreover, the equations (3.805) are tensor equations, which, in the language of Sec. 2.4, state that *the vectorial divergence of the energy-tensor vanishes identically*, all the Christoffel symbols for (3.601) being zero.

This generalization has, however, introduced a new element in the relationship between the density and the pressure of a fluid. Consider the component T^{44} of the energy-tensor which, by (3.701) and (3.803), may be written

$$T^{44} = \left(\rho + \frac{p}{c^2}\right)\left(1 - \frac{q^2}{c^2}\right)^{-1} - \frac{p}{c^2}.$$

In the Newtonian case the terms in $1/c^2$ vanish and this component is simply the density; but in the special relativity generalization this is true only if the fluid is at rest in the inertial system ($q = 0$). The density ρ may therefore be called the *proper-density* of the fluid[1], the expression $\left(\rho + \frac{p}{c^2}\right)\left(1 - \frac{q^2}{c^2}\right)^{-1} - \frac{p}{c^2}$ being the relative density. Whereas in Newtonian hydrodynamics the density and pressure of the fluid are regarded as independent attributes, this is now no longer the case. They have become intermingled, a possibility which is also suggested by the physical dimensions of ρ and of p/c^2, which are (mass)/(length)^3. Just as the mass and kinetic energy of a particle have been shown to be attributes of the same kind through the four-dimensional representation implicit in special relativity, so now the density and stress of a perfect fluid are no longer independent properties but aspects of the same physical characteristic, which may be called energy in a general sense. Moreover, it is not beyond the bounds of possibility that density and stress may be interchangeable into one another[4].

The covariant form of the energy-tensor is obtained from (3.804) by lowering the indices and is

$$T_{\mu\nu} = \left(\rho + \frac{p}{c^2}\right)u_\mu u_\nu - g_{\mu\nu}\frac{p}{c^2}, \tag{3.806}$$

while the mixed form is

$$T_\nu^\mu = \left(\rho + \frac{p}{c^2}\right)u^\mu u_\nu - \delta_\nu^\mu \frac{p}{c^2}. \tag{3.807}$$

From the latter, there is obtained by contraction the *invariant density*

$$\begin{aligned}
T_\mu^\mu &= \left(\rho + \frac{p}{c^2}\right)u^\mu u_\mu - \delta_\mu^\mu \frac{p}{c^2} \\
&= \left(\rho + \frac{p}{c^2}\right) - 4\frac{p}{c^2} \\
&= \rho - \frac{3p}{c^2},
\end{aligned}$$

which again emphasizes that the invariant associated with the energy-tensor is neither the density nor the pressure alone, but a combination of the two.

The four equations (3.805) which now replace the Newtonian equations (3.801) still form an indeterminate set, in spite of the existence of the additional relationship (3.802). The reason, of course, is that there are now *four* functions u^μ, which together with ρ and p, give six unknowns satisfying five equations. Nor is it now easy to find additional relationships by an appeal to thermodynamics because no generally accepted extension of thermodynamics to both special and general relativity has yet been developed, a point to be borne in mind when Newtonian hydrodynamics is extended to general relativity.

CHAPTER 4

The Principles of General Relativity

4.1. Riemannian Space-time and Einstein's Equations

The Minkowski space-time used in special relativity is a very special kind of four-dimensional Riemannian space. Since the coefficients of its metric are all constants, the Christoffel symbols are all identically zero and consequently the Riemann-Christoffel tensor also vanishes. The space-time is therefore flat in the sense of Sec. 2.5. The removal of this limitation will lead to general relativity and to the solution of the gravitational problem.

The events now under contemplation by the investigator are constituted by the history of a distribution of matter, its density and pressure at a sequence of points in space and at successive instants in time, the motion of its various parts and the gravitational effects that are present, etc. It will be assumed that each event still requires four numbers (x^4, x^1, x^2, x^3) to specify it, and these numbers will be called the coordinates of the event. The coordinates of all events under examination by the investigator are presumed to be assigned in the same way, but the particular method employed is not specified *a priori*. A corollary therefore is that x^4 is not necessarily a time-specification nor are (x^1, x^2, x^3) necessarily spatial coordinates. It may be that the investigator finds it convenient to specify the time of occurrence of an event by some function of x^4 and x^1, for example. The only stipulation then made is that he use the *same function* of x^4 and x^1 for the time-specifications of all events. This vagueness in the procedure of assigning coordinates has been criticized by certain applied mathematicians, who maintain that a satisfactory theory must begin by describing the observational methods – actual or conceptual – through which the coordinates are to be set up. Such a restriction on the freedom of the investigator does not seem to be legitimate and an analogy drawn from Newtonian mechanics may serve to clarify this point. It is well known that a Newtonian mechanical system can often be described by means of Lagrange's equations and great advantages result by so doing. Yet in establishing these equations, generalized coordinates are used, for the setting up of which no specific *a priori* rules are usually given. Indeed, it may well be argued that the whole value of Lagrange's method lies precisely in this lack of rules. When Lagrange's equations come to be applied to a particular physical situation, the investigator certainly assigns physical meanings to the generalized coordinates, but it is also often true that he can do this in more than one way. Exactly the same type of procedure is followed in general relativity, the interpretation of the four coordinates of an event being reached *a posteriori* for each physical situation contemplated and not laid down beforehand as an essential element of the theory.

The next stop is to plot, or represent, all the events under consideration as points in a four-dimensional Riemannian space having the following two properties: (*a*) the Riemann-Christoffel tensor and the Ricci tensor have non-zero values at one point of the space, at least; (*b*) when local Cartesian co-ordinates are set up at any event, the metric takes the form

$$ds^2 = (dX^4)^2 - \frac{1}{c^2} \sum_{i=1}^{3} (dX^i)^2, \qquad (4.101)$$

in other words, the Riemannian space is such that it is 'locally' identical with the Minkowski space-time. This does not occur in a four-dimensional Rie-mannian space chosen at random, and therefore the sub-class of spaces used in general relativity will be called *Riemannian space-times* by analogy with the Minkowski space-time of special relativity. Requirement (*a*) restricts Rie-mannian space-times to be curved, and their metrics, in terms of the co-ordinates (*x*) are, of course,

$$ds^2 = g_{\mu\nu}(x)dx^\mu dx^\nu. \qquad (4.102)$$

The distribution of matter whose history has thus been 'plotted' has now to be specified. As an over-all guide, the *principle of covariance* is employed; it states that there must be no preferred coordinate-system, but that the investigator must be free to choose any such system without thereby modify-ing essentially the equations he is using. A satisfactory way of ensuring this is to use tensors and tensor equations and this principle will now be applied to the description of the distribution of matter. The investigations in Sec. 3.8 suggest how this can be done, provided that the material is envisaged as a perfect fluid. At each event in a Riemannian space-time the fluid will be characterized by a velocity 4-vector u^μ, a scalar density ρ and a scalar pressure p, all six quantities being regarded as functions of the four coordinates of the event. If there is, in fact, no material present at the event, then u^μ, ρ and p will be zero there. The velocity 4-vector is a unit vector and therefore satisfies, by (2.213),

$$1 = u^\mu u_\mu = g_{\mu\nu} u^\mu u^\nu, \qquad (4.103)$$

and the energy-tensor of the fluid is then defined to be

$$T^{\mu\nu} = \left(\rho + \frac{p}{c^2}\right) u^\mu u^\nu - g^{\mu\nu} \frac{p}{c^2}, \qquad (4.104)$$

which has the same symmetry properties as the tensor (3.804) of special relativity, with covariant and mixed forms analogous to (3.806), (3.807). The energy-tensor in special relativity satisfies the four equations (3.805) which state that its vectorial divergence is zero. They are therefore tensor equations and so may be taken to apply to any Riemannian space-time with metric (4.102). Since, however, the coefficients of the metric are no longer constants, the vanishing of the vectorial divergence is now expressed with the aid of (2.407) by

$$\frac{1}{\sqrt{(-g)}} \frac{\partial \sqrt{(-g)}T^{\mu\lambda}}{\partial x^\lambda} + \begin{Bmatrix} \mu \\ \lambda\sigma \end{Bmatrix} T^{\lambda\sigma} = 0, \qquad (\mu = 1, 2, 3, 4). \qquad (4.105)$$

These four equations are to be regarded as the generalizations in general relativity of the Newtonian equations (3.202) and (3.203).

It is possible to generalize these results and to deal in similar fashion with distributions of matter and energy other than perfect fluids. Any symmetrical energy-tensor which, in special relativity, possesses a vanishing vectorial divergence can be regarded in general relativity as obeying the equations (4.105).

The Riemannian space-time used as the representation of the distribution of matter must now be connected with the physical characteristics of the distribution. In this book, the energy-tensor will be regarded as summarizing the physical characteristics of the matter and energy constituting the distribution. At events where these physical entities are present the energy-tensor does not vanish, even if this non-vanishing occurs only through the presence of a mathematical singularity in the value of the tensor. Conversely, where matter (or energy) is absent, the energy-tensor is strictly zero. The essential characteristic of the energy-tensor is its possession of a zero vectorial divergence. Now the simplest tensor with a vanishing vectorial divergence that is deducible from the metrical tensor is

$$R^{\mu\nu} - \tfrac{1}{2}g^{\mu\nu}R^\rho_\rho,$$

as may be seen by reference to Sec. 2.7. Einstein could have made the connection between this tensor and the energy-tensor by merely asserting that the vectorial divergences were proportional to one another, so that

$$- \kappa c^2 T^{\mu\nu}_{,\nu} = (R^{\mu\nu} - \tfrac{1}{2}g^{\mu\nu}R^\rho_\rho)_{,\nu}, \qquad (4.106)$$

where $- \kappa c^2$ is the proportionality constant. Though he certainly did this, his peculiar stroke of genius was to do more. He established a relation between the tensors themselves, and not merely between their vectorial divergences. To obtain this relation it is necessary to reverse the process of covariant differentiation, in other words, to perform an integration. But integration necessarily introduces the equivalent of the 'constant of integration' of the elementary calculus. Since the metrical tensor has a vanishing covariant derivative, the appropriate 'constant of integration' is now $\Lambda g^{\mu\nu}$ where Λ is a constant independent of the coordinates. Hence the integrals of the equations (4.106) are the ten equations

$$- \kappa c^2 T^{\mu\nu} = R^{\mu\nu} - \tfrac{1}{2}g^{\mu\nu}(R^\rho_\rho - 2\Lambda), \qquad (4.107)$$

and they are known as *Einstein's equations*. They relate *the metrical tensor of the Riemannian space-time which represents the distribution of matter (or of energy) to the energy-tensor of the distribution.* Since it has been shown in Sec. 2.7 that the Einstein tensor has a vanishing vectorial divergence, it follows automatically from (4.107) that the equations (4.105) are satisfied.

Historically, the constant Λ was introduced by Einstein in the course of working out a cosmological problem and it is therefore known as the *cosmical constant*. This cosmical significance is accidental; the presence of Λ is due to the extraction of (4.107) from (4.106) and therefore arises through a purely mathematical operation. The cosmical constant would, in fact, still be present in Einstein's equations even if cosmology had never been thought of.

By lowering indices, Einstein's equations may be thrown into either of the equivalent forms

$$- \kappa c^2 T^\mu_\nu = R^\mu_\nu - \tfrac{1}{2}\delta^\mu_\nu(R^\sigma_\sigma - 2\Lambda), \tag{4.108}$$

$$- \kappa c^2 T_{\mu\nu} = R_{\mu\nu} - \tfrac{1}{2}g_{\mu\nu}(R^\sigma_\sigma - 2\Lambda). \tag{4.109}$$

At an event, or set of events, where the energy-tensor is zero, Einstein's equations take the simpler form

$$R^\mu_\nu - \tfrac{1}{2}\delta^\mu_\nu(R^\sigma_\sigma - 2\Lambda) = 0.$$

By contraction, it follows that $R^\sigma_\sigma = 4\Lambda$ and hence Einstein's equations may be written in one or other of the alternative forms

$$R^{\mu\nu} = \Lambda g^{\mu\nu}, \qquad R^\mu_\nu = \Lambda \delta^\mu_\nu, \qquad R_{\mu\nu} = \Lambda g_{\mu\nu}. \tag{4.110}$$

Finally, if it proves to be the case that the cosmical constant has the value zero, (4.110) becomes

$$R^{\mu\nu} = 0, \qquad R^\mu_\nu = 0, \qquad R_{\mu\nu} = 0. \tag{4.111}$$

4.2. Determination of the Constant κ

In Sec. 3.8 it has been shown that the history of a distribution of matter can be represented in the Minkowski space-time by defining a velocity 4-vector, a density and a pressure, and then asserting that the energy-tensor of the distribution satisfies the equations (3.805). Einstein's equations, however, do more than this for they relate the energy-tensor to the metrical tensor of the space-time. It may therefore be asked: what happens when these equations are applied to the Minkowski space-time itself? Since the space-time is flat, the tensors $R^{\mu\nu}$ and R^σ_σ are zero and the equations (4.107) become

$$- \kappa c^2 T^{\mu\nu} = \Lambda g^{\mu\nu}. \tag{4.201}$$

The metrical tensor is given by (3.701) and the energy-tensor by (4.104). Remembering that *lmn* stands for any cyclic permutation of 123 and abandoning the summation convention, the ten equations (4.201) become

$$- \kappa c^2 T^{44} = - \kappa c^2\left\{\left(\rho + \frac{p}{c^2}\right)(u^4)^2 - \frac{p}{c^2}\right\} = \Lambda, \tag{4.202}$$

$$- \kappa c^2 T^{l4} = - \kappa c^2\left\{\left(\rho + \frac{p}{c^2}\right)u^l u^4\right\} = 0, \tag{4.203}$$

$$- \kappa c^2 T^{ll} = - \kappa c^2 \left\{ \left(\rho + \frac{p}{c^2} \right)(u^l)^2 + p \right\} = - c^2 \Lambda \qquad (4.204)$$

$$- \kappa c^2 T^{lm} = - \kappa c^2 \left\{ \left(\rho + \frac{p}{c^2} \right)u^l u^m \right\} = 0, \qquad (4.205)$$

to which must be added (4.103), viz.:

$$1 = (u^4)^2 - \frac{1}{c^2} \sum_{i=1}^{3} (u^i)^2. \qquad (4.206)$$

The equations (4.203), (4.205) and (4.206) show that

$$u^l = 0, \qquad u^4 = 1,$$

so that the distribution of matter is at rest in the inertial system. Equations (4.202), (4.204) then give, whatever κ may be,

$$\rho = - \frac{\Lambda}{\kappa c^2}, \qquad p = \frac{\Lambda}{\kappa},$$

and therefore the density and pressure are constant and are necessarily of opposite sign, except when $\Lambda = 0$, when they are zero. These results are therefore either physically unacceptable, or trivial, and the conclusion is drawn that Einstein's equations do not give significant results when applied to the Minkowski space-time nor can a physical interpretation of κ be arrived at in this way.

A different situation arises when Einstein's equations are applied to a Riemannian space-time whose metrical tensor differs only slightly from that of the Minkowski space-time. Consideration of the cosmical constant will be postponed until Chap. 6 and for the moment this constant will be regarded as negligibly small. It will be assumed that the space-time is, firstly, *statical*, which means that its metrical tensor does not vary with the time; secondly, that it is *isotropic* so that there is no preferred direction at any point; and thirdly, that it is orthogonal. The metric of space-time is therefore

$$ds^2 = g_{44}(dx^4)^2 + \sum_{i=1}^{3} g_{ii}(dx^i)^2,$$

where

$$\left. \begin{aligned} g_{44} &= 1 + \varepsilon f, \\ g_{ii} &= - \frac{1}{c^2}(1 + \varepsilon h), \end{aligned} \right\} \qquad (4.207)$$

ε is a small constant whose square and higher powers are negligible, and f, h are functions of the three spatial coordinates (x^1, x^2, x^3) alone. As in the Minkowski space-time, s and x^4 will be regarded as having the physical dimensions of time and x^1, x^2, x^3, those of length. Hence εf and εh have zero physical dimensions. By (4.207)

$$g = - \frac{1}{c^6}(1 + 3\varepsilon h)(1 + \varepsilon f),$$

and therefore

$$g^{44} = 1 - \varepsilon f, \quad g^{ii} = -c^2(1 - \varepsilon h), \\ g^{\lambda\mu} = 0, \quad (\lambda \neq \mu).$$

(4.208)

The energy-tensor (4.104) therefore has the following components

$$T^{44} = \left(\rho + \frac{p}{c^2}\right)(u^4)^2 - \frac{p}{c^2}(1 - \varepsilon f),$$

$$T^{l4} = \left(\rho + \frac{p}{c^2}\right)u^l u^4,$$

$$T^{ll} = \left(\rho + \frac{p}{c^2}\right)(u^l)^2 + p(1 - \varepsilon h),$$

$$T^{lm} = \left(\rho + \frac{p}{c^2}\right)u^l u^m.$$

(4.209)

The calculation of the Einstein tensor is, for this special case, most easily performed starting from the Riemann-Christoffel tensor (2.504). Since a Christoffel symbol involves only partial derivatives of the $g_{\mu\nu}$ it must be of order ε, and therefore a product of Christoffel symbols is of order ε^2 and so negligible. Hence (2.504) reduces to

$$R_{\kappa\lambda\mu\nu} = \tfrac{1}{2}\left\{\frac{\partial^2 g_{\nu\kappa}}{\partial x^\lambda \partial x^\mu} + \frac{\partial^2 g_{\lambda\mu}}{\partial x^\mu \partial x^\kappa} - \frac{\partial^2 g_{\lambda\nu}}{\partial x^\mu \partial x^\kappa} - \frac{\partial^2 g_{\mu\kappa}}{\partial x^\nu \partial x^\lambda}\right\},$$

(4.210)

and the components of this tensor are therefore also of order ε. Now the Ricci tensor is

$$R_{\lambda\mu} = g^{\nu\kappa}R_{\kappa\lambda\mu\nu}$$
$$= R_{4\lambda\mu4} - c^2(R_{1\lambda\mu1} + R_{2\lambda\mu2} + R_{3\lambda\mu3}),$$

(4.211)

since the terms in ε in the $g^{\mu\nu}$ given by (4.208) would produce terms of order ε^2 in $R_{\lambda\mu}$. Using (4.207), (4.210) and (4.211), and writing

$$\nabla^2 = \frac{\partial^2}{(\partial x^1)^2} + \frac{\partial^2}{(\partial x^2)^2} + \frac{\partial^2}{(\partial x^3)^2},$$

(4.212)

we obtain

$$R_{44} = -\tfrac{1}{2}\varepsilon c^2 \nabla^2 f, \quad R_{l4} = 0,$$

$$R_{ll} = \tfrac{1}{2}\varepsilon\left\{\frac{\partial^2(f+h)}{(\partial x^l)^2} + \nabla^2 h\right\},$$

$$R_{lm} = \tfrac{1}{2}\varepsilon\frac{\partial^2(f+h)}{\partial x^l \partial x^m}.$$

Raising one suffix we have

$$R_4^4 = g^{44}R_{44} = -\tfrac{1}{2}\varepsilon c^2 \nabla^2 f,$$

$$R_l^l = g^{ll}R_{ll} = -c^2 R_{ll} = -\frac{c^2\varepsilon}{2}\left\{\frac{\partial^2(f+h)}{(\partial x^l)^2} + \nabla^2 h\right\},$$

and therefore

$$R_\sigma^\sigma = R_4^4 + \sum_{i=1}^{3}(R_i^i) = -\varepsilon c^2 \nabla^2(f + 2h).$$

(4.213)

Raising both suffixes there comes

$$R^{44} = -\tfrac{1}{2}\varepsilon c^2 \nabla^2 f, \qquad R^{l4} = 0,$$
$$R^{ll} = \tfrac{1}{2}\varepsilon c^4 \left\{ \frac{\partial^2 (f+h)}{(\partial x^l)^2} + \nabla^2 h \right\},$$
$$R^{lm} = \tfrac{1}{2}\varepsilon c^4 \frac{\partial^2 (f+h)}{\partial x^l \partial x^m}. \tag{4.214}$$

Hence, by (4.107), (4.209), (4.213) and (4.214), Einstein's equations with $\varLambda = 0$ are

$$-\kappa c^2 \left\{ \left(\rho + \frac{p}{c^2} \right)(u^4)^2 - \frac{p}{c^2}(1 - \varepsilon f) \right\} = \varepsilon c^2 \nabla^2 h, \tag{4.215}$$

$$-\kappa c^2 \left(\rho + \frac{p}{c^2} \right) u^l u^4 = 0, \tag{4.216}$$

$$-\kappa c^2 \left\{ \left(\rho + \frac{p}{c^2} \right)(u^l)^2 + p(1 - \varepsilon h) \right\}$$
$$= \tfrac{1}{2}\varepsilon c^4 \left\{ \frac{\partial^2 (f+h)}{(\partial x^l)^2} - \nabla^2 (f+h) \right\}, \tag{4.217}$$

$$-\kappa c^2 \left\{ \left(\rho + \frac{p}{c^2} \right) u^l u^m \right\} = \tfrac{1}{2}\varepsilon c^4 \frac{\partial^2 (f+h)}{\partial x^l \partial x^m}, \tag{4.218}$$

where by (4.103), (4.207), the velocity 4-vector satisfies

$$1 = (1 + \varepsilon f)(u^4)^2 - \frac{1 + \varepsilon h}{c^2} \sum_{i=1}^{3} (u^i)^2. \tag{4.219}$$

The equations (4.216) and (4.219) show that

$$u^i = 0, \qquad (i = 1, 2, 3), \qquad u^4 = 1 - \tfrac{1}{2}\varepsilon f,$$

so that the distribution of matter is at rest relative to the coordinate-system in use. Hence by (4.218)

$$\frac{\partial^2 (f+h)}{\partial x^l \partial x^m} = 0, \tag{4.220}$$

and the three equations (4.217) become

$$-\kappa c^2 p (1 - \varepsilon h) = \tfrac{1}{2}\varepsilon c^4 \left\{ \frac{\partial^2 (f+h)}{(\partial x^l)^2} - \nabla^2 (f+h) \right\} \tag{4.221}$$

At this stage there emerges a type of relation which will be of importance in the sequel. The three equations (4.221) are consistent only if

$$\frac{\partial^2 (f+h)}{(\partial x^1)^2} = \frac{\partial^2 (f+h)}{(\partial x^2)^2} = \frac{\partial^2 (f+h)}{(\partial x^3)^2}, \tag{4.222}$$

which is a restriction on the possible choice of the functions f and h dictated by the algebraic form of the energy-tensor combined with the *a priori* selection of the form (4.207) for the metrical tensor. Equations arising in this way will be called *Consistency Relations*; they are not tensor equations but nevertheless they will play a fundamental role in applications of Einstein's equations. The equations (4.220) and (4.222) are obviously satisfied by

$$f = - h,$$

and therefore the surviving Einstein equations are, by (4.215) and (4.221),

$$- \kappa\rho(1 + \varepsilon h) = \varepsilon \nabla^2 h, \qquad (4.223)$$

$$\kappa p(1 - \varepsilon h) = 0, \qquad (4.224)$$

the last of which shows that the pressure is zero to the order to which we are working. At this point it will be assumed, firstly, that general relativity is to involve – apart from Λ – the two constants of nature κ and c; and secondly, that general relativity is then to reduce to Newtonian gravitational theory when c is identified with $\mathscr{C}$. The first assumption is satisfied by setting $\varepsilon = 1/c^2$, which is in agreement with the postulated smallness of this constant. The second assumption is consistent with the existence of a factor $1/c^2$ in κ and with the hypothesis that ρ, p, f and h contain no factors of order c^2. Then the Newtonian approximation to (4.223) is

$$- \mathop{\mathrm{Lim}}_{c \to \mathscr{C}} (\kappa c^2 \rho) = \nabla^2 h,$$

an equation that may be identified with Poisson's equation $- 4\pi G\rho = \nabla^2 V$ if $h = 2V$ and

$$\kappa = \frac{8\pi G}{c^2} = 1{\cdot}864 \times 10^{-27} \text{ cm. gr.}^{-1}, \qquad (4.225)$$

which therefore determines κ. If, instead of V, the potential $\psi = V/(4\pi G)$ is used, we have

$$\varepsilon h = - \varepsilon f = \frac{8\pi G}{c^2} \psi = \kappa\psi,$$

and therefore the metric of the space-time which represents a static distribution of matter whose Newtonian gravitational potential is $4\pi G\psi(x^1, x^2, x^3)$, is by (4.207)

$$ds^2 = (1 - \kappa\psi)(dx^4)^2 - \frac{(1 + \kappa\psi)}{c^2}\{(dx^1)^2 + (dx^2)^2 + (dx^3)^2\}, \qquad (4.226)$$

provided that squares and higher powers of $1/c^2$ are neglected in the calculation of Einstein's equations.

4.3. The Geodesic Principle

It was pointed out in Sec. 3.7. that a time-like geodesic of the Minkowski space-time represented the history of the motion of a particle moving in accordance with Newton's First Law of Motion. Moreover, in Sec. 3.3. it was indicated that the motion of a particle in a uniform gravitational field had all the characteristics of motion under Newton's First Law, apart from the fact that the motion was accelerated. We may therefore guess that the geodesics of a Riemannian space-time might represent the history of the motion of a particle subject to a gravitational acceleration, a speculation which can be substantiated by examining the geodesics of the space-time (4.226). The metric being orthogonal, equations (2.807) apply and the geodesic equations become

$$\frac{d}{ds}\left\{(1 - \kappa\psi)\frac{dx^4}{ds}\right\} = 0, \qquad (4.301)$$

$$\frac{d}{ds}\left\{(1 + \kappa\psi)\frac{dx^i}{ds}\right\} - \frac{\kappa c^2}{2}\frac{\partial\psi}{\partial x^i}\left\{\left(\frac{dx^4}{ds}\right)^2\right.$$
$$\left. + \frac{1}{c^2}\sum_{j=1}^{3}\left(\frac{dx^j}{ds}\right)^2\right\} = 0, \qquad (i = 1, 2, 3). \qquad (4.302)$$

The first equation is integrable to give

$$\frac{dx^4}{ds} = \beta(1 + \kappa\psi), \qquad (4.303)$$

where β is a constant of integration. But now the integral (2.808) is

$$(1 - \kappa\psi)\left(\frac{dx^4}{ds}\right)^2 - \frac{1 + \kappa\psi}{c^2}\sum_{j=1}^{3}\left(\frac{dx^j}{ds}\right)^2 = 1,$$

and therefore

$$\frac{1}{c^2}\sum_{j=1}^{3}\left(\frac{dx^j}{ds}\right)^2 = \beta^2 - (1 - \kappa\psi).$$

Thus the equations (4.302) may be written

$$\frac{d}{ds}\left\{(1 + \kappa\psi)\frac{dx^i}{ds}\right\} - \frac{\kappa c^2}{2}\frac{\partial\psi}{\partial x^i}\{2\beta^2 - 1 + \kappa\psi(1 + 2\beta^2)\} = 0. \qquad (4.304)$$

The Newtonian approximation is obtained by identifying c with $\mathscr{C}$ so that by (4.226)

$$s \equiv x^4 \equiv T, \qquad (4.305)$$

and then (x^1, x^2, x^3) become the rectangular coordinates (X_1, X_2, X_3) of a Newtonian inertial system. Moreover, $\kappa \rightarrow 8\pi G/\mathscr{C}^2 \rightarrow 0$, $\kappa c^2 \rightarrow 8\pi G$, and, by (4.303), (4.305), $\beta \rightarrow 1$. Hence the equations (4.304) become

$$\frac{d^2 X_i}{dT^2} = 4\pi G\frac{\partial\psi}{\partial X_i} = \frac{\partial V}{\partial X_i}, \qquad (i = 1, 2, 3),$$

which are the Newtonian equations of motion of a particle moving in a gravitational field of potential V, the particle's own gravitational effect being neglected.

This result suggests the following postulate: In any Riemannian space-time with metric (4.102), representing a distribution of matter, a time-like geodesic represents the history of the motion of a particle, of negligibly small gravitational effect, in the gravitational field of the distribution. Since in terms of the Riemannian coordinates of Sec. 2.6., which are valid locally at any event, the geodesic equations become

$$\frac{d^2 y^\sigma}{ds^2} = 0, \qquad (\sigma = 1, 2, 3, 4),$$

the motion of the particle is locally identical with motion under Newton's First Law and the results of Sec. 3.7 apply, in particular, the restriction to time-like geodesics only. In physical terms, these local Riemannian coordinates may be said to form a system which is falling freely in the gravitational field of the distribution of matter at the event in question. This is one formulation of the *principle of equivalence* which states that the effects of a gravitational field can be removed, locally at least, by employing an appropriately chosen accelerated coordinate system.

For a general coordinate system (x) in which the metric of the Riemannian space-time has the form (4.102), the velocity 4-vector of the particle will be defined by analogy with the case of the Minkowski space-time as in Sec. 3.7. If dx^σ/ds ($\sigma = 1, 2, 3, 4$) are the components of the unit tangent vector to the time-like geodesic representing the motion of the particle, then the particle's velocity 4-vector is

$$v^\sigma = \frac{dx^\sigma}{ds}, \qquad (\sigma = 1, 2, 3, 4), \qquad (4.306)$$

which, since it is a unit vector, must satisfy by (2.213) the equation

$$1 = g_{\mu\nu} v^\mu v.. \qquad (4.307)$$

The history of the motion of a light-ray will be represented by a null-geodesic of the Riemannian space-time. This is an obvious generalization from the case of the Minkowski space-time, if it is assumed that in Riemannian coordinates the results of Sec. 3.7 are valid. The representation of the history of the motions of small test-particles and of light-rays by time-like geodesics and by null-geodesics, respectively, together form the *geodesic principle*.

As stated above, the geodesic principle presupposes that the distribution of matter is given through its energy-tensor, that the appropriate Riemannian space-time has been determined through Einstein's equations and that the particle itself contributes nothing to the distribution under whose gravitational influence it moves. But it may be argued that a small particle is itself the limit of a distribution of matter as the volume occupied by the distribution tends to zero and the following question arises: If the distribution itself consists of two or more particles, defined by an energy-tensor, is it possible to find the corresponding Riemannian space-time by means of Einstein's equations and also prove from these equations that the motion of each particle is represented by a time-like geodesic? This question can be answered in the affirmative[1] for the special case when Einstein's equations reduce to (4.111) except

F

in the (limited) regions occupied by the particles. This means that the space-times represent distributions of matter consisting of discrete lumps of matter separated by empty regions. More than this, however, is needed in applications of general relativity to cosmology where continuous distributions of matter are in question. At the present stage of development of the theory it is therefore better to regard the geodesic principle as independent of Einstein's equations, whilst noting that, in certain cases, the principle can be deduced from them.

4.4. Orthogonal Space-times and Einstein's Equations

There are several qualitative aids to the determination of the Riemannian space-time representing a distribution of matter. For example, if the distribution is symmetrical about a point in space, the coefficients of the metric will also exhibit symmetry about that point. Or the distribution might be plane symmetrical, the properties of the material being the same at every point in each of a series of planes perpendicular to a given direction. Or cylindrical symmetry might exist, with the material having identical properties at all points on each of a series of coaxial cylinders. In each case the coefficients of the metric would possess the corresponding symmetry property.

In addition to the simplifications introduced by considerations of this kind, investigations in general relativity have usually, though not exclusively, been conducted by postulating that the Riemannian space-time is of the type that admits orthogonal coordinate-systems. This mathematical restriction has been adopted because of the forbidding complexity of Einstein's equations in non-orthogonal cases. Dingle[2] has worked out the explicit forms of Einstein's equations for the general orthogonal case in which

$$ds^2 = D(dx^4)^2 - A(dx^1)^2 - B(dx^2)^2 - C(dx^3)^2, \tag{4.401}$$

where $D, -A, -B, -C$ are the coefficients of the metric and are functions of all four coordinates. Dingle's formulae may be regarded as forming a fundamental table of reference in general relativity. Writing

$$\frac{\partial D}{\partial x^\lambda} = D_\lambda, \qquad \frac{\partial^2 D}{\partial x^\lambda \partial x^\mu} = D_{\lambda\mu} \qquad (\lambda, \mu = 1, 2, 3, 4),$$

with a similar notation for the partial derivatives of A, B, C, Dingle's expressions for the Christoffel symbols of (4.401) are:

$$\{^1_{11}\} = \frac{A_1}{2A} \qquad \{^1_{21}\} = \frac{A_2}{2A} \qquad \{^1_{31}\} = \frac{A_3}{2A} \qquad \{^1_{41}\} = \frac{A_4}{2A}$$

$$\{^2_{11}\} = -\frac{A_2}{2B} \qquad \{^2_{21}\} = \frac{B_1}{2B} \qquad \{^2_{31}\} = 0 \qquad \{^2_{41}\} = 0$$

$$\{^3_{11}\} = -\frac{A_3}{2C} \qquad \{^3_{21}\} = 0 \qquad \{^3_{31}\} = \frac{C_1}{2C} \qquad \{^3_{41}\} = 0$$

$$\{^4_{11}\} = \frac{A_4}{2D} \qquad \{^4_{21}\} = 0 \qquad \{^4_{31}\} = 0 \qquad \{^4_{41}\} = \frac{D_1}{2D}$$

$$\{^1_{12}\} = \frac{A_2}{2A} \qquad \{^1_{22}\} = -\frac{B_1}{2A} \qquad \{^1_{32}\} = 0 \qquad \{^1_{42}\} = 0$$

$$\{^2_{12}\} = \frac{B_1}{2B} \qquad \{^2_{22}\} = \frac{B_2}{2B} \qquad \{^2_{32}\} = \frac{B_3}{2B} \qquad \{^2_{42}\} = \frac{B_4}{2B}$$

$$\{^3_{12}\} = 0 \qquad \{^3_{22}\} = -\frac{B_3}{2C} \qquad \{^3_{32}\} = \frac{C_2}{2C} \qquad \{^3_{42}\} = 0$$

$$\{^4_{12}\} = 0 \qquad \{^4_{22}\} = \frac{B_4}{2D} \qquad \{^4_{32}\} = 0 \qquad \{^4_{42}\} = \frac{D_2}{2D}$$

$$\{^1_{13}\} = \frac{A_3}{2A} \qquad \{^1_{23}\} = 0 \qquad \{^1_{33}\} = -\frac{C_1}{2A} \qquad \{^1_{43}\} = 0$$

$$\{^2_{13}\} = 0 \qquad \{^2_{23}\} = \frac{B_3}{2B} \qquad \{^2_{33}\} = -\frac{C_2}{2B} \qquad \{^2_{43}\} = 0$$

$$\{^3_{13}\} = \frac{C_1}{2C} \qquad \{^3_{23}\} = \frac{C_2}{2C} \qquad \{^3_{33}\} = \frac{C_3}{2C} \qquad \{^3_{43}\} = \frac{C_4}{2C}$$

$$\{^4_{13}\} = 0 \qquad \{^4_{23}\} = 0 \qquad \{^4_{33}\} = \frac{C_4}{2D} \qquad \{^4_{43}\} = \frac{D_3}{2D}$$

$$\{^1_{14}\} = \frac{A_4}{2A} \qquad \{^1_{24}\} = 0 \qquad \{^1_{34}\} = 0 \qquad \{^1_{44}\} = \frac{D_1}{2A}$$

$$\{^2_{14}\} = 0 \qquad \{^2_{24}\} = \frac{B_4}{2B} \qquad \{^2_{34}\} = 0 \qquad \{^2_{44}\} = \frac{D_2}{2B}$$

$$\{^3_{14}\} = 0 \qquad \{^3_{24}\} = 0 \qquad \{^3_{34}\} = \frac{C_4}{2C} \qquad \{^3_{44}\} = \frac{D_3}{2C}$$

$$\{^4_{14}\} = \frac{D_1}{2D} \qquad \{^4_{24}\} = \frac{D_2}{2D} \qquad \{^4_{34}\} = \frac{D_3}{2D} \qquad \{^4_{44}\} = \frac{D_4}{2D} \qquad (4.402)$$

The ten Einstein equations (4.107) are:

$$
\begin{aligned}
\kappa c^2 A T^{11} = {}& \tfrac{1}{2}\left\{ \frac{B_{33} + C_{22}}{BC} - \frac{B_{44} - D_{22}}{BD} - \frac{C_{44} - D_{33}}{CD} \right\} \\
& - \tfrac{1}{4}\left\{ \frac{B_3 C_3 + C_2^2}{BC^2} + \frac{C_2 B_2 + B_3^2}{CB^2} - \frac{B_4 D_4 - D_2^2}{BD^2} + \frac{D_2 B_2 - B_4^2}{DB^2} \right. \\
& \qquad - \frac{C_4 D_4 - D_3^2}{CD^2} + \frac{D_3 C_3 - C_4^2}{DC^2} \\
& \qquad - \frac{C_2 D_2 + B_3 D_3 - B_4 C_4}{BCD} \\
& \qquad \left. - \frac{DB_1 C_1 + CB_1 D_1 + BC_1 D_1}{ABCD} \right\} + \varLambda, \qquad (4.403)
\end{aligned}
$$

$$\kappa c^2 BT^{22} = \tfrac{1}{2}\left\{\frac{A_{33} + C_{11}}{AC} - \frac{A_{44} - D_{11}}{AD} - \frac{C_{44} - D_{33}}{CD}\right\}$$

$$-\tfrac{1}{4}\left\{\frac{A_3 C_3 + C_1^2}{AC^2} + \frac{C_1 A_1 + A_3^2}{CA^2} - \frac{A_4 D_4 - D_1^2}{AD^2} + \frac{D_1 A_1 - A_4^2}{DA^2}\right.$$

$$-\frac{C_4 D_4 - D_3^2}{CD^2} + \frac{D_3 C_3 - C_4^2}{DC^2}$$

$$-\frac{C_1 D_1 + A_3 D_3 - A_4 C_4}{ACD}$$

$$\left. -\frac{DA_2 C_2 + CA_2 D_2 + AC_2 D_2}{ABCD}\right\} + \Lambda, \qquad (4.404)$$

$$\kappa c^2 CT^{33} = \tfrac{1}{2}\left\{\frac{A_{22} + B_{11}}{AB} - \frac{A_{44} - D_{11}}{AD} - \frac{B_{44} - D_{22}}{BD}\right\}$$

$$-\tfrac{1}{4}\left\{\frac{A_2 B_2 + B_1^2}{AB^2} + \frac{B_1 A_1 + A_2^2}{BA^2} - \frac{A_4 D_4 - D_1^2}{AD^2} + \frac{D_1 A_1 - A_4^2}{DA^2}\right.$$

$$-\frac{B_4 D_4 - D_2^2}{BD^2} + \frac{D_2 B_2 - B_4^2}{DB^2}$$

$$-\frac{B_1 D_1 + A_2 D_2 - A_4 B_4}{ABD}$$

$$\left. -\frac{DA_3 B_3 + BA_3 D_3 + AB_3 D_3}{ABCD}\right\} + \Lambda, \qquad (4.405)$$

$$-\kappa c^2 DT^{44} = \tfrac{1}{2}\left\{\frac{A_{22} + B_{11}}{AB} + \frac{A_{33} + C_{11}}{AC} + \frac{B_{33} + C_{22}}{BC}\right\}$$

$$-\tfrac{1}{4}\left\{\frac{A_2 B_2 + B_1^2}{AB^2} + \frac{B_1 A_1 + A_2^2}{BA^2} + \frac{A_3 C_3 + C_1^2}{AC^2} + \frac{C_1 A_1 + A_3^2}{CA^2}\right.$$

$$+\frac{B_3 C_3 + C_2^2}{BC^2} + \frac{C_2 B_2 + B_3^2}{CB^2} - \frac{B_1 C_1 + A_2 C_2 + A_3 B_3}{ABC}$$

$$\left. +\frac{CA_4 B_4 + BA_4 C_4 + AB_4 C_4}{ABCD}\right\} + \Lambda, \qquad (4.406)$$

$$+\kappa c^2 ABT^{12} = \kappa c^2 ABT^{21}$$

$$= -\tfrac{1}{2}\left\{\frac{DC_{12} + CD_{12}}{CD}\right\}$$

$$+\tfrac{1}{4}\left\{\frac{C_1 C_2}{C^2} + \frac{D_1 D_2}{D^2} + \frac{A_2 C_1}{AC} + \frac{A_2 D_1}{AD} + \frac{B_1 C_2}{BC} + \frac{B_1 D_2}{BD}\right\}, \qquad (4.407)$$

$$+\kappa c^2 ACT^{13} = \kappa c^2 ACT^{31}$$

$$= -\tfrac{1}{2}\left\{\frac{DB_{13} + BD_{13}}{BD}\right\}$$

$$+\tfrac{1}{4}\left\{\frac{B_1 B_3}{B^2} + \frac{D_1 D_3}{D^2} + \frac{A_3 B_1}{AB} + \frac{A_3 D_1}{AD} + \frac{C_1 B_3}{CB} + \frac{C_1 D_3}{CD}\right\}, \qquad (4.408)$$

$$+ \kappa c^2 BCT^{23} = \kappa c^2 BCT^{32}$$

$$= -\tfrac{1}{2}\left\{\frac{DA_{23} + AD_{23}}{AD}\right\}$$

$$= \tfrac{1}{4}\left\{\frac{A_2A_3}{A^2} + \frac{D_2D_3}{D^2} + \frac{A_2B_3}{AB} + \frac{A_3C_2}{AC} + \frac{D_2B_3}{DB} + \frac{D_3C_2}{DC}\right\}, \quad (4.409)$$

$$- \kappa c^2 ADT^{14} = - \kappa c^2 ADT^{41}$$

$$= -\tfrac{1}{2}\left\{\frac{CB_{14} + BC_{14}}{BC}\right\}$$

$$+ \tfrac{1}{4}\left\{\frac{B_1B_4}{B^2} + \frac{C_1C_4}{C^2} + \frac{A_4B_1}{AB} + \frac{A_4C_1}{AC} + \frac{B_4D_1}{BD} + \frac{C_4D_1}{CD}\right\}, \quad (4.410)$$

$$- \kappa c^2 BDT^{24} = - \kappa c^2 BDT^{42}$$

$$= -\tfrac{1}{2}\left\{\frac{CA_{24} + AC_{24}}{AC}\right\}$$

$$+ \tfrac{1}{4}\left\{\frac{A_2A_4}{A^2} + \frac{C_2C_4}{C^2} + \frac{A_2B_4}{AB} + \frac{C_2B_4}{BC} + \frac{A_4D_2}{AD} + \frac{C_4D_2}{CD}\right\}, \quad (4.411)$$

$$- \kappa c^2 CDT^{34} = - \kappa c^2 CDT^{43}$$

$$= -\tfrac{1}{2}\left\{\frac{BA_{34} + AB_{34}}{AB}\right\}$$

$$+ \tfrac{1}{4}\left\{\frac{A_3A_4}{A^2} + \frac{B_3B_4}{B^2} + \frac{A_3C_4}{AC} + \frac{B_3C_4}{BC} + \frac{A_4D_3}{AD} + \frac{B_4D_3}{BD}\right\}. \quad (4.412)$$

Before discussing special cases of (4.401), it must be pointed out that the notation (x^4, x^1, x^2, x^3) for coordinates is very cumbersome in practice and it is advantageous to use a separate letter for each coordinate. With practice, the assigning of the indices 1, 2, 3, 4 to the coordinates – for example in the calculation of Christoffel symbols – can be performed mentally. We now proceed to list three classes of space-times, all of which come under the category (4.401), that have particular symmetry properties. The proofs that the space-times do, in fact, possess the properties will not be given for they would lead too far afield into group theory and into the theory of differential equations. The reader who is interested in these questions should consult the references given.

(i) *Plane symmetry.* Those space-times in which each plane $x = constant$ is a plane of symmetry have metrics of the form[3]

$$ds^2 = e^{2f}dt^2 - \frac{1}{c^2}\{e^{2f}dx^2 + e^{2h}(dy^2 + dz^2)\}, \quad (4.413)$$

where f, h are arbitrary functions of x, t. The indices are to be assigned to the coordinates in (4.413) thus:

$$t = x^4, \qquad x = x^1, \qquad y = x^2, \qquad z = x^3. \quad (4.414)$$

(ii) *Spherical symmetry.* The metrics of such space-times can be built up by considering first the Euclidean 3-space whose metric in spherical polar co-ordinates was found in Sec. 2.2 to be

$$ds^2 = dr^2 + r^2 d\theta^2 + r^2 \sin^2 \theta \, d\phi^2.$$

There are then two useful forms for the metric of an orthogonal space-time, spherically symmetric about the point $r = 0$, viz.

$$ds^2 = e^\nu dt^2 - \frac{1}{c^2}\{e^\mu dr^2 + r^2 d\theta^2 + r^2 \sin^2 \theta \, d\phi^2\}, \qquad (4.415)$$

where ν, μ are arbitrary functions of r, t; and

$$ds^2 = e^\nu dt^2 - \frac{e^\mu}{c^2}\{dr^2 + r^2 d\theta^2 + r^2 \sin^2 \theta \, d\phi^2\}, \qquad (4.416)$$

where ν, μ are again arbitrary functions of r, t. The second form is called *isotropic* and it can be proved that (4.415) and (4.416) are convertible into one another[4]. But the r, t and ν, μ in these two expressions are not identical; for example, the r of (4.416) is a complicated function of the r and t of (4.415) and the same is true for t, ν and μ. The angular coordinates θ and ϕ are, however, unchanged by passing from one form to the other. The coordinate identification is now

$$t = x^4, \qquad r = x^1, \qquad \theta = x^2, \qquad \phi = x^3. \qquad (4.417)$$

The isotropic form (4.416) is of particular interest and therefore the explicit forms of Einstein's equations to which it gives rise will be worked out in detail, the energy-tensor (4.104) being that for a perfect fluid. We have

$$D = e^\nu, \qquad A = \frac{e^\mu}{c^2}, \qquad B = \frac{e^\mu r^2}{c^2}, \qquad C = \frac{e^\mu r^2 \sin^2 \theta}{c^2}.$$

Inspection of the formulae for T^{24}, T^{34}, T^{12}, T^{23} and T^{13} on pp. 72, 73 shows that these components are identically zero and hence $u^2 = 0$, $u^3 = 0$. The fluid-velocity 4-vector therefore satisfies

$$1 = e^\nu (u^4)^2 - \frac{e^\mu (u^1)^2}{c^2} \qquad (4.418)$$

The surviving Einstein equations are, by (4.406), (4.403), (4.404) and (4.405), and (4.410),

$$\kappa\left\{\left(\rho + \frac{p}{c^2}\right)(u^4)^2 + e^{-\nu}\frac{p}{c^2}\right\}e^\nu$$

$$= -e^{-\mu}\left\{\mu_{rr} + \tfrac{1}{4}\mu_r^2 + \frac{2}{r}\mu_r\right\} + \frac{3}{4}\frac{e^{-\nu}}{c^2}\mu_t^2 - \frac{\Lambda}{c^2}, \qquad (4.419)$$

$$\kappa\left\{\left(\rho + \frac{p}{c^2}\right)(u^1)^2 + e^{-\mu}p\right\}e^\mu$$

$$= c^2 e^{-\mu}\left\{\frac{1}{r}(\mu + \nu)_r + \tfrac{1}{4}\mu_r^2 + \tfrac{1}{2}\mu_r \nu_r\right\} - e^{-\nu}(\mu_{tt} + \tfrac{3}{4}\mu_t^2 - \tfrac{1}{2}\mu_t \nu_t) + \Lambda, \qquad (4.420)$$

$$\kappa p = c^2 e^{-\mu}\left\{\tfrac{1}{2}(\mu + \nu)_{rr} + \frac{1}{2}\frac{1}{r}(\mu + \nu)_r + \tfrac{1}{4}\nu_r^2\right\}$$

$$- e^{-\nu}(\mu_{tt} + \tfrac{3}{4}\mu_t^2 - \tfrac{1}{2}\mu_t \nu_t) + \Lambda, \qquad (4.421)$$

$$\kappa\left(\rho + \frac{p}{c^2}\right)u^4u^1 = e^{-(\mu+\nu)}(\mu_{rt} - \tfrac{1}{2}\mu_t\nu_r),\qquad(4.422)$$

where subscripts denote partial derivatives with respect to r and t.

(iii) *Cylindrical symmetry*[5]. The axis of symmetry being $z = 0$, space-times possessing this type of symmetry and whose metrics are orthogonal have

$$ds^2 = e^\nu dt^2 - \frac{1}{c^2}\{e^\mu(dr^2 + r^2d\theta^2) + e^\lambda dz^2\},\qquad(4.423)$$

where ν, μ, λ are arbitrary functions of t, r, z, and the coordinate identification is now

$$t = x^4,\qquad r = x^1,\qquad \theta = x^2,\qquad z = x^3,\qquad(4.424)$$

The metrics (4.413), (4.416) and (4.423) are all reducible in the first approximation to the form (4.226) by assuming that the metrical tensors are independent of $t\ (\equiv x^4)$ and by making the following adjustments: For (4.413): Let

$$x^1 = \int e^{f-h}dx,\qquad x^2 = y,\qquad x^3 = z,$$

and

$$e^{2f} = 1 - \kappa\psi(x^1),\qquad e^{2h} = 1 + \kappa\psi(x^1).$$

For (4.416): Let

$$x^1 = r\sin\theta\cos\phi,\qquad x^2 = r\sin\theta\sin\phi,\qquad x^3 = r\cos\phi,$$

and

$$e^{\nu(r)} = 1 - \kappa\psi(r),\qquad e^{\mu(r)} = 1 + \kappa\psi(r).$$

For (4.423): Let

$$x^1 = r\cos\theta,\qquad x^2 = r\sin\theta,\qquad x^3 = z$$

and

$$e^{\nu(r,z)} = 1 - \kappa\psi(r,z),\qquad e^{\mu(r,z)} = e^{\lambda(r,z))} = 1 + \kappa\psi(r,z).$$

4.5. Gravitation and the Curvature of Space-time

The Riemann-Cristoffel tensor for the space-time (4.226) is not zero as may easily be verified from (4.210). For example, the component R_{4141} is

$$R_{4141} = -\tfrac{1}{2}\frac{\partial^2 g_{44}}{(\partial x^1)^2} = \frac{\kappa}{2}\frac{\partial^2 \psi}{(\partial x^1)^2},$$

and similarly all the other non-vanishing components are proportional to κ. Thus, when the distribution of matter is statical and the coefficients of the metric involve terms in the first power of κ only, space-time is curved and a free test-particle is subject to a purely gravitational acceleration as was indicated in Sec. 4.3. When, as happened in the early days of general relativity, attention is concentrated on statical space-times, it is natural to conclude that the curvature of space-time (i.e. the existence of a non-null Riemann-Christoffel tensor) is associated with the presence of a gravitational field. From this to the assertion that gravitation is a property of space-time itself, and not of the distribution of matter it describes, is but a small further step. Such a statement, however, would imply that *any* curved space-time must necessarily correspond to a gravitational field, irrespective of whether or not a distribution of matter responsible for the field can be indicated. It will now be shown that, at the present stage of development of the theory, such a view is of doubtful validity.

Consider the space-time whose metric is

$$ds^2 = dt^2 - \frac{e^{2\sqrt{(\Lambda/3)t}}}{c^2}(dx^2 + dy^2 + dz^2), \tag{4.501}$$

where Λ is the cosmical constant. This space-time is not statical, the coefficients of its metric being functions of the time-coordinate t. In the notation of formula (4.401) they are

$$D = 1, \qquad A = B = C = \frac{e^{2\sqrt{(\Lambda/3)t}}}{c^2}, \tag{4.502}$$

where

$$t = x^4, \qquad x = x^1, \qquad y = x^2, \qquad z = x^3. \tag{4.503}$$

Using Dingle's formulae (4.402) for the Christoffel symbols together with (2.501) for the Riemann-Christoffel tensor, the component R^1_{441}, for example, is found to be

$$R^1_{441} = \frac{\Lambda}{3}.$$

Hence one component of the tensor in this particular coordinate-system is different from zero and therefore the tensor is not a null-tensor, which means that the space-time (4.501) is curved. Again, the Einstein equations (4.407) to (4.412) show that those components of the energy-tensor for which

$$\mu\nu = 12, 13, 23, 14, 24, 34,$$

are identically zero because A, B, C, D are functions of one coordinate only. Equation (4.406) becomes

$$- 8\pi G T^{44} = -\tfrac{1}{4}\left(\frac{CA_4B_4 + BA_4C_4 + AB_4C_4}{ABCD}\right) + \Lambda$$
$$= -\tfrac{3}{4}(\tfrac{4}{3}\Lambda) + \Lambda$$
$$= 0, \tag{4.504}$$

whilst (4.403), (4.404) and (4.405) yield

$$8\pi G \frac{e^{2\sqrt{(\Lambda/3)t}}}{c^2} T^{ii} = -e^{-2\sqrt{(\Lambda/3)t}}\frac{d^2 e^{2\sqrt{(\Lambda/3)t}}}{dt^2} + \tfrac{1}{4}\left(\frac{d \log e^{2\sqrt{(\Lambda/3)t}}}{dt}\right)^2 + \Lambda$$
$$= (-\tfrac{4}{3}\Lambda + \tfrac{1}{3}\Lambda) + \Lambda$$
$$= 0, \qquad (i = 1, 2, 3). \tag{4.505}$$

Hence every component of the energy-tensor is identically zero at all events (t, x, y, z) of the space-time (4.501) and there are, moreover, no singular events at which $T^{\mu\nu}$ could be regarded as undefined owing to some infinity, or other singularity, in the right-hand sides of equations (4.403) to (4.412). This space-time does not therefore represent any distribution of matter at all and there is no gravitational field which might correspond to its curvature.

The foregoing example has been known since 1917, equation (4.501) being one form of the metric of the de Sitter universe (see model A2(vi—b) of Appendix). It has been speculated that the space-time might represent the limit of a distribution of matter whose energy-tensor has tended to zero with the passage of time, having once been non-zero, but no proof of this speculation is known to the author. Alternatively, the responsibility for the null character of the energy-tensor has been placed on the cosmical constant, which, as will be shown in Sec. 6.5, has a gravitational effect equivalent to that of a distribution of matter. Indeed, it is obvious that if $\Lambda = 0$ in (4.501) the metric becomes that of the Minkowski space-time whose curvature is zero. This interpretation might once have seemed satisfactory, but solutions of Einstein's equations with $\Lambda = 0$ have now been discovered in which the components of the Ricci tensor (2.507) are all zero whereas the Riemann-Christoffel tensor is not zero. The vanishing of the Ricci tensor implies, of course, that the energy-tensor is zero. Thus there is no gravitating matter present. The first solution was found by A. H. Taub[3] in 1951, the second by I. Ozsvath and E. Shücking[6] in 1962. It has been objected to Taub's solution that it must contain a singularity of the energy-tensor though the physical system represented by the singularity has not been indicated. A corresponding objection to the Ozsvath and Schücking case has not been raised.

These examples therefore demonstrate that, whether the cosmical constant is included in Einstein's equations or not, it is not possible to say that the curvature of space-time is the cause of gravitation. What can be asserted is that, if a space-time is to represent the gravitational and mechanical properties of a distribution of matter, the Ricci tensor must be different from zero, which in turn implies that the Riemann-Christoffel tensor cannot be a null-tensor and therefore that the space-time must be curved. But it cannot be asserted with certainty that the converse is true; every curved space-time may not necessarily represent a distribution of matter: some may correspond to null energy-tensors while others may even represent distributions of matter whose energy-tensors, though not null, are inadmissible for physical reasons.

4.6. Accelerated Coordinate-systems

It has been mentioned in Sec. 4.3 that the existence of Riemannian coordinates at every event in space-time expresses the principle of equivalence and indicates that the effect of a gravitational field can be abolished locally by the choice of a suitably accelerated coordinate-system. This result has led to some confusion for it has been interpreted as equivalent to the statement that the essence of general relativity consists in the use of accelerated coordinate-systems, in contrast to special relativity, where relatively unaccelerated coordinate-systems are employed. The statement is, however, misleading because there is nothing to prevent the investigator from using accelerated coordinate-systems in special relativity if he choses to do so. We shall now examine, by means of an example, the consequences of such a step. Let (x^4, x^1, x^2, x^3) be the coordinates of an inertial system S in the Minkowski space-time, so that the metric is

$$ds^2 = (dx^4)^2 - \frac{1}{c^2} \sum_{j=1}^{3} (dx^j)^2. \qquad (4.601)$$

Consider the non-inertial coordinate-system A in which the coordinates are (t, x, y, z) where

$$\begin{aligned} t + \frac{x}{c} &= \frac{1}{\alpha + \beta} \log\left\{ (\alpha + \beta)\left(x^4 + \frac{x^1}{c} \right) \right\}, \\ t - \frac{x}{c} &= \frac{1}{\alpha - \beta} \log\left\{ (\alpha - \beta)\left(x^4 - \frac{x^1}{c} \right) \right\}, \\ y &= x^2, \qquad z = x^3, \end{aligned} \qquad (4.602)$$

and α, β are constants with the physical dimensions of $(\text{time})^{-1}$. If differentials of these equations are taken, it is easy to show that the metric (4.601) is transformed into

$$ds^2 = e^X\left\{ dt^2 - \frac{dx^2}{c^2} \right\} - \frac{1}{c^2}(dy^2 + dz^2), \qquad (4.603)$$

where

$$X = 2\alpha t + 2\beta x/c.$$

The transformation (4.602) does not, of course, alter the null-character of the Riemann-Christoffel tensor of the Minkowski space-time which remains a flat space-time whether the formula for the metric is (4.601) or (4.603). Hence the Ricci tensor is still identically zero and so is the energy-tensor, in spite of the fact that the coefficients of the metric in (4.603) are no longer constants. Thus (4.603) does not represent any distribution of matter and therefore no gravitational field is present. Nevertheless consider a test-particle whose motion is given by a time-like geodesic of (4.601). In the frame S its motion is governed by the equations

$$\frac{d^2x^\mu}{ds^2} = 0, \qquad (\mu = 1, 2, 3, 4),$$

and so is unaccelerated. For simplicity, suppose that the particle moves parallel to the x^1-axis of S and therefore parallel to the x-axis of the system A. In this system, the particle's motion is governed by the geodesic equations (2.807), (2.808) applied to (4.603), namely,

$$\frac{d}{ds}\left(e^X \frac{dt}{ds} \right) - \alpha e^X\left\{ \left(\frac{dt}{ds} \right)^2 - \frac{1}{c^2}\left(\frac{dx}{ds} \right)^2 \right\} = 0, \qquad (4.604)$$

$$\frac{d}{ds}\left(e^X\frac{dx}{ds}\right) + \beta ce^X\left\{\left(\frac{dt}{ds}\right)^2 - \frac{1}{c^2}\left(\frac{dx}{ds}\right)^2\right\} = 0, \qquad (4.605)$$

$$1 = e^X\left\{\left(\frac{dt}{ds}\right)^2 - \frac{1}{c^2}\left(\frac{dx}{ds}\right)^2\right\}. \qquad (4.606)$$

The integrals of the first two equations are

$$\left.\begin{array}{l} \dfrac{dt}{ds} = \alpha(a + s)e^{-X}, \\[2mm] \dfrac{dx}{ds} = c\beta(b - s)e^{-X}, \end{array}\right\} \qquad (4.607)$$

where a, b are the constants of integration. Substitution into (4.606) gives

$$e^X = \alpha^2(a + s)^2 - \beta^2(b - s)^2. \qquad (4.608)$$

Differentiating the second of equations (4.607) with respect to s, and using (4.608) one finds, after some calculation, that

$$\frac{d^2x}{ds^2} = - c\beta e^{-2X}\{\alpha^2(a + s)(a + 2b - s) + \beta^2(b - s)^2\}.$$

This equation shows that the geodesic motion of the particle in A is accelerated, whereas it was unaccelerated in S. The passage from the inertial system S to the non-inertial system A has had two consequences; firstly, the co-efficients of the metric in (4.603) have become functions of the coordinates, whereas they were constants when the coordinates of S were used; secondly, accelerations, which are reflections of the motion of the system A relative to S, are introduced in the motions of free particles. But these accelerations are quite arbitrary because special relativity provides no prescriptions by which they could be connected with physical effects, gravitation for example. There is, for instance, no rule by which α and β could be interpreted physically. General relativity therefore does more than employ accelerated coordinate-systems and the variable coefficients of the metric to which such systems give rise. Its essential feature is to provide a link through non-vanishing Ricci tensors with gravitational fields. Accelerated coordinate-systems are merely incidental consequences of this linkage.

CHAPTER 5

The Schwarzschild Space-time

It is well known in Newtonian gravitational theory that the potential of a particle of mass M at a point distant r from the particle is $\psi = M/r$ and that this is the so-called elementary solution of Laplace's equation,

$$\nabla^2 \psi = 0.$$

But it is also true that $\psi = M/r$ is the gravitational potential of a sphere of mass M, of finite size, at a point outside it distant r from its centre. Thus from the elementary solution of Laplace's equation alone, and without additional information, it is impossible to distinguish between a particle (a mass-point) and a finite sphere. This point must be borne in mind in the interpretation of the analogue of the elementary solution of Laplace's equation which will now be obtained from Einstein's equations.

5.1. Metric of the Schwarzschild Space-time

Consider a space-time with spherical symmetry, whose coefficients are independent of the time, and which by (4.415) therefore has the form

$$ds^2 = e^{\nu(r)}dt^2 - \frac{1}{c^2}\{e^{\mu(r)}dr^2 + r^2d\theta^2 + r^2\sin^2\theta\,d\phi^2\}, \tag{5.101}$$

where ν, μ are functions of r to be determined. Suppose that the centre of the spherical mass M is located at $r = 0$, and let the energy-tensor outside this mass be identically zero. Assume also that the cosmical constant is zero. Then referring to Sec. 2.8 and to formulae (2.507) and (4.111), Einstein's equations are

$$R_{\lambda\mu} = \frac{\partial^2 \log \sqrt{(-g)}}{\partial x^\mu \partial x^\lambda} - \frac{\partial}{\partial x^\sigma}\begin{Bmatrix}\sigma\\\lambda\mu\end{Bmatrix} + \begin{Bmatrix}\tau\\\lambda\sigma\end{Bmatrix}\begin{Bmatrix}\sigma\\\mu\tau\end{Bmatrix} - \begin{Bmatrix}\tau\\\lambda\mu\end{Bmatrix}\frac{\partial \log \sqrt{(-g)}}{\partial x^\tau} = 0. \tag{5.102}$$

For the space-time (5.101), assigning indices as in (4.417), we have

$$\begin{aligned}\sqrt{(-g)} &= \{e^{\frac{1}{2}(\nu+\mu)}r^2 \sin\theta\}/c^3, \\ g^{44} &= e^{-\nu}, \quad g^{11} = -c^2 e^{-\mu}, \quad g^{22} = -c^2 r^{-2}, \quad g^{33} = -c^2 r^{-2}\sin^{-2}\theta,\end{aligned} \tag{5.103}$$

and, if a prime denotes a derivative with respect to r, the non-zero Christoffel symbols of the second kind are

$$\left.\begin{array}{l} \{^1_{11}\} = \tfrac{1}{2}\mu', \quad \{^2_{21}\} = \{^2_{12}\} = \{^3_{31}\} = \{^3_{13}\} = \dfrac{1}{r}, \\[2mm] \{^4_{14}\} = \{^4_{41}\} = \tfrac{1}{2}\nu', \quad \{^1_{22}\} = -re^{-\mu}, \\[2mm] \{^3_{23}\} = \{^3_{32}\} = \cot\theta, \quad \{^1_{33}\} = -re^{-\mu}\sin^2\theta, \\[2mm] \{^2_{33}\} = -\sin\theta\cos\theta, \quad \{^1_{44}\} = \tfrac{1}{2}c^2 e^{\nu-\mu}\nu'. \end{array}\right\} \tag{5.104}$$

The non-zero components of the tensor $R_{\lambda\mu}$ turn out to be four in number and the ten equations (5.102) reduce to the following:

$$R_{44} = c^2 e^{\nu-\mu}\left\{-\tfrac{1}{2}\nu'' - \frac{\nu'}{r} + \tfrac{1}{4}\mu'\nu' - \tfrac{1}{4}(\nu')^2\right\} = 0, \tag{5.105}$$

$$R_{11} = \tfrac{1}{2}\nu'' - \frac{\mu'}{r} - \tfrac{1}{4}\mu'\nu' + \tfrac{1}{4}(\nu')^2 = 0, \tag{5.106}$$

$$R_{33} = \sin^2\theta\, R_{22} = \sin^2\theta\{e^{-\mu} + \tfrac{1}{2}re^{-\mu}(\nu' - \mu') - 1\} = 0. \tag{5.107}$$

Clearly the equation $R_{11} + \dfrac{1}{c^2}e^{\mu-\nu}R_{44} = 0$ is satisfied if $\mu' + \nu' = 0$ which means that

$$\mu = -\nu,$$

whilst (5.107) is satisfied if

$$(1 + r\nu')e^{\nu} = 1,$$

i.e. if

$$e^{\nu} = 1 - \frac{\alpha}{r},$$

where α is a constant of integration. It is now easy to verify that the functions

$$e^{\nu} = e^{-\mu} = 1 - \frac{\alpha}{r}, \tag{5.108}$$

satisfy the three equations (5.105) to (5.107) individually. Obviously, e^{ν} and e^{μ} tend to unity as $r \to \infty$, and therefore for large values of r the space-time degenerates to the Minkowski space-time. It is not, however, flat because, for small values of r, the Riemann-Christoffel tensor (2.504) has some non-zero components. Thus the space-time (5.101) has the metric

$$ds^2 = \left(1 - \frac{\alpha}{r}\right)dt^2 - \frac{1}{c^2}\left\{\frac{dr^2}{1 - \dfrac{\alpha}{r}} + r^2 d\theta^2 + r^2\sin^2\theta\, d\phi^2\right\}, \tag{5.109}$$

the tensor $g_{\mu\nu}$ having one infinite and one zero component at $r = \alpha$ whose signs are reversed for $r < \alpha$. Thus (5.109) is the space-time representing the gravitational field outside a spherically symmetric distribution of matter with centre at $r = 0$. There is a singular region within $0 \leq r \leq \alpha$, which could only become a point-singularity if $\alpha = 0$. But $\alpha = 0$ is the condition for reducing (5.109) to the Minkowski space-time and thus making the gravitational field disappear.

The determination of α depends on a reduction to Newtonian theory and this may be conveniently made through the geodesic equations. Using (2.807) with (5.103), (5.108) we have, for $\lambda = 4, 2$ and 3, respectively,

$$\frac{d}{ds}\left(e^\nu \frac{dt}{ds}\right) = 0, \tag{5.110}$$

$$\frac{d}{ds}\left(r^2 \frac{d\theta}{ds}\right) - r^2 \sin\theta \cos\theta \left(\frac{d\phi}{ds}\right)^2 = 0, \tag{5.111}$$

$$\frac{d}{ds}\left(r^2 \sin^2\theta \frac{d\phi}{ds}\right) = 0, \tag{5.112}$$

and, in place of the equation for $\lambda = 1$, we can use the integral (2.808), viz.

$$1 = e^\nu \left(\frac{dt}{ds}\right)^2 - \frac{1}{c^2}\left\{e^\mu \left(\frac{dr}{ds}\right)^2 + r^2 \left(\frac{d\theta}{ds}\right)^2 + r^2 \sin^2\theta \left(\frac{d\phi}{ds}\right)^2\right\}. \tag{5.113}$$

These four equations, in accordance with the geodesic principle, represent the motion of a particle in the gravitational field represented by the space-time (5.109). Equation (5.110) may be integrated to give

$$\frac{dt}{ds} = \beta e^{-\nu} = \beta \left(1 - \frac{\alpha}{r}\right)^{-1}, \tag{5.114}$$

where β is a constant of integration. Using this integral in (5.113) there comes

$$\frac{1}{\beta^2}\left(1 - \frac{\alpha}{r}\right)^2 = \left(1 - \frac{\alpha}{r}\right) - \frac{1}{c^2}\left\{\frac{1}{1 - \alpha/r}\left(\frac{dr}{dt}\right)^2 + r^2 \left(\frac{d\theta}{dt}\right)^2 + r^2 \sin^2\theta \left(\frac{d\phi}{dt}\right)^2\right\}. \tag{5.115}$$

If the motion is purely radial, then $d\theta/dt$ and $d\phi/dt$ are both zero and

$$\left(\frac{dr}{dt}\right)^2 = \left(1 - \frac{\alpha}{r}\right)^2 c^2 - \frac{c^2}{\beta^2}\left(1 - \frac{\alpha}{r}\right)^3. \tag{5.116}$$

Suppose also that the particle can attain values of r which are infinitely large compared with α. If dr/dt has the value V in such regions, then

$$\beta = \left(1 - \frac{V^2}{c^2}\right)^{-1/2}. \tag{5.117}$$

On differentiating (5.116) with respect to t, it follows that

$$\frac{d^2r}{dt^2} = \frac{\alpha c^2}{r^2}\left(1 - \frac{\alpha}{r}\right) - \frac{3\alpha c^2}{2r^2}\left(1 - \frac{V^2}{c^2}\right)\left(1 - \frac{\alpha}{r}\right)^2.$$

Hence, if α/r and V/c are both small, we have approximately

$$\frac{d^2r}{dt^2} = -\tfrac{1}{2}\frac{\alpha c^2}{r^2}$$

and this is of the same mathematical form as the Newtonian equation of (radial) motion for a particle in the external gravitational field of a spherical mass M, if

$$\alpha = \frac{2GM}{c^2},$$

which determines α. It is usual to replace α by a constant $2m$ where

$$m = \tfrac{1}{2}\alpha = \frac{GM}{c^2} \qquad (5.118)$$

and then the metric (5.109) may be written

$$ds^2 = \left(1 - \frac{2m}{r}\right)dt^2 - \frac{1}{c^2}\left\{\frac{dr^2}{1 - 2m/r} + r^2 d\theta^2 + r^2 \sin^2 \theta \, d\phi^2\right\}, \qquad (5.119)$$

which is the standard form for the Schwarzschild space-time. It represents in general relativity the gravitational field outside a spherical mass M whose centre lies at $r = 0$. Since the singular region, $0 \le r \le 2m$, is of finite size for $M \ne 0$, it would seem appropriate to regard (5.119) as the generalization of the solution of Laplace's equation for the field external to a finite sphere rather than as referring to the analogue of the mass-point of Newtonian theory

If the space-time refers to the gravitational field of the sun,

$$2m = \frac{2GM_\odot}{c^2} = 2{\cdot}956 \text{ km} \qquad (5.120)$$

and, since the physical radius of the Sun is 6.960×10^5 km, the singular region is deeply embedded in it. This means, of course, that long before the singular region is attained, the material of the Sun is encountered and the solution (5.119) of Einstein's equations no longer applies, because the energy-tensor is no longer zero when the physical surface of the Sun is penetrated. A similar conclusion holds for all other stars, since their physical radii are always far larger than $2G/c^2$ times their masses.

For the local gravitational field of the Earth we have

$$2m = \frac{2GM_\oplus}{c^2} = 0{\cdot}887 \text{ cm}. \qquad (5.121)$$

A new radial coordinate, $\bar{r}$, may be introduced in the Schwarzschild space-time by

$$r = \left(1 + \frac{m}{2\bar{r}}\right)^2 \bar{r},$$

so that

$$dr = \left(1 - \frac{m^2}{4\bar{r}^2}\right)d\bar{r},$$

$$1 - \frac{2m}{r} = \left(1 - \frac{m}{2\bar{r}}\right)^2 \Big/ \left(1 + \frac{m}{2\bar{r}}\right)^2.$$

Then (5.119) becomes

$$ds^2 = \frac{(1 - m/2\bar{r})^2}{(1 + m/2\bar{r})^2}dt^2 - \frac{1}{c^2}\left(1 + \frac{m}{2\bar{r}}\right)^4 \{d\bar{r}^2 + \bar{r}^2 \, d\theta^2 + \bar{r}^2 \sin^2 \theta \, d\phi^2\}, \qquad (5.122)$$

which is the isotropic form of the metric. Making the further substitution

$$t = x^4, \qquad x^1 = \bar{r} \sin \theta \cos \phi, \qquad x^2 = \bar{r} \sin \theta \sin \phi, \qquad x^3 = \bar{r} \cos \theta,$$

we obtain

$$ds^2 = \frac{(1 - m/2\bar{r})^2}{(1 + m/2\bar{r})^2}(dx^4)^2 - \frac{1}{c^2}\left(1 + \frac{m}{2\bar{r}}\right)^4\{(dx^1)^2 + (dx^2)^2 + (dx^3)^2\}, \qquad (5.123)$$

with

$$\bar{r}^2 = (x^1)^2 + (x^2)^2 + (x^3)^2.$$

Neglecting terms of order $(m/r)^2$ in (5.123) it becomes

$$ds^2 = \left(1 - \frac{2m}{\bar{r}}\right)(dx^4)^2 - \frac{1}{c^2}\left(1 + \frac{2m}{\bar{r}}\right)\{(dx^1)^2 + (dx^2)^2 + (dx^3)^2\},$$

and is therefore of the form (4.226) with

$$\kappa\psi = \frac{8\pi G}{c^2}\psi = \frac{2G}{c^2}\frac{M}{\bar{r}}.$$

Thus the first approximation to the Schwarzschild space-time corresponds to a Newtonian gravitational field of potential

$$4\pi\psi = \frac{M}{\bar{r}}$$

which is the elementary solution of Laplace's equation

$$\nabla^2\psi = 0.$$

The Lorentz transformation (3.401) leaves the mathematical form of the metric of the Minkowski space-time (3.601) unchanged. There are no analogous transformations in the Schwarzschild space-time (5.123) because of the presence of the singular region $0 \leq \bar{r} \leq m/2$. But, of course, local Cartesians can be set up for events in the neighbourhood of a given event in the Schwarzschild space-time and Lorentz transformations exist between these coordinates. Special relativity, whilst not applicable in the large, is therefore valid locally in the Schwarzschild space-time.

The form (5.123) for the metric yields a definition of the velocity of a moving particle. At the event $(x_0^4, x_0^1, x_0^2, x_0^3)$, introduce local Cartesian coordinates (see Sec. 2.6) by the definitions

$$X^4 = \frac{1 - m/2\bar{r}_0}{1 + m/2\bar{r}_0}(x^4 - x_0^4),$$

$$X^i = \left(1 + \frac{m}{2\bar{r}_0}\right)^2(x^i - x_0^i), \qquad (i = 1, 2, 3).$$

The metric becomes

$$ds^2 = (dX^4)^2 - \frac{1}{c^2}\sum_{i=1}^{3}(dX^i)^2.$$

Hence at the event (x_0), the local velocity of the particle may be defined in a manner analogous to that implied by (3.705) and (3.707) as

$$q_0 = \left\{\frac{(\Sigma(dX^i)^2)^{1/2}}{dX^4}\right\}_0 = \frac{(1 + m/2\bar{r}_0)^3}{1 - m/2\bar{r}_0}\left\{\frac{\Sigma(dx^i)^2}{dx^4}\right\}_0.$$

Local Cartesians may be set up at any event and one may also work back to the system (t, r, θ, ϕ). Then the velocity of the particle at (r, θ, ϕ) at time t is found to be

$$q = \frac{1}{(1 - 2m/r)^{1/2}}\left\{\frac{1}{1 - 2m/r}\left(\frac{dr}{dt}\right)^2 + r^2\left(\frac{d\theta}{dt}\right)^2 + r^2\sin^2\theta\left(\frac{d\phi}{dt}\right)^2\right\}^{1/2} \quad (5.124)$$

This definition implies that the equation (5.115) may also be written

$$\frac{1}{\beta^2} = \left(1 - \frac{q^2}{c^2}\right)\left(1 - \frac{2m}{r}\right)^{-1}, \quad (5.125)$$

a relation that now refers to the geodesic motion of a particle. It is clear that so long as q is very much smaller than c and if this occurs only for values of r that are very much larger than $2m$, the value of β lies very close to unity.

5.2. The Ordinary Geodesics of the Schwarzschild Space-time

The equations of the ordinary geodesics (5.110) to (5.113) must now be studied in detail, and we begin by discussing the significance of the constant β in the equation (5.115). The equation (5.125) may be written

$$q = c\left(1 - \frac{1 - 2m/r}{\beta^2}\right)^{\frac{1}{2}}, \quad (5.201)$$

and if $q = V$ when $r = \infty$, it follows that β and V are again related by (5.117). Thus V is imaginary, zero, or real according as $\beta < 1$, $\beta = 1$, $\beta > 1$. If $\beta < 1$ the particle can never attain to an infinite value of r; in the other two cases, the constant β may be interpreted thus: At $r = \infty$ the Schwarzschild space-time degenerates to the Minkowski space-time of special relativity and (5.117) then shows that β is the factor occurring in the Lorentz transformation from the coordinate system (t, r, θ, ϕ) to the inertial system in which the particle is at rest. The system (t, r, θ, ϕ) is in fact the inertial system in which a particle whose velocity at $r = \infty$ is zero will be at rest. A particle is thus limited to a velocity $V \leq c$ at infinity, in contrast to the case of Newtonian gravitational theory, where the velocity at infinity may have any value. Now suppose that at infinity the particle is moving with speed V directly towards the centre of the central body. Since (5.201) can then also be written

$$q = -V\left\{1 + \frac{2m}{r}\left(\frac{c^2}{V^2} - 1\right)\right\}^{\frac{1}{2}},$$

it follows that the magnitude of q continually increases as r decreases. But this does not continue without limit for at $r = 2m$ the magnitude of q would be c, whatever the initial speed had been. In practice, of course, the particle would reach the outer physical boundary of the central body long before the value $r = 2m$ had been attained.

A geodesic which represents the motion of a particle in a plane passing

G

through $r = 0$, and which traces out an orbit about this point, may be found by setting

$$\frac{d\theta}{ds} = 0, \qquad \theta = \tfrac{1}{2}\pi,$$

in the geodesic equations. Thus (5.111) is identically satisfied and (5.112), (5.114) give, respectively,

$$r^2\frac{d\phi}{ds} = h, \qquad \frac{dt}{ds} = \beta\left(1 - \frac{2m}{r}\right)^{-1}, \tag{5.202}$$

where h, β are constants of integration. Hence (5.115) becomes

$$1 = \frac{\beta^2}{1 - 2m/r} - \frac{h^2}{c^2}\left\{\frac{1}{(1 - 2m/r)r^4}\left(\frac{dr}{d\phi}\right)^2 + \frac{1}{r^2}\right\},$$

which can be transformed by writing $u = 1/r$ into

$$\left(\frac{du}{d\phi}\right)^2 = 2mu^3 - u^2 + \frac{2mc^2}{h^2}u - \gamma, \tag{5.203}$$

where

$$\gamma = \frac{c^2}{h^2}(1 - \beta^2). \tag{5.204}$$

The solution of this equation will be discussed with reference to the Sun as the central body, the particle being identified with a planet. However, exactly the same procedure applies to the case of an artificial earth satellite, the centre of the (spherical) Earth then being at $r = 0$.

If the term $2mu^3$ is omitted from (5.203), the resulting equation is known to have the solution

$$u = \frac{1}{r} = \frac{1 + e\cos\phi}{p},$$

where

$$\frac{1}{p} = \frac{mc^2}{h^2}, \qquad \gamma = \frac{1 - e^2}{p^2}.$$

This is a conic-section of eccentricity e and semi-latus-rectum p, the angle ϕ being the true anomaly. When $e < 1$ (ellipse) the perihelion and aphelion points are given by

$$u = \frac{1 + e}{p} \quad, \quad u = \frac{1 - e}{p} \quad, \tag{5.205}$$

and if $2a$ is the length of the major-axis, then $a = p(1 - e^2)^{-1}$. The perihelion and aphelion points are also defined by the condition that $du/d\phi = 0$ at both of them.

It will now be proved that the complete equation (5.203) also has solutions in which the perihelion and aphelion points are defined in terms of two constants e and p by the formulae (5.205) and that these two points are such that

$du/d\phi = 0$ at both of them. Introduce the dimensionless variable w and the dimensionless constant ε by

$$w = pu = \frac{p}{r}, \qquad \varepsilon = \frac{m}{p}, \qquad (5.206)$$

so that (5.203) becomes

$$\left(\frac{dw}{d\phi}\right)^2 = 2\varepsilon w^3 - w^2 + \frac{2\varepsilon p^2 c^2}{h^2}w - \gamma p^2, \qquad (5.207)$$

and then the conditions to be satisfied are that $dw/d\phi = 0$ at $w = 1 + e$ and $w = 1 - e$, respectively. Thus (5.207) is

$$\left(\frac{dw}{d\phi}\right)^2 = 2\varepsilon\{w - (1 + e)\}\{w - (1 - e)\}\left\{w - \frac{1 - 4\varepsilon}{2\varepsilon}\right\}, \qquad (5.208)$$

with

$$\left.\begin{array}{l} \dfrac{c^2}{h^2} = \dfrac{1}{\varepsilon p^2}\{1 - \varepsilon(3 + e^2)\}, \\[3mm] \gamma = \dfrac{1 - e^2}{p^2}(1 - 4\varepsilon). \end{array}\right\} \qquad (5.209)$$

The required solution is best expressed in terms of the relativistic true anomaly[1], ϕ', in terms of which perihelia occur at $\phi' = 0, 2\pi, 4\pi, \ldots$ and aphelia at $\phi' = \pi, 3\pi, 5\pi, \ldots$. With

$$w = 1 + e\cos\phi', \qquad (5.210)$$

the equation (5.208) becomes†

$$\left(\frac{d\phi'}{d\phi}\right)^2 = 1 - 2\varepsilon(3 + e\cos\phi'). \qquad (5.211)$$

When ε is small, so that its square and higher powers may be neglected compared with unity, the last equation gives

$$\phi - \omega = \int_0^{\phi'}\{1 + \varepsilon(3 + e\cos\phi')\}d\phi'$$
$$= (1 + 3\varepsilon)\phi' + e\varepsilon\sin\phi', \qquad (5.212)$$

where the constant of integration has been adjusted so that $\phi = \omega$ at $\phi' = 0$.

Since $w = p/r$, it follows from (5.210) that the relation between r and ϕ' represents an ellipse of constant eccentricity e and constant semi-latus-rectum p, its major-axis therefore also being of constant length. But the direction of the major-axis rotates in the plane of the orbit, a result deducible from

---

† Let $\phi' = 2\chi + \pi$ so that $\chi = 0$ corresponds to the aphelion defined by $\phi' = \pi$. Let $\phi = \phi_a$ at this aphelion. Then

$$\phi - \phi_a = \frac{2}{(1 - 6\epsilon + 2e\epsilon)^{1/2}}\int_0^\chi \frac{d\chi}{(1 - k^2\sin^2\chi)^{1/2}}$$

where

$$k^2 = \frac{4e\epsilon}{(1 - 6\epsilon + 2e\epsilon)^{1/2}}.$$

This expresses ϕ in terms of an elliptic integral of the first kind.

(5.211) in general, and, for small ε, from (5.212). Suppose that a perihelion $\phi' = 0$ occurs at $\phi = \omega$; the next perihelion will occur at $\phi' = 2\pi$ for which the value of ϕ will be

$$\phi = 2\pi + \omega + \frac{6\pi m}{p}.$$

The next revolution may therefore be regarded as starting with $\phi' = 0$ at $\phi = \omega + 6\pi m/p$; in other words, the perihelion advances in one revolution by an amount

$$\Delta\omega = \frac{6\pi m}{p}. \tag{5.213}$$

In order to interpret this result in the solar system it is first necessary to identify the coordinates (t, r, θ, ϕ) with those used by astronomers. The observational method of determining distances in the solar system is, in principle, the following. Newtonian gravitational theory, with its underlying assumption that Euclidean geometry prevails, is first used to construct through Kepler's Third Law and the classical elliptic orbits, a scale-model of the solar system. The scale factor is then found by measuring the distance from the Earth to one of the planets, for example, to the minor planet Eros at opposition. This part of the procedure is trigonometric and entails laying out a base-line on the Earth's surface. It is sometimes argued that, because the length of this base-line is involved, all distances in the solar system ultimately depend on rigid measuring rods. This is, however, obviously not the case since the chains with which surveyors measure the base-line are certainly not rigid. The essential criterion is not the rigidity or otherwise of the measuring apparatus, but the internal consistency of the surveyor's mapping of the Earth's surface. At any rate, these operations lead to distances in the solar system whose uncertainties are estimated to be one part in two thousand, though higher accuracies are said to be possible from radar distances from the Earth to Venus. To show that heliocentric distance found in this way can be identified with the r of the Schwarzschild space-time, we may argue thus: if $R_\odot$ is the physical radius of the Sun, then the metric (5.119) applies only for $r > R_\odot$. By considering the coefficient of $(d\theta^2 + \sin^2 d\phi^2)$ in (5.119), it follows that, at any instant t, the difference of the radii, R and $R_\odot$, of spheres centred at the Sun, is $R - R_\odot$. The increment of r between these spheres is, however,

$$\int_{R_\odot}^{R} \frac{dr}{\left(1 - \dfrac{2m}{r}\right)^{\frac{1}{2}}} = (R - R_\odot)\left\{1 + \frac{m}{R - R_\odot}\log_e \frac{R}{R_\odot} + \frac{3}{2}\frac{m^2}{RR_\odot} + \ldots\right\},$$

and the departure from Euclidean geometry is represented by the terms involving m on the right-hand side. But even if R is as small as $2\cdot48 R_\odot$, the quantity $m(R - R_\odot)^{-1}\log_e (R/R_\odot)$ is of the order of $(8 \times 10^6)^{-1}$ and therefore the identification of r with the heliocentric distances computed by astronomers on the hypothesis of Euclidean geometry introduces an error no larger than one part in eight millions, which is far below the errors in the distances themselves. Similarly, the nearly Euclidean character of the geometry suggests that ϕ is identifiable with the angle measuring the displacement of the planet from the direction Sun to First Point of Aries, and that θ is an angle measured from the normal to the plane of the orbit.

The meaning to be assigned to the time-coordinate t is much more difficult to find. The astronomers' ephemeris time is arrived at by interpreting the motions of the planets and satellites of the solar system through Newtonian gravitational theory, due allowance being made for the mutual perturbations of these bodies on one another. Allowance is also made for the effects of the terms in $2mu^3$ in the orbital equations such as (5.203), by treating these as if they arose from small perturbations to the inverse square law of attraction. Ephemeris time, t_e, is then a time which proceeds at such a rate that all observations of the solar system during the eighteenth and nineteenth centuries are most accurately described by the theory. But if the Earth is now identified with a general relativity particle whose orbit is given by (5.207), the second of equations (5.202) must also be taken into account. Should t_e then be identified with t or with the time-like interval (proper-time) s of the Earth measured along its geodesic orbit? Some light may be thrown on this question by considering the Earth to have a circular orbit $r = p$. Equations (5.204) and (5.209) then yield

$$\beta = \frac{1 - 2\varepsilon}{(1 - 3\varepsilon)^{1/2}}, \qquad h = \frac{(mc^2 p)^{1/2}}{(1 - 3\varepsilon)^{1/2}}.$$

Thus by (5.202)

$$\frac{d\phi}{ds} = \frac{(mc^2)^{1/2}}{p^{3/2}} \frac{1}{(1 - 3\varepsilon)^{1/2}}, \qquad \frac{d\phi}{dt} = \frac{(mc^2)^{1/2}}{p^{3/2}},$$

and the sidereal periods of the Earth in proper-time (s) and coordinate-time (t) are, respectively

$$\left.\begin{aligned} S &= 2\pi \frac{p^{3/2}}{(GM_\odot)^{1/2}} \left(1 - \frac{3m}{p}\right)^{1/2}, \\ T &= 2\pi \frac{p^{3/2}}{(GM_\odot)^{1/2}}. \end{aligned}\right\} \tag{5.214}$$

It will be observed that the formula for T is identical with the expression in Newtonian gravitational theory of Kepler's Third Law, if the radius p of the Earth's orbit is measured by the astronomer's usual methods. To the extent that the periods of planets and satellites are based on this form of Kepler's Third Law, it may be argued with some plausibility that t_e should be identified with t rather than with the proper-time s. This conclusion is reinforced by reflecting on the method by which ephemeris time is set up. It depends on a version of Newtonian gravitational theory modified by ad hoc terms which allow for the fact that the two-body orbit in general relativity differs from an ellipse. That this procedure should give rise to an (invariant) proper-time in the sense of general relativity would be very hard to prove. It seems much more likely to produce a coordinate-time, whose rate could be changed as more observations of the solar system were accumulated.

After this digression, we return to (5.213) which will be converted into a displacement of the planet's perihelion in 100 terrestrial years by the use of the Newtonian form of Kepler's Third Law. Let A ($= 1 \cdot 496 \times 10^{13}$ cm) be the astronomical unit and let the semi-major axis of the planet's orbit be $a = nA$. Then if T is the period in years of the planet, we have $T = n^{3/2}$. Also $p = nA(1 - e^2)$ where e is the eccentricity of the planet's orbit. Thus if $\Delta\omega_{100}$ seconds of arc is the displacement of the perihelion in 100 years, (5.213) gives

$$\Delta\omega_{100} = \frac{6\pi GM_\odot}{c^2 A} \frac{100}{n^{5/2}(1 - e^2)} 206265''$$

$$= \frac{3'' \cdot 84}{n^{5/2}(1 - e^2)}. \qquad (5.215)$$

Newtonian gravitational theory shows that the perihelion of a given planet will be displaced because of the perturbations of the remaining planets and from other causes. Thus in 1949, Clemence[2] found that the total angular displacement of the perihelion of Mercury in 100 years due to these effects was $5,557'' \cdot 18 \pm 0'' \cdot 85$. Rather less than ten per cent of this total was due to the perturbations of the other planets and to the oblateness of the Sun. The remainder arose from the general precession of the Earth which affects the system of reference to which the observations are referred. The corresponding observed displacement was $5,599'' \cdot 74 \pm 0'' \cdot 41$. The figures for the Earth were $6,179'' \cdot 1 \pm 2'' \cdot 5$ and $6,183'' \cdot 7 \pm 1'' \cdot 1$. These residual differences for three of the planets, as they were given by Duncombe[3] in 1956, are listed in Table I under $\Delta\omega_{100}$ (obs). The column headed $\Delta\omega_{100}$ (calc) gives the values obtained

TABLE I

	n	e	$\Delta\omega_{100}$ (obs)	$\Delta\omega_{100}$ (calc)
Mercury	$0 \cdot 3871$	$0 \cdot 2056$	$43'' \cdot 11 \pm 0'' \cdot 45$	$43'' \cdot 03$
Venus	$0 \cdot 7233$	$0 \cdot 0068$	$8'' \cdot 4 \pm 4'' \cdot 8$	$8'' \cdot 64$
Earth	$1 \cdot 0000$	$0 \cdot 0167$	$5'' \cdot 0 \pm 1'' \cdot 2$	$3'' \cdot 84$

from (5.215). It is clear that the identification of a planet with a particle tracing out a geodesic in the Schwarzschild space-time accounts in a satisfactory way for an effect in the motion of its perihelion that Newtonian gravitational theory left unaccounted for.

A corresponding displacement of the perigee of the orbit of an artificial earth satellite may be derived from (5.213). For this purpose, the Earth must be regarded as a sphere of radius $R_\oplus$, say. Let the semi-major axis of the satellite's orbit be $a = nR_\oplus$ and its eccentricity be e. Then n and e

must be related in such a way that the perigee distance is greater than $R_\oplus$, which means that $n(1 - e) > 1$. If the period of the satellite is taken to be $2\pi a^{3/2}(GM_\oplus)^{-1/2}$ it follows that the displacement of the perigee in one sidereal year of $3 \cdot 156 \times 10^7$ sec is

$$\Delta\omega_1 = \frac{3(GM_\oplus)^{3/2}(3 \cdot 156 \times 10^7)206265}{c^2 R_\oplus^{5/2}} \cdot \frac{1}{n^{5/2}(1 - e^2)}$$

$$= \frac{16'' \cdot 87}{n^{5/2}(1 - e^2)},$$

where $R_\oplus$ has been identified with the mean radius of the Earth, $6 \cdot 371 \times 10^8$ cm, and $M_\oplus = 5 \cdot 977 \times 10^{27}$ gr. Clearly $\Delta\omega_1$ is the larger, the closer n, e lie to unity and zero, respectively. For example, if $n = 1 \cdot 1$ and $e = 0 \cdot 04$, so that the perigee height is 357 km above the Earth's surface, it follows that $\Delta\omega_1 = 13'' \cdot 3$. But if $n = 2$, $e = 0 \cdot 45$, with perigee height of 637 km, the value of $\Delta\omega_1$ is reduced to $3'' \cdot 7$. These relativistic displacements of the perigee are, of course, additional to those which are produced by the oblateness of the Earth.

5.3. Null-geodesics of the Schwarzschild Space-time

The equations of the null-geodesics of (5.119) follow from (2.807), with s replaced by a non-zero parameter μ, and have the integral (2.809). These equations are

$$\frac{d}{d\mu}\left\{\left(1 - \frac{2m}{r}\right)\frac{dt}{d\mu}\right\} = 0, \tag{5.301}$$

$$\frac{d}{d\mu}\left(r^2\frac{d\theta}{d\mu}\right) - r^2 \sin\theta \cos\theta\left(\frac{d\phi}{d\mu}\right)^2 = 0, \tag{5.302}$$

$$\frac{d}{d\mu}\left(r^2 \sin^2\theta\frac{d\phi}{d\mu}\right) = 0, \tag{5.303}$$

$$0 = \left(1 - \frac{2m}{r}\right)\left(\frac{dt}{d\mu}\right)^2 - \frac{1}{c^2}\left\{\left(1 - \frac{2m}{r}\right)^{-1}\left(\frac{dr}{d\mu}\right)^2\right.$$
$$\left. + r^2\left(\frac{d\theta}{d\mu}\right)^2 + r^2 \sin^2\theta\left(\frac{d\phi}{d\mu}\right)^2\right\}. \tag{5.304}$$

If the definition (5.124) is also used for the velocity of the light-ray, equation (5.304) gives

$$q^2 = c^2, \tag{5.305}$$

and therefore the magnitude of q always has the constant value c. Motion in a plane may again be defined by

$$\frac{d\theta}{d\mu} = 0, \quad \theta = \tfrac{1}{2}\pi,$$

and in this case the integrals of (5.301) and (5.303) are, respectively,

$$\frac{dt}{d\mu} = \beta*\left(1 - \frac{2m}{r}\right)^{-1}, \quad r^2\frac{d\phi}{d\mu} = h\beta*c,$$

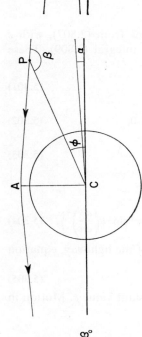

where β^* and $h\beta^*c$ are constants of integration. Equation (5.304) becomes, on writing $u = r^{-1}$,

$$\left(\frac{du}{d\phi}\right)^2 = \frac{1}{h^2} - u^2 + 2mu^3, \qquad (5.306)$$

which gives the path of the light-ray in the (r, ϕ) plane. This equation may be solved as follows: The angle between the radius vector and the tangent to the path at the point (r, ϕ) is β where

$$\tan \beta = \frac{rd\phi}{(-dr)} = u\left(\frac{1}{h^2} - u^2 + 2mu^3\right)^{-1/2},$$

since r decreases as ϕ increases (see Fig. 2 at P). In all cases of interest $h \gg m$ and there is a point A on the path at which $\beta = \frac{1}{2}\pi$. If $r = R$ at A then it follows that

$$\frac{1}{h^2} = \frac{1}{R^2}\left(1 - \frac{2m}{R}\right). \qquad (5.307)$$

Let

$$w = R/r = Ru, \qquad \varepsilon = 2m/R, \qquad (5.308)$$

and then (5.306) becomes with the aid of (5.307),

$$\left(\frac{dw}{d\phi}\right)^2 = 1 - w^2 - \varepsilon(1 - w^3),$$

which may also be written

$$\left(\frac{dw}{d\phi}\right)^2 = \varepsilon(1 - w)(w_1 - w)(w_2 + w), \quad (5.309)$$

where

$$
\left.
\begin{aligned}
w_1 &= \frac{1-\varepsilon}{2\varepsilon}\left\{1 + \left(1 + \frac{4\varepsilon}{1-\varepsilon}\right)^{1/2}\right\} \\
&= \frac{1-\varepsilon}{\varepsilon}\left\{1 + \frac{\varepsilon}{1-\varepsilon} - \left(\frac{\varepsilon}{1-\varepsilon}\right)^2 + \ldots\right\}, \\
w_2 &= \frac{1-\varepsilon}{2\varepsilon}\left\{\left(1 + \frac{4\varepsilon}{1-\varepsilon}\right)^{1/2} - 1\right\} \\
&= 1 - \frac{\varepsilon}{1-\varepsilon} + \ldots
\end{aligned}
\right\} (5.310)
$$

By means of the substitution

$$\frac{R}{r} = w = -w_2 + \tfrac{1}{2}(1 + w_2)(1 - \cos 2\chi), \quad (5.311)$$

FIG. 2.

one obtains

$$\left(\frac{d\chi}{d\phi}\right)^2 = \frac{\varepsilon}{4}(w_1 + w_2)(1 - k^2 \sin^2 \chi), \tag{5.312}$$

where

$$k^2 = (1 + w_2)/(w_1 + w_2). \tag{5.313}$$

At A, $w = 1$ and so $\chi = \pi/2$. Thus the constant of integration in the solution of (5.312) can be adjusted so that $\phi = \phi_0$ when $\chi = \pi/2$. Therefore

$$\phi - \phi_0 = \frac{2}{\{\varepsilon(w_1 + w_2)\}^{1/2}} \int_{\pi/2}^{\chi} \frac{d\chi}{(1 - k^2 \sin^2 \chi)^{1/2}}, \tag{5.314}$$

which shows that ϕ is determined as an elliptic integral of the first kind. The path of the light-ray is therefore expressed in parametric form by the equations (5.311) and (5.314).

In all cases of interest, ε is a small number and its square and higher powers may be neglected. We then have

$$\varepsilon(w_1 + w_2) = 1 + \varepsilon, \qquad k^2 = 2\varepsilon,$$

and so (5.314) is

$$\phi - \phi_0 = 2(1 - \tfrac{1}{2}\varepsilon)\int_{\pi/2}^{\chi} (1 + \varepsilon \sin^2 \chi)d\chi$$

$$= 2\left(\chi - \frac{\pi}{2}\right) - \frac{\varepsilon}{2} \sin 2\chi.$$

Inverting this relation, one finds

$$2\chi = \pi + (\phi - \phi_0) - \frac{\varepsilon}{2} \sin (\phi - \phi_0),$$

and therefore substitution in (5.311) yields for the equation of the path

$$\frac{R}{r} = -(1 - \varepsilon) + (1 - \tfrac{1}{2}\varepsilon)\left\{1 + \cos (\phi - \phi_0)\right\} + \frac{\varepsilon}{2} \sin^2 (\phi - \phi_0). \tag{5.315}$$

This formula may be used to interpret the phenomenon of the bending of light-rays observed at a total eclipse of the Sun. In Fig. 2, C is the Sun's centre and S is a star at (D, α) which is observed past the limb of the Sun during a total eclipse by an observer at O (a, π), where a is the mean distance of the Earth from the Sun. Six months later the observer is at O' $(a, 0)$. At O the ray is seen in a direction which makes an angle β_0 with the radius vector CO where

$$\tan \beta_0 = \frac{R}{a}\left\{1 - \frac{R^2}{a^2} - \frac{2m}{R}\left(1 - \frac{R^3}{a^3}\right)\right\}^{-1/2}. \tag{5.316}$$

Since R is of the order of magnitude of the radius of the Sun, R/a is a small fraction and, to a sufficient degree of approximation, $\beta_0 = R/a$. But now the path of the ray must pass through S and therefore (5.315) gives

$$\frac{R}{D} = -(1 - \varepsilon) + (1 - \tfrac{1}{2}\varepsilon)\left\{1 + \cos (\phi_0 - \alpha)\right\} + \frac{\varepsilon}{2} \sin^2 (\phi_0 - \alpha).$$

Because R/D is effectively zero, this becomes

$$1 - \frac{\varepsilon}{2} = 1 + \cos(\phi_0 - \alpha) + \frac{\varepsilon}{2}\{1 - \cos^2(\phi_0 - \alpha)\},$$

an equation whose solution is

$$\phi_0 = \frac{\pi}{2} + \varepsilon + \alpha.$$

The ray must also pass through O and therefore

$$\frac{R}{a} = -(1 - \varepsilon) + (1 - \tfrac{1}{2}\varepsilon)\left\{1 - \cos\phi_0\right\} + \frac{\varepsilon}{2}\sin^2\phi_0.$$

The angle $\alpha \ (= \angle O'CS)$ is clearly very small and so is ε. Therefore, ignoring the product $\alpha\varepsilon$, we have

$$\beta_0 = \frac{R}{a} = -(1 - \varepsilon) + (1 - \tfrac{1}{2}\varepsilon)(1 + \alpha + \varepsilon) + \tfrac{1}{2}\varepsilon$$

$$= 2\varepsilon + \alpha.$$

When the observer is at O', the path SO' of the light-ray differs from a Euclidean straight line only by terms of order $(2m/R)(R/a) = \varepsilon(R/a)$ or less. These are negligible. Since moreover the star is extremely remote, the line SO' is effectively parallel to SC. Thus the star is seen from O' in a direction inclined to CO' at the angle α. Hence the directions in which the star are seen from O and O', respectively, differ by $\varDelta\beta = \beta_0 - \alpha$ and therefore by (5.308)

$$\varDelta\beta = \frac{4m}{R}.$$

In practice R is a small multiple, $n(\geq 1)$, of the solar radius $R_\odot$. Converting also to seconds of arc, using (5.121) and $R_\odot = 6\cdot960 \times 10^5$ km, one finds

$$\varDelta\beta = \frac{4m}{nR_\odot}(2\cdot06265 \times 10^5) = \frac{1''\cdot75}{n}, \qquad (5.317)$$

which is the angular displacement of the star at the eclipse compared with its position when viewed in the absence of an eclipse.

In practice the stars photographed on the eclipse plate are not found at grazing incidence ($n = 1$), nor can their displacement relative to the mathematical line OCO' be directly observed. The angular separations of the stars from one another on the eclipse plate must be compared with their separations on the comparison plate taken some months later, and the value of $n\varDelta\beta$ deduced therefrom. The effect of the eclipsed Sun on the stellar positions is indistinguishable from a change in the scale of the eclipse, as compared with the comparison, plate. It has proved extremely difficult to allow properly for a change of scale, if any has occurred; indeed, not until the 1947 eclipse was a satisfactory device invented to identify such a change. During the eclipse, a check star-field at 90° from the Sun is projected onto the eclipse plate and photographed simultaneously with the field beyond the Sun. This same check field is recorded in the same way on the comparison plate, and thus serves to detect the change of scale.

The various observational determinations[4] of $n\Delta\beta$ are shown in Table II, with their probable or mean errors when these were specifically mentioned by the computers. For a writer who is not himself a practical astronomer, it is difficult to know what to make of such discordant conclusions. However, the best star-field occurred at the 1919 eclipse, when the stars were distributed regularly round the Sun. The fields at the other eclipses were poor: in 1929, a solar diameter could be drawn so that 17 stars lay on one side of it and only one on the other. In 1936, the field was so unfavourable that Mikhailov had to use, in the main, stars located near the edges of his plates. His result can therefore have little weight. Apart from the Sobral II, Kosimizu and Bocajuva values, which were vitiated by obvious instrumental troubles, it is remarkable that the observers find values in consonance with the theory, except in the case of the 1929 eclipse. The re-reductions give different values, apparently because of differences of opinion as to the effect of the scale factor. But Trumpler finds $1''\cdot75 \pm 0\cdot19$ from the controversial 1929 data. In this matter, the opinion of a solar expert must carry great weight and it is interesting to note that S. A. Mitchell[5] concludes that the 1919, 1922 and 1929 eclipses give

$$n\Delta\beta = 1''\cdot79 \pm 0\cdot06, \qquad (5.318)$$

a value since apparently confirmed by the 1952 eclipse. Those who argue that observation gives $n\Delta\beta \geq 2''$ would seem to accept Freundlich's $2''\cdot24 \pm 0\cdot10$ for 1929 as indisputably correct, to regard the re-reductions for Sobral I and Wallal II as preferable to the observers' conclusions, and to ignore Trumpler's and Jackson's re-reductions for 1929. If (5.318) is accepted as the observed value, the theoretical prediction can only be regarded as being in agreement with the data.

The bending of light-rays does not produce, as might be thought at first sight, any significant enlargement of the apparent angular diameter of the Sun, or of any star. If the ray starts from the point A on the Sun itself, then by (5.316)

$$\beta_0 = \frac{R}{a}\left(1 + \frac{m}{R}\right).$$

The angular diameter of the Sun is $2\beta_0$ and R is approximately equal to $R_\odot$. Thus

$$2\beta_0 = \frac{2R_\odot}{a}\left(1 + \frac{m}{R_\odot}\right),$$

where $2R_\odot/a$ is the Sun's apparent angular diameter as it would be computed by classical optics. Since $m/R_\odot = 2 \times 10^{-6}$, the increase of angular diameter is negligible. The corresponding ratio for the white dwarf 40 Eri. B is about twenty-seven times that for the Sun; hence even in this case the fractional increase of apparent angular diameter is negligible.

TABLE II

Date	Station	INSTRUMENTS Ap.	F/L	No. of plates	No. of stars	Result observed "	Observers	Re-reductions "
1919 May 29	Sobral I	4"	19'	7	7	1·98 ± 0·12 (pe)	{Crommelin[a], Davidson}	{Danjon[j] 2·05 ± 0·20 (me), Hopman[k] 2·16 ± 0·14 "}
	Sobral II	8"	11'	16†	6-12	0·93 ± ?	{Cottingham[a], Eddington}	
	Principe	8"	11'	2	5	1·61 ± 0·3	"	{Chant[b], Young}
1922 Sept. 21	Wallal I	6"	10'	2	18	1·74 ± 0·3	"	
	Wallal II	5"	15'	4	62-85	1·72 ± 0·11	{Campbell[c], Trumpler}	{Danjon[j] 2·05 ± 0·13, Freundlich[l] 2·07 ± ?, Hopman[k] 2·14 ± 0·18 ?, Jackson[m] 2·12 ± ? ?}
	Wallal III	4"	5'	6	134-143	1·82 ± 0·15	{Campbell[c], Trumpler}	Danjon[j] 2·07 ± ?
	Cordillo Downs	3"	5'	2	14	1·77 ± 0·3	{Davidson[a], Dodwell}	
1929 May 9	Takengon	8"	28'	4	17-18	2·24 ± 0·10 (me)	{Freundlich[e], v. Brunn, v. Kluber}	{Danjon[j] 2·04 ± 0·27, Jackson[m] 1·98 ± 0·14, Trumpler[n] 1·75 ± 0·19}
1936 June 19	Kuybyshevka	6"	20'	2	?	2·71 ± 0·26	Michailov[f]	
	Kosimizu	8"	16'	1	10	{2·13 ± 1·5 ‡, 1·28 ± 2·67}	Matukuma[g]	
1947 May 20	Bocajuva	6"	20'	1§	51	2·01 ± 0·27	v. Biesbroeck[h]	
1952 Feb. 25	Khartoum	6"	20'	2	9-11	1·70 ± 0·10	v. Biesbroeck[i]	

† Poor focus caused by distortion of mirrors.
‡ Two comparison plates gave these alternatives when in different combinations with the eclipse plate.
§ Distortion of mirrors due to heating.

5.4. Gravitational and Doppler Displacements of Spectral Lines

The null-geodesic treatment of the motion of light used in general relativity corresponds to the geometrical optics of classical physics: it does not require the consideration of light as a periodic phenomenon. If it is now postulated that light is a wave-phenomenon, and that each light-wave is characterized by a time-interval called its period, some new conclusions may be drawn. However, these conclusions follow only if some addition to general relativity is made, an extension that goes beyond Einstein's equations and the theory of null-geodesics. This extension may consist of a re-formulation of the basic equations for the energy levels of an atom[6] so as to make these equations valid in any space-time and not merely in the Minkowski space-time. In this way, the energy levels, and consequently the radiations emitted by the atom, are made to depend on the gravitational potential at the point at which the atom is located[†]. Alternatively, an analogous modification of the classical theory of the propagation of electromagnetic energy may be made[8]. Still

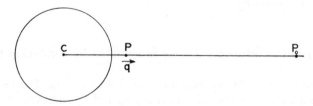

FIG. 3.

another procedure is to employ the hypothesis that the rate of emission of photons by a source, and the rate of receipt of photons by a recorder, are both proportional to the frequencies of the photons themselves[9]. Though a number of devices of this kind have been employed, there does not appear to be agreement as to which is the correct one. Therefore we shall give a treatment of the problem which depends on a definition, namely, that the emission, and also the receipt, of a light-wave, or of a photon, are occurrences each of which is characterized by a *pair* of events.

The principle of the method is illustrated by the Schwarzschild space-time (5.119). In Fig. 3, let P be a source of radiation near the surface of the central body, whose centre is at C $(r = 0)$, and let the observer be located at $P_0(r = r_0)$ on the 'radius' CP produced. Suppose in the first instance that P is at rest in the coordinate-system employed in (5.119), and that P emits a light-wave of frequency ν. This means that the light-wave is associated with a coordinate-period dt whose relation to ν will be found presently. The emission of the wave will then be defined as the pair of events (t, r, θ, ϕ) and $(t + dt, r, \theta, \phi)$.

† This should also be a necessary preliminary to the method of 'standard clocks' if these are regarded as 'atomic clocks'[7].

However, suppose that P is moving directly towards the observer at P_0 and that during the time dt its r-coordinate alters by dr. Then, for this moving source, the pair of events defining the emission of the light-wave are E and E', whose coordinates are (t, r, θ, ϕ) and $(t + dt, r + dr, \theta, \phi)$. Also E and E' are separated by the invariant proper-time interval ds where

$$ds^2 = \left(1 - \frac{2m}{r}\right)dt^2 - \frac{1}{c^2}\frac{dr^2}{1 - 2m/r}.$$

Since P is moving radially, its velocity as defined by (5.124) is

$$q = \frac{1}{1 - 2m/r}\frac{dr}{dt}, \tag{5.401}$$

and therefore

$$ds = \left(1 - \frac{2m}{r}\right)^{1/2}(1 - q^2/c^2)^{1/2}dt. \tag{5.402}$$

The frequency, ν, and wave-length, λ, of the emitted wave may be defined in an invariant fashion by

$$\nu = \frac{1}{ds}, \qquad \lambda = cds. \tag{5.403}$$

Thus the relation between ν and dt is obtained by combining (5.402) and (5.403).

The observer at P_0 is, by definition, at rest at $r = r_0$. The receipt of the light-wave is defined as the pair of events, E_0 and E_0', whose coordinates are, respectively, (t_0, r_0, θ, ϕ) and $(t_0 + dt_0, r_0, \theta, \phi)$. These events are separated by the interval

$$ds_0 = \left(1 - \frac{2m}{r_0}\right)^{1/2}dt_0, \tag{5.404}$$

and therefore the frequency, $\nu + d\nu$, and wave-length, $\lambda + d\lambda$, of the received wave are

$$\nu + d\nu = \frac{1}{ds_0}, \qquad \lambda + d\lambda = cds_0. \tag{5.405}$$

The events E, E_0 and E', E_0' lie on the null-geodesic through P and P_0 whose differential equation is

$$\frac{dr}{dt} = c\left(1 - \frac{2m}{r}\right).$$

Thus for the pair E and E_0, we have, on integration,

$$t_0 - t = \frac{1}{c}\int_r^{r_0} \frac{dr}{1 - 2m/r},$$

and for the pair E', E_0',

$$t_0 + dt_0 - (t + dt) = \frac{1}{c}\int_{r+dr}^{r_0} \frac{dr}{1 - 2m/r}.$$

Hence subtracting the two formulae,

$$dt_0 - dt = -\frac{1}{c}\frac{dr}{1 - 2m/r} = -\frac{q}{c}dt,$$

and this gives

$$dt_0 = \left(1 - \frac{q}{c}\right)dt. \tag{5.406}$$

It will be noticed that the coordinate periods dt_0 and dt are equal when $q = 0$; the coordinate period is therefore transferred along the null-geodesic without change of magnitude in this case. In general, the equations (5.402), (5.404) and (5.406) yield for the ratio of the invariant periods

$$\frac{ds_0}{ds} = \left(\frac{1 - 2m/r_0}{1 - 2m/r}\right)^{1/2}\left(\frac{1 - q/c}{1 + q/c}\right)^{1/2}.$$

Therefore, by (5.403) and (5.405), we have

$$\left(1 + \frac{dv}{v}\right)^{-1} = 1 + \frac{d\lambda}{\lambda} = \left(\frac{1 - 2m/r_0}{1 - 2m/r}\right)^{1/2}\left(\frac{1 - q/c}{1 + q/c}\right)^{1/2}. \tag{5.407}$$

The arriving wave at P_0, whose frequency and wave-length are $v + dv$ and $\lambda + d\lambda$, respectively, is compared with a similar wave in the laboratory at P_0. This is a wave emitted by a light source at P_0 whose frequency, v, and wave-length, λ, are also defined by (5.403). Thus the properties of the arriving wave and of the similar wave are related by (5.407).

The formula (5.407) shows firstly that, when source and observer are at relative rest ($q = 0$), dv and $d\lambda$ are nevertheless not zero because r and r_0 are unequal. In the first approximation, mc^2/r is the Newtonian gravitational potential at a point distant r from C. The displacement $d\lambda$ would be ascribed, in Newtonian theory, to the difference in the values of the gravitational potential at source and observer, respectively. The light emitted by the source will normally exhibit spectral lines; the lines will be displaced from their laboratory positions by amounts obtained from (5.407) with $q = 0$. These displacements are known as the *gravitational displacements* of the spectral lines. However, (5.407) also reveals another point: the gravitational displacement will be inextricably intermingled with any *Doppler effect* of the spectral lines which may be present, this type of displacement of the spectral lines being represented by the factor involving q/c.

When m/r_0, m/r and q/c are all small compared with unity, we have from (5.407)

$$-\frac{dv}{v} = \frac{d\lambda}{\lambda} = \frac{m}{r} - \frac{m}{r_0} - \frac{q}{c}. \tag{5.408}$$

Terrestrial experiments can be employed to detect this change of wave-length. In Fig. 3, C is taken to be the centre of the Earth and the configuration shown in this figure will be described by saying that the source is 'below' the observer. We have also to consider the opposite configuration, shown in Fig. 4, in which the source is 'above' the observer. In both cases the source is presumed to be moving towards the observer. The direction of motion of the radiation is also, of course, reversed in Fig. 4 as compared with Fig. 3. It is then easy to show that (5.408) applies also to the case when the source is above the observer. Let (5.119) now describe the gravitational field of the earth and let P_0 and P, whichever is above the other, be close to the surface of the earth and at a distance h apart. Then in Fig. 3, $r = R_\oplus - h$, $r_0 = R_\oplus$ whereas in Fig. 4, $r = R_\oplus + h$, $r_0 = R_\oplus$. Hence, for the Fig. 3 configuration, the change of frequency or of wave-length is given by

$$-\frac{(dv)_b}{v} = \frac{(d\lambda)_b}{\lambda} = \frac{GM_\oplus}{R_\oplus^2}\frac{h}{c^2} - \frac{q}{c},$$

whereas for the Fig. 4 configuration the result is

$$-\frac{(dv)_a}{v} = \frac{(d\lambda)_a}{\lambda} = -\frac{GM_\oplus}{R_\oplus^2}\frac{h}{c^2} - \frac{q}{c}.$$

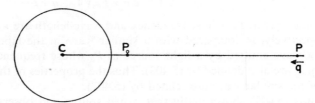

FIG. 4.

Therefore if care is taken that the source shall move towards the observer with the same speed q in both cases, it follows that

$$\frac{(dv)_a - (dv)_b}{v} = \frac{(d\lambda)_b - (d\lambda)_a}{\lambda} = \frac{GM_\oplus}{R_\oplus^2}\frac{2h}{c^2}. \qquad (5.409)$$

This result is the basis of the experiment of Pound and Rebka[10] who used a source of 14.4 kev. gamma-rays with an 'observer' which absorbed this radiation by the Mössbauer effect in Fe^{57}. The distance h was 74 ft ($= 22.55$ m) and $M_\oplus = 5.975 \times 10^{27}$ gr, $R_\oplus = 6367.65$ km. Thus the expected value of the right-hand side of (5.409) is 4.93×10^{-15} and the observed value was $(5.13 \pm 0.51) \times 10^{-15}$. It may be concluded that this experiment provides a very satisfactory confirmation of the prediction of general relativity that the wave-length of electromagnetic radiation will be modified as it moves through a gravitational field whose strength varies from one point to another.

The astronomical applications of (5.408) have produced unexpected results. Suppose that the source P is at rest on the solar surface and that the observer P_0 is regarded as being at rest at the distance of the Earth from the Sun. Then in (5.408), $q = 0$, $r = R_\odot$ and m/r_0 is negligible. It is the practice among astronomers to multiply observed displacements $d\lambda/\lambda$ by c and thus to express them in velocity units. Hence, for the Sun,

$$c\frac{d\lambda}{\lambda} = \frac{GM_\odot}{cR_\odot} = 0.64 \text{ km/sec}^{-1}.$$

Since $d\lambda$ is positive, the spectral lines are displaced towards the red and therefore the effect is also known as the *gravitational red-shift*. The most extensive study of solar spectral line displacements has been carried out by Dr M. G. Adam[11] and her co-workers. The measurements are made at points such as B (Fig. 5) on a solar meridian $NBAS$ in order to avoid introducing Doppler

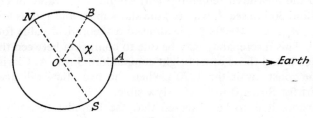

FIG. 5

corrections produced by the solar rotation. Allowance must also be made for the Doppler shifts due to the rotational and orbital motions of the Earth. When all known effects have been allowed for, apart from the gravitational red-shift, the displacements deduced from the observations are shown in Table III. Whatever the origin of these displacements may be, they cannot be

TABLE III

$\cos\chi$	1.000	0.817	0.639	0.468	0.398	0.282	0.181	0.1726	0.1411	0.0998	0.000
$cd\lambda/\lambda$ (km.sec^{-1})	0.246	0.261	0.256	0.290	0.354	0.448	0.634	0.767	0.793	0.828	0.912

due to the gravitational red-shift alone. For it is only towards the limb, at χ equal to about 79°, that the observed value coincides with 0.64 km.sec^{-1}. The fact that at the centre of the disc the displacement is less than the gravitational red-shift whereas it is greater at the limb, precludes an interpretation in terms of a radial velocity q for the solar gases responsible for the spectral lines. At present, therefore, the origin of the displacements listed in Table III is unknown, though presumably the gravitational red-shift must somehow be involved.

The displacements to the red of a solar strontium resonance line have been measured by Blamont and Roddier[12]. They too observe a smaller displacement at the centre of the disk than they do at the limb.

H

For a star of mass M_S and radius R_S with the source of radiation at rest on its surface, we have

$$c\frac{d\lambda}{\lambda} = \frac{GM_S}{cR_S}.$$

White dwarf stars have large M_S/R_S ratios, but there are only one or two of these stars for which the mass and radius can be independently estimated. For 40 Eri B, Popper[13] has measured displacements corresponding to $cd\lambda/\lambda = 21 \pm 4$ km.sec^{-1}. He estimates that the mass and radius of the star are respectively $M_S = 0\cdot43 \pm 0\cdot04M_\odot$ and $R_S = 0\cdot016 \pm 0\cdot002R_\odot$, which lead to $cd\lambda/\lambda = 17 \pm 3$ km.sec^{-1}, in good agreement with the observed value. But for Sirius B the measured red-shift[14] corresponds to a value of $cd\lambda/\lambda$ lying between 10 and 30 km.sec^{-1}, whereas the star's mass and radius are believed to be $M_S = M_\odot$, $R_S = 0\cdot008R_\odot$, leading to a theoretical value for $cd\lambda/\lambda$ of 79 km.sec^{-1}. This discrepancy may be due to confusion between the spectral lines of Sirius B and those of its bright companion, Sirius A. Clarification of this question must await the 1970's when the two stars will again be far enough apart for Sirius B to be clearly visible.

In conclusion, it is to be observed that the Doppler formula of special relativity may be deduced from (5·407). If $2m = 0$, the metric (5.119) reduces to that of the Minkowski space-time (3.601) with $x^4 = t$ and the coordinates (x^1, x^2, x^3) replaced by polar coordinates (r, θ, ϕ) through formulae of type (2.102). Then (5.407) with $2m = 0$ is the special relativity Doppler formula for the case of a source moving directly towards the observer. The opposite case, when the source recedes directly from the observer, is of greater interest. It is obtained by writing $-q$ for q in (5.407) and thus

$$\left(1 + \frac{dv}{v}\right)^{-1} = 1 + \frac{d\lambda}{\lambda} = \left(\frac{1 + q/c}{1 - q/c}\right)^{1/2}. \qquad (5.410)$$

The classical relation between $d\lambda/\lambda$ and q is deduced through the assumption that both quantities are small compared with unity. One then has

$$\frac{d\lambda}{\lambda} = \frac{q}{c}. \qquad (5.411)$$

Considerable errors can be made if q is computed from the second formula when $d\lambda/\lambda$ is large, as it is, for example, in the spectra of remote galaxies. In Table IV are shown the values of the ratio q/c for various $d\lambda/\lambda$ computed from (5.410). In particular, it is evident that $d\lambda/\lambda = 1$ corresponds to $q = 0\cdot6c$, and not to $q = c$ which would be the classical value. In fact $q = c$ corresponds to an infinite value of $d\lambda/\lambda$ which presumably means that the radiation from a source moving in this fashion could not be detected.

TABLE IV

$d\lambda/\lambda$	0·2	0·4	0·5	0·6	0·8	1·0	2·0	3·0	5	10	∞
q/c	0·18	0·32	0·38	0·44	0·53	0·60	0·80	0·88	0·95	0·98	1·00

Approximations to Einstein's Equations and Newtonian Gas-dynamics

In expositions of general relativity it has become traditional to show, as was done in Sec. 4.2, that a space-time whose coefficients have the very special form (4.207) leads to Poisson's equation, and to let the matter rest there. We propose to push a little deeper into the question of approximations to Einstein's equations with two ends in view. In the first place, wider implications of these equations will thus be revealed; and, secondly, an important by-product will emerge in the shape of a method for the solution of the equations of classical gas-dynamics.

6.1. First Approximation to a General Orthogonal Space-time

It will be assumed for the sake of mathematical simplicity that the metric of space-time is of the orthogonal form (4.401) and that its coefficients differ by small quantities from those of the Minkowski space-time. The smallness will be defined in terms of the constant κ that was given by (4.225), by saying that the square and higher powers of this constant are negligible.† The coefficients of the metric, in Dingle's notation, will be taken to be

$$D = 1 - \kappa\psi, \qquad A = \frac{1}{c^2}\left\{1 + \kappa\left(\psi + \frac{2\psi_1}{c^2}\right)\right\},$$

$$B = \frac{1}{c^2}\left\{1 + \kappa\left(\psi + \frac{2\psi_2}{c^2}\right)\right\}, \qquad C = \frac{1}{c^2}\left\{1 + \kappa\left(\psi + \frac{2\psi_3}{c^2}\right)\right\}, \tag{6.101}$$

where ψ, ψ_1, ψ_2, ψ_3 are functions of all four coordinates x^4, x^1, x^2, x^3. Since

---

† Strictly speaking the metric and Einstein's equations should first be expressed in terms of dimensionless variables[1]. It then emerges that two independent approximation parameters are available. One is $\eta = \kappa V$ where V is an arbitrary fixed gravitational potential, the other is $\varepsilon = v/c$ where v is the ratio of an arbitrary fixed length to an arbitrary fixed time-interval. The first approximation of Sec. 6.1 corresponds to working to order η, the second approximation of Sec. 6.4, to order η^2. The replacement of c by $\mathscr{C}$ amounts to putting $\varepsilon^2 = 0$ *after* a factor η/ε^2 has been cancelled on both sides of Einstein's equations.

powers of κ higher than the first are to be neglected, it is evident by inspection of Dingle's formulae that it is sufficient to take

$$\frac{1}{D} = 1, \quad \frac{1}{A} = \frac{1}{B} = \frac{1}{C} = c^2, \quad \sqrt{(-g)} = \frac{1}{c^3}. \tag{6.102}$$

If lmn stands for any cyclic permutation of 123, the expressions (6.101) substituted into Dingle's formulae, lead to the following approximate forms for Einstein's equations:

$$\left.\begin{aligned}
\kappa T^{lm} &= -\kappa \frac{\partial^2 \psi_n}{\partial x^l \partial x^m}, \\[2mm]
\kappa T^{l4} &= \kappa \frac{\partial^2}{\partial x^l \partial x^4}\left\{\psi + \frac{\psi_m + \psi_n}{c^2}\right\} \\[2mm]
\kappa T^{ll} &= \kappa\left\{-\frac{\partial^2}{(\partial x^4)^2}\left(\psi + \frac{\psi_m + \psi_n}{c^2}\right) + \frac{\partial^2 \psi_m}{(\partial x^n)^2} + \frac{\partial^2 \psi_n}{(\partial x^m)^2}\right\} + \Lambda, \\[2mm]
\kappa T^{44} &= -\kappa\left\{\nabla^2\psi + \frac{1}{c^2}\sum_{l,m,n}\left(\frac{\partial^2}{(\partial x^m)^2} + \frac{\partial^2}{(\partial x^n)^2}\right)\psi_l\right\} - \frac{\Lambda}{c^2},
\end{aligned}\right\} \tag{6.103}$$

where ∇^2 is the Laplacian operator (4.212) for the spatial coordinates x^1, x^2, x^3. It is then easy to prove by direct partial differentiation that the expressions (6.103) for the $T^{\mu\nu}$ satisfy identically the four relations

$$\frac{\partial(\kappa T^{\mu\sigma})}{\partial x^\sigma} = 0, \quad (\mu, \sigma = 1, 2, 3, 4), \tag{6.104}$$

provided that terms multiplied by squares and higher powers of κ are omitted. Hence neglect of second order terms in κ is equivalent to omitting from the left-hand sides of (4.105) the terms involving the Christoffel symbols. This arises because the Christoffel symbols are themselves proportional to κ. Cancelling the factor κ, the equations (6.104) are of the same mathematical form as (3.805) and they are therefore the equations of motion and the equation of continuity of a fluid in special relativity, when the only force acting is the pressure-gradient. It may therefore be concluded that Einstein's equations in their exact forms will contain, not only a theory of gravitation, but also a generalization of Newtonian hydrodynamics.

If the fluid is perfect, its energy-tensor is given by (4.104) and equations (6.103) become, with $\sigma = \rho = + p/c^2$,

$$\left.\begin{aligned}
\sigma u^l u^m &= -\frac{\partial^2 \psi_n}{\partial x^l \partial x^m}, \\[2mm]
\sigma u^l u^4 &= \frac{\partial^2}{\partial x^l \partial x^4}\left(\psi + \frac{\psi_m + \psi_n}{c^2}\right), \\[2mm]
\sigma(u^l)^2 + p &= -\frac{\partial^2}{(\partial x^4)^2}\left(\psi + \frac{\psi_m + \psi_n}{c^2}\right) + \frac{\partial^2 \psi_m}{(\partial x^n)^2} + \frac{\partial^2 \psi_n}{(\partial x^m)^2} + \frac{\Lambda}{\kappa}, \\[2mm]
\sigma(u^4)^2 - \frac{p}{c^2} &= -\nabla^2\psi - \frac{1}{c^2}\sum_{l,m,n}\left(\frac{\partial^2}{(\partial x^n)^2} + \frac{\partial^2}{(\partial x^m)^2}\right)\psi_l - \frac{\Lambda}{\kappa c^2},
\end{aligned}\right\} \tag{6.105}$$

where, to a sufficient approximation, the velocity 4-vector satisfies

$$(u^4)^2 - \frac{1}{c^2} \sum_{j=1}^{3} (u^j)^2 = 1.$$ (6.106)

There are eleven equations in the set (6.105) and (6.106), whose left-hand sides contain the six functions of the coordinates $\rho, p, u^\mu, (\mu = 1, 2, 3, 4)$, their right-hand sides involving the four functions $\psi, \psi_1, \psi_2, \psi_3$. Obviously, there-fore, there must be additional relations between these two sets of functions; such as, for example, the four equations (6.104), which are differential equa-tions governing $\rho, p, u^\mu, (\mu = 1, 2, 3, 4)$. But it is also, in principle at least, possible to eliminate these six functions from (6.105) and (6.106) and thus obtain differential equations involving only $\psi, \psi_1, \psi_2, \psi_3$. Such equations are indeed *consistency relations* of the kind referred to in Sec. 4.2 because, unless $\psi, \psi_1, \psi_2, \psi_3$ satisfy them, the eleven equations (6.105) and (6.106) will be mutually incompatible.

The coordinate-system $(x^4, x^1, x^2, x^3) = (x)$ is, however, not unique, in the sense that there are in general other systems in terms of which the metric of space-time is orthogonal and differs infinitesimally from that of the Minkow-ski space-time. It is sufficient to consider the effect of making an infinitesimal transformation from (x) to a new system (y) which may be conveniently taken as

$$x^\mu = y^\mu + \frac{\kappa}{2} \frac{\xi^\mu}{c^2}, \quad (\mu = 1, 2, 3, 4),$$ (6.107)

where the ξ^μ are four functions of the coordinates (y). It then follows that the coefficients of the metric are

$$D = 1 - \kappa\bar{\psi}, \quad A = \frac{1}{c^2}\left\{1 + \kappa\left(\bar{\psi} + \frac{2\bar{\psi}_1}{c^2}\right)\right\},$$

$$B = \frac{1}{c^2}\left\{1 + \kappa\left(\bar{\psi} + \frac{2\bar{\psi}_2}{c^2}\right)\right\}, \quad C = \frac{1}{c^2}\left\{1 + \kappa\left(\bar{\psi} + \frac{2\bar{\psi}_3}{c^2}\right)\right\},$$

where (the summation convention being suspended)

$$\bar{\psi} = \psi - \frac{1}{c^2}\frac{\partial\xi^4}{\partial y^4},$$
$$\bar{\psi}_i = \psi_i + \frac{1}{2}\left(\frac{\partial\xi^i}{\partial y^i} + \frac{\partial\xi^4}{\partial y^4}\right), \quad (i = 1, 2, 3),$$ (6.108)

the ψ and ψ_i being the *same* functions of the (y) as they were of the (x). If the metric is still to be orthogonal, the ξ^μ must satisfy

$$\frac{\partial\xi^4}{\partial y^i} - \frac{1}{c^2}\frac{\partial\xi^i}{\partial y^4} = 0, \quad (i = 1, 2, 3)$$
$$\frac{\partial\xi^l}{\partial y^m} + \frac{\partial\xi^m}{\partial y^l} = 0,$$ (6.109)

lmn being any cyclic permutation of 123. These equations are not the only ones, however, which govern the ξ^μ; further relations are obtained by considering the transformation of equations (6.103). The transform of the energy-tensor is

$$T^{\mu\nu} = \frac{\partial x^\mu}{\partial y^\alpha}\frac{\partial x^\nu}{\partial y^\beta}\bar{T}^{\alpha\beta} = \left(\delta^\mu_\alpha + \frac{\kappa}{2c^2}\frac{\partial\xi^\mu}{\partial y^\alpha}\right)\left(\delta^\nu_\beta + \frac{\kappa}{2c^2}\frac{\partial\xi^\nu}{\partial y^\beta}\right)\bar{T}^{\alpha\beta}.$$

But the left-hand sides of equations (6.103) are of order κ and it is therefore sufficient to take

$$\bar{T}^{\mu\nu}(y) = T^{\mu\nu}(y).$$

Now consider, for example, the first of equations (6.103) which is, in the coordinate-system (y),

$$\kappa\bar{T}^{lm} = -\kappa\frac{\partial^2\bar{\psi}_n}{\partial y^l\partial y^m},$$

or

$$\kappa T^{lm}(y) = -\kappa\left\{\frac{\partial^2\psi_n}{\partial y^l\partial y^m} + \frac{1}{2}\frac{\partial^2}{\partial y^l\partial y^m}\left(\frac{\partial\xi^n}{\partial y^n} + \frac{\partial\xi^4}{\partial y^4}\right)\right\}.$$

But ψ_n is the same function of the (y) as it was of the (x) and therefore

$$\kappa T^{lm}(y) = -\kappa\frac{\partial^2\psi_n}{\partial y^l\partial y^m}.$$

Hence the ξ^μ must satisfy

$$\frac{\partial^2}{\partial y^l\partial y^m}\left(\frac{\partial\xi^n}{\partial y^n} + \frac{\partial\xi^4}{\partial y^4}\right) = 0, \tag{6.110}$$

and proceeding in this way with the remaining equations of the set (6.103) we find

$$\left.\begin{aligned} &\frac{\partial^2}{\partial y^l\partial y^4}\left(\frac{\partial\xi^m}{\partial y^m} + \frac{\partial\xi^n}{\partial y^n}\right) = 0, \\ &-\frac{1}{c^2}\frac{\partial^2}{(\partial y^4)^2}\left(\frac{\partial\xi^m}{\partial y^m} + \frac{\partial\xi^n}{\partial y^n}\right) \\ &\quad + \frac{\partial^2}{(\partial y^n)^2}\left(\frac{\partial\xi^m}{\partial y^m} + \frac{\partial\xi^4}{\partial y^4}\right) + \frac{\partial^2}{(\partial y^m)^2}\left(\frac{\partial\xi^n}{\partial y^n} + \frac{\partial\xi^4}{\partial y^4}\right) = 0, \\ &\sum_{l,m,n}\frac{\partial^2}{(\partial y^l)^2}\left(\frac{\partial\xi^m}{\partial y^m} + \frac{\partial\xi^n}{\partial y^n}\right) = 0. \end{aligned}\right\} \tag{6.110}$$

If therefore the ξ^μ satisfy (6.109) and (6.110), Einstein's equations have the same form in the (y) coordinate-system as they had in the (x).

Returning to the coordinate-system (x) and to Einstein's equations in the form (6.105), we consider the case of a statical space-time in which therefore ψ and the ψ_i are functions of (x^1, x^2, x^3) alone. The equations for the three combinations $\sigma u^l u^4$ then give

$$u^i = 0, \qquad (i = 1, 2, 3)$$

and the distribution of matter is at rest in the coordinate-system. From the equations for the $\sigma u^l u^m$ we find

$$\frac{\partial^2 \psi_n}{\partial x^l \partial x^m} = 0,$$

whilst the three equations for p are

$$p - \frac{\Lambda}{\kappa} = \frac{\partial^2 \psi_m}{(\partial x^n)^2} + \frac{\partial^2 \psi_n}{(\partial x^m)^2} = \frac{\partial^2 \psi_l}{(\partial x^m)^2} + \frac{\partial^2 \psi_m}{(\partial x^n)^2} = \frac{\partial^2 \psi_l}{(\partial x^n)^2} + \frac{\partial^2 \psi_n}{(\partial x^l)^2}.$$

Hence

$$\frac{\partial p}{\partial x^l} = \frac{\partial}{\partial x^n}\left(\frac{\partial^2 \psi_m}{\partial x^l \partial x^n}\right) + \frac{\partial}{\partial x^m}\left(\frac{\partial^2 \psi_n}{\partial x^l \partial x^m}\right) = 0,$$

and similarly

$$\frac{\partial p}{\partial x^m} = 0, \qquad \frac{\partial p}{\partial x^n} = 0,$$

and thus p is a constant. Therefore the general theorem, of which a special case was considered in Sec. 4.2, is:

When the metric of space-time is orthogonal and statical and the co-efficients of the metric differ by terms of order κ from those of the Minkowski space-time, then the corresponding distribution of matter is at rest in the coordinate-system and its pressure is constant, in the first approximation with respect to κ.

6.2. Newtonian Gas-dynamics

The approximation used in the preceding section is essentially based on the smallness of the constant κ and therefore, apart from the presence of the cosmical constant, leads to special relativity hydrodynamics. If now the constant c is replaced by the infinite velocity $\mathscr{C}$ and terms in $1/\mathscr{C}^2$ are neglected, the Newtonian approximation to equations (6.105) and (6.106) should result. In performing this further approximation it will be assumed that ρ, p and the four u^n do not contain a factor of order c^2. As to ψ, ψ_1, ψ_2, ψ_3, two alternative procedures are possible: in the first method the four functions are also assumed to contain no terms of order c^2. The consequences of this assumption will be explored in this, and the next two, sections. But an alternative device is available, which consists in permitting terms of order c^2 in ψ, ψ_1, ψ_2, ψ_3 and 'cancelling' them with the help of the cosmical constant, as will be shown in Sec. 6.5.

If then there are no terms of order c^2 in the right-hand sides of equations (6.105), and the pressure and density are to remain finite in the Newtonian approximation, it is obvious that the cosmical constant must be chosen so that, as c tends to $\mathscr{C}$, the limits of both Λ/κ and $\Lambda/\kappa c^2$ shall be finite or zero.

This can be achieved by assuming that Λ contains at most a factor $1/c^2$ and that

$$\operatorname*{Lim}_{c \to \mathscr{C}} \frac{\Lambda}{\kappa} = \lambda, \qquad \operatorname*{Lim}_{c \to \mathscr{C}} \frac{\Lambda}{\kappa c^2} = 0, \tag{6.201}$$

where λ is a finite constant. These conditions will be said to define a *small cosmical constant*. Again, in (6.106), $u^4 = 1$ when terms in $1/c^2$ are neglected, and (u^1, u^2, u^3) become respectively the Newtonian velocity components of the fluid (U_1, U_2, U_3). The coordinates (x^4, x^1, x^2, x^3) degenerate to the Newtonian coordinates (T, X_1, X_2, X_3), s becoming identical with T and x^4. Finally replacing c by $\mathscr{C}$ in (6.105) and omitting all terms in $1/\mathscr{C}^2$, we have

$$\rho U_l U_m = - \frac{\partial^2 \psi_n}{\partial X_l \partial X_m}, \tag{6.202}$$

$$\rho U_i = \frac{\partial^2 \psi}{\partial X_i \partial T}, \qquad (i = 1, 2, 3), \tag{6.203}$$

$$\rho (U_i)^2 + p = - \frac{\partial^2 \psi}{\partial T^2} + \frac{\partial^2 \psi_n}{\partial X_m^2} + \frac{\partial^2 \psi_m}{\partial X_n^2} + \lambda, \tag{6.204}$$

$$\rho = - \nabla^2 \psi. \tag{6.205}$$

In the ten equations (6.202) to (6.205) ρ, p stand for the Newtonian density and pressure, respectively.

Elimination of ρ, U_1, U_2, U_3 from equations (6.202), (6.203) and (6.205) yields the three equations

$$\frac{\partial^2 \psi_l}{\partial X_m \partial X_n} = \left(\frac{\partial^2 \psi}{\partial X_m \partial T} \cdot \frac{\partial^2 \psi}{\partial X_n \partial T} \right) \Big/ \nabla^2 \psi. \tag{6.206}$$

Again elimination of p, ρ, U_1, U_2, U_3 from (6.203), (6.204) and (6.205) yields

$$\left. \begin{aligned} \left(\frac{\partial^2 \psi}{\partial X_1 \partial T} \right)^2 \Big/ \nabla^2 \psi + \frac{\partial^2 \psi_2}{\partial X_3^2} + \frac{\partial^2 \psi_3}{\partial X_2^2} &= \left(\frac{\partial^2 \psi}{\partial X_2 \partial T} \right)^2 \Big/ \nabla^2 \psi + \frac{\partial^2 \psi_1}{\partial X_3^2} + \frac{\partial^2 \psi_3}{\partial X_1^2} \\ &= \left(\frac{\partial^2 \psi}{\partial X_3 \partial T} \right)^2 \Big/ \nabla^2 \psi + \frac{\partial^2 \psi_1}{\partial X_2^2} + \frac{\partial^2 \psi_2}{\partial X_1^2}. \end{aligned} \right\} \tag{6.207}$$

Equations (6.206) and (6.207) are the consistency relations for the ten equations (6.202) to (6.205). If, for convenience, the three expressions in (6.207) are denoted by E_1, E_2, E_3 respectively, and their common value is $\chi - \lambda$, then

$$\frac{\partial \chi}{\partial X_l} = \frac{\partial E_l}{\partial X_l} = \frac{\partial}{\partial X_l} \left\{ \left(\frac{\partial^2 \psi}{\partial X_l \partial T} \right)^2 \Big/ \nabla^2 \psi \right\}$$
$$+ \frac{\partial}{\partial X_m} \left(\frac{\partial^2 \psi_n}{\partial X_m \partial X_l} \right) + \frac{\partial}{\partial X_n} \left(\frac{\partial^2 \psi_m}{\partial X_n \partial X_l} \right), \tag{6.208}$$

there being no summation over repeated indices. Hence by (6.206)

$$\frac{\partial \chi}{\partial X_i} = \sum_{i=1}^{3} \frac{\partial}{\partial X_i} \left\{ \left(\frac{\partial^2 \psi}{\partial X_i \partial T} \cdot \frac{\partial^2 \psi}{\partial X_i \partial T} \right) \middle/ \nabla^2 \psi \right\}, \tag{6.209}$$

and therefore χ is determined in terms of ψ. By an algebraic solution of (6.202) to (6.205), making use also of (6.207) and the definition of χ,

$$\left. \begin{aligned} U_i &= - \frac{\partial^2 \psi}{\partial X_i \partial T} \middle/ \nabla^2 \psi, \quad (i = 1, 2, 3), \\ \rho &= - \nabla^2 \psi, \\ p &= - \frac{\partial^2 \psi}{\partial T^2} + \chi. \end{aligned} \right\} \tag{6.210}$$

These equations show that the cosmical constant has disappeared from the final result, a consequence of the postulated non-existence of large terms in ψ, ψ_1, ψ_2, ψ_3. The same result would, of course, have been obtained if the cosmical constant had been equated to zero in Einstein's equations in the first instance.

The reader will easily verify by direct substitution and the use of (6.209), that the foregoing expressions for ρ, p and the three U_i satisfy (3.201) and (3.202) identically for all ψ, *provided that* $F_i = 0$. Since ρ is in general a function of T as well as of (X_1, X_2, X_3), the expressions (6.210) are solutions, in terms of one indeterminate function ψ, of the classical equations for the motion of a gas (a fluid of variable density) when the only force acting is the pressure-gradient. The indeterminacy is inherent in the problem, for as was shown in Sec. 3.2, the four equations (3.201) and (3.202) cannot determine all five unknowns. No limitation, however, has been placed on the magnitude of the velocity. The fact that ρ and ψ in (6.210) are connected by Poisson's equation must not be taken to mean that the gravitational self-attraction of the gas plays a part in controlling its motion. If this were the case F_i could not be zero; to the order of approximation to which we are working the gravitational potential ψ enters only as an auxiliary function in the solution of the hydrodynamical equations.

The vector

$$\Omega_i = \frac{\partial \rho U_m}{\partial X_n} - \frac{\partial \rho U_n}{\partial X_m},$$

may be called the *momentum-vorticity* of the fluid. It is easy to verify from (6.210) that $\Omega_i = 0$ so that there is a restriction on the possible types of motion. The limitation is traceable[1] to the choice of mathematical form for the four non-zero coefficients of the metric in (6.101). It can be removed by more elaborate initial assumptions.

It is now necessary to investigate the effect of the non-unique character of the initial coordinate-system. Suppose, indeed, that the approximation process had had for its starting point the coordinate-system (y) of (6.107), instead of (x), would the end-result be significantly different from (6.210)? To answer this question with a sufficient degree of generality for the present purpose, it will be assumed that the functions ξ^μ in (6.107) are of the form

$$\left.\begin{array}{l} \xi^4 = -c^2 \int \xi dy^4, \\[2mm] \xi^l = c^2 \int \left(\xi + \dfrac{\zeta_l}{c^2}\right) dy^l + c^4 \eta_l(y^4, y^m, y^n), \end{array}\right\} \tag{6.211}$$

where the integrations are partial, ξ and ζ_l may be functions of all four coordinates, but each η_l $(l = 1, 2, 3)$ is independent of the corresponding y^l. The conditions (6.109) and (6.110) then read, respectively,

$$\left.\begin{array}{l} \dfrac{\partial}{\partial y^l}\left(\int \xi dy^4\right) + \dfrac{\partial \eta_l}{\partial y^4} = -\dfrac{1}{c^2}\dfrac{\partial}{\partial y^4}\left\{\int\left(\xi + \dfrac{\zeta_l}{c^2}\right)dy^l\right\}, \\[4mm] \dfrac{\partial \eta_l}{\partial y^m} + \dfrac{\partial \eta_m}{\partial y^l} = -\dfrac{1}{c^2}\left[\dfrac{\partial}{\partial y^m}\left\{\int\left(\xi + \dfrac{\zeta_l}{c^2}\right)dy^l\right\} + \dfrac{\partial}{\partial y^l}\left\{\int\left(\xi + \dfrac{\zeta_m}{c^2}\right)dy^m\right\}\right], \end{array}\right\} \tag{6.212}$$

$$\left.\begin{array}{l} \dfrac{\partial^2 \zeta_n}{\partial y^l \partial y^m} = 0, \qquad \dfrac{\partial^2}{\partial y^l \partial y^4}\left(2\xi + \dfrac{\zeta_m + \zeta_n}{c^2}\right) = 0, \\[4mm] \dfrac{\partial^2}{(\partial y^4)^2}\left(2\xi + \dfrac{\zeta_m + \zeta_n}{c^2}\right) = \dfrac{\partial^2 \zeta_m}{(\partial y^n)^2} + \dfrac{\partial^2 \zeta_n}{(\partial y^m)^2}, \\[4mm] \displaystyle\sum_{l,m,n} \dfrac{\partial^2}{(\partial y^l)^2}\left(2\xi + \dfrac{\zeta_m + \zeta_n}{c^2}\right) = 0. \end{array}\right\} \tag{6.213}$$

Now consider the transition to Newtonian mechanics, replacing c by $\mathscr{C}$ and discarding terms in $1/\mathscr{C}^2$ or $1/\mathscr{C}^4$. By hypothesis, the system (x) becomes the Newtonian system (T, X_1, X_2, X_3); let the system (y) become the Newtonian system (Y_4, Y_1, Y_2, Y_3). Then, introducing (6.211) into (6.107) and omitting all terms containing a factor $1/c^2$, we have

$$\left.\begin{array}{l} Y^4 = T. \\[2mm] X_l = Y_l + 4\pi G \eta_l(T, Y_m, Y_n). \end{array}\right\} \tag{6.214}$$

Thus the transformation (6.211) preserves the uniqueness of Newtonian time. Differentiating the first of equations (6.212) once with respect to y^4 and then omitting all terms containing a factor $1/c^2$ in this and all other equations in the sets (6.212) and (6.213), we find the Newtonian forms

$$\left.\begin{array}{l} \dfrac{\partial \xi}{\partial Y_l} + \dfrac{\partial^2 \eta_l}{\partial T^2} = 0, \qquad \dfrac{\partial \eta_l}{\partial Y_m} + \dfrac{\partial \eta_m}{\partial Y_l} = 0, \\[4mm] \dfrac{\partial^2 \zeta_n}{\partial Y_l \partial Y_m} = 0, \qquad \dfrac{\partial^2 \xi}{\partial Y_l \partial T} = 0, \\[4mm] \dfrac{\partial^2 \xi}{\partial T^2} = \dfrac{1}{2}\left(\dfrac{\partial^2 \zeta_m}{\partial Y_n^2} + \dfrac{\partial^2 \zeta_n}{\partial Y_m^2}\right), \qquad \nabla^2 \xi = 0. \end{array}\right\} \tag{6.215}$$

The reader may easily verify that a solution of these equations is provided by

$$\left.\begin{aligned}
\xi &= \sum_{j=1}^{3} \alpha_j Y_j + f(T), \\
\zeta_i &= \sum_{j=1}^{3} Y_j^2 h_{ij}(T), \qquad (i = 1, 2, 3) \\
\eta_l &= (\beta_{lm} Y_m + \beta_{ln} Y_n)T - \tfrac{1}{2}\alpha_l T^2,
\end{aligned}\right\} \tag{6.216}$$

where the α_j and β_{ij} are constants of which the latter satisfy

$$\beta_{lm} + \beta_{ml} = 0;$$

and the h_{ij} and f are any functions of T that satisfy

$$\frac{d^2 f}{dT^2} = h_{12} + h_{21} = h_{31} + h_{13} = h_{23} + h_{32}. \tag{6.217}$$

Hence (6.211) and (6.216) turn the formulae (6.108) into

$$\left.\begin{aligned}
\bar{\psi} &= \psi + \sum_{j=1}^{3} \alpha_j Y_j + f(T), \\
\bar{\psi}_i &= \psi_i + \tfrac{1}{2}\zeta_i = \psi_i + \tfrac{1}{2}\sum_{j=1}^{3} Y_j^2 h_{ij}(T), \qquad (i = 1, 2, 3).
\end{aligned}\right\} \tag{6.218}$$

The new consistency relations differ from (6.206) and (6.207) in having $\bar{\psi}$, $\bar{\psi}_i$ and (Y_1, Y_2, Y_3) written for ψ, ψ_i and (X_1, X_2, X_3), e.g. (6.206) is replaced by

$$\frac{\partial^2 \bar{\psi}_l}{\partial Y_m \partial Y_n} = \left(\frac{\partial^2 \bar{\psi}}{\partial Y_m \partial T} \cdot \frac{\partial^2 \bar{\psi}}{\partial Y_n \partial T}\right) \Big/ \nabla^2 \bar{\psi}.$$

But by (6.218) this equation becomes

$$\frac{\partial^2 \psi_l}{\partial Y_m \partial Y_n} = \left(\frac{\partial^2 \psi}{\partial Y_m \partial T} \cdot \frac{\partial^2 \psi}{\partial Y_n \partial T}\right) \Big/ \nabla^2 \psi,$$

and therefore, since the ψ, ψ_i are the same functions of (T, Y_1, Y_2, Y_3) as they were of (T, X_1, X_2, X_3) no significant change in this consistency relation has been made. The same property holds for (6.207), the relations (6.217) being borne in mind, and for (6.208). Lastly, if $\bar{U}_i$, $\bar{\rho}$, $\bar{p}$ refer to the (Y) system, equations (6.218) then show that

$$\left.\begin{aligned}
\bar{U}_i &= -\frac{\partial^2 \psi}{\partial Y_i \partial T} \Big/ \nabla^2 \psi, \qquad (i = 1, 2, 3) \\
\bar{\rho} &= -\nabla^2 \psi, \\
\bar{p} &= -\frac{\partial^2 \psi}{\partial T^2} + \chi,
\end{aligned}\right\} \tag{6.219}$$

in other words, the formulae for the velocity, density and pressure of the fluid have the same functional forms in the (Y) coordinates as they had in the (X). Hence, provided that boundary and initial conditions in the two coordinate-systems are made to agree by the use of (6.214), the equations (6.210) and (6.219) may be said to describe exactly the same distribution of matter and the change in the initial coordinate-system has produced no alteration in the physical situation.

6.3. The Geodesic Principle and Newtonian Theory

An uncritical application of the geodesic principle can lead to an apparent contradiction with the conclusion stated at the end of the previous section. An ordinary geodesic of the space-time whose coefficients are listed in (6.101), describes the history of the motion of a free test-particle subjected to the gravitational effects of the distribution of matter (6.105), the gravitational contribution of the particle itself being ignored. Writing $v^\mu = dx^\mu/ds$ for the particle's velocity 4-vector and using (2.807) and (6.101), the geodesic equations are, to the first order in κ,

$$
\left.
\begin{aligned}
&\frac{dv^4}{ds} - \frac{\kappa}{2}\left\{ 2\sum_{\mu=1}^{4}\frac{\partial\psi}{\partial x^\mu}v^4 v^\mu - \frac{\partial\psi}{\partial x^4}(v^4)^2 - \sum_{j=1}^{3}\left(\frac{\partial\psi}{\partial x^4} + \frac{2}{c^2}\frac{\partial\psi_j}{\partial x^4}\right)\frac{(v^j)^2}{c^2} \right\} = 0, \\
&\frac{dv^i}{ds} - \frac{\kappa c^2}{2}\frac{\partial\psi}{\partial x^i}(v^4)^2 - \frac{\kappa}{2}\sum_{j=1}^{3}\left(\frac{\partial\psi}{\partial x^i} + \frac{2}{c^2}\frac{\partial\psi_j}{\partial x^i}\right)(v^j)^2 \\
&\qquad\qquad + \kappa\sum_{\mu=1}^{4}\left(\frac{\partial\psi}{\partial x^\mu} + \frac{2}{c^2}\frac{\partial\psi_i}{\partial x^\mu}\right)v^i v^\mu = 0, \qquad (i = 1, 2, 3).
\end{aligned}
\right\} \tag{6.301}
$$

On replacing c by $\mathscr{C}$, κ tends to zero and κc^2 to $8\pi G$; also $s \equiv T$, $v^4 = 1$ and $v^i = dX_i/dT$. Hence the three surviving equations of the set (6.301) are

$$
\frac{d^2 X_i}{dT^2} = 4\pi G\frac{\partial\psi}{\partial X_i}, \qquad (i = 1, 2, 3). \tag{6.302}
$$

But had we used the coordinate-system (y) of (6.107) in the first instance, instead of the system (x), the geodesic equations would have degenerated to

$$
\frac{d^2 Y_i}{dT^2} = 4\pi G\frac{\partial\bar\psi}{\partial Y_i}, \qquad (i = 1, 2, 3), \tag{6.303}
$$

where $\bar\psi$ is given in (6.218). Hence

$$
\frac{d^2 Y_i}{dT^2} = 4\pi G\left(\frac{\partial\psi}{\partial Y_i} + \alpha_i\right), \qquad (i = 1, 2, 3), \tag{6.304}
$$

and thus an apparent additional constant gravitational force $4\pi G\alpha_i$ per unit mass has appeared. Yet this is in no way reflected by a change in the distribution of matter, described by (6.210) or by (6.219), which is responsible for the gravitational field. In fact, the additional 'gravitational force' is merely a reflection of the fact that the (Y) and (X) coordinate-systems are relatively accelerated. For by (6.214) and (6.216)

$$
\frac{d^2 X_i}{dT^2} = \frac{d^2 Y_i}{dT^2} - 4\pi G\alpha_i, \qquad (i = 1, 2, 3), \tag{6.305}
$$

and

$$\frac{\partial \psi}{\partial Y_l} = \sum_{j=1}^{3} \frac{\partial \psi}{\partial X_j} \frac{\partial X_j}{\partial Y_l} = \frac{\partial \psi}{\partial X_l} + 4\pi G\left(\beta_{ml}\frac{\partial \psi}{\partial X_m} + \beta_{nl}\frac{\partial \psi}{\partial X_n}\right)T.$$

Neglecting terms in $(4\pi G)^2$, which corresponds in the Newtonian approximation to the neglect of terms in κ^2, the equations (6.304) transform into (6.302). Equations (6.305), however, reveal that the relative acceleration of the two coordinate systems is precisely $4\pi G\alpha_i$. That this acceleration is not a genuine gravitational acceleration is emphasized by the fact that it persists even when $\psi \equiv 0$, $\psi_i \equiv 0$, so that there is no matter present to produce a gravitational field. The space-time with coefficients (6.101) then reduces to the Minkowski space-time and the coordinate-system (y) becomes an accelerated system in the sense of Sec. 4.6. It is to be expected that spurious gravitational accelerations due to the use of inappropriate coordinate-systems, will also occur when Einstein's equations are solved in their exact forms, and too great a reliance on the geodesic principle may well lead to physical error.

6.4. Second Approximations. Gas-dynamics with Gravitation

The expansions of the coefficients of the metric in Einstein's equations will now be pushed to terms in κ^2 and it will be shown that the resulting Newtonian approximations lead to motions of a fluid (gas or liquid) under the action of both its pressure-gradient and its gravitational self-attraction. A general attack on the problem produces very complicated formulae and therefore the method will be illustrated through two important special cases.

(i) *Plane symmetry*. – It will be assumed that the cosmical constant is zero in this part of the investigation. Referring to (4.413) and (4.414) the coefficients of the metric are, in Dingle's notation,

$$D = Ac^2 = e^{2f}, \qquad B = C = \frac{e^{2h}}{c^2}. \tag{6.401}$$

Inspection of the formulae for T^{12}, T^{13}, T^{23}, T^{24} and T^{34} shows that all these components are identically zero. This implies that $u^2 = 0$ and $u^3 = 0$ and the identity satisfied by the velocity 4-vector therefore becomes

$$1 = D(u^4)^2 - A(u^1)^2. \tag{6.402}$$

It is also convenient to introduce the following symbols:

$$L = e^f u^4, \qquad U = e^f u^1, \qquad \sigma = \rho + \frac{p}{c^2}, \tag{6.403}$$

and to denote partial derivatives of f and h with respect to $x = x^1$ and $t = x^4$ by suffixes. The surviving Einstein equations given below correspond to the energy-tensor components T^{11}, $T^{22} = T^{33}$, T^{44}, $T^{14} = T^{41}$, respectively:

$$\kappa(\sigma U^2 + p) = e^{-2f}\{- 2h_{tt} + c^2(h_x^2 + 2h_x f_x) - (3h_t^2 - 2h_t f_t)\}, \tag{6.404}$$

$$\kappa p = e^{-2f}\{- h_{tt} - f_{tt} + c^2(h_{xx} + f_{xx}) + c^2 h_x^2 - h_t^2\}, \tag{6.405}$$

$$- \kappa\left(\sigma L^2 - \frac{p}{c^2}\right) = e^{-2f}\left\{2h_{xx} + 3h_x^2 - 2h_x f_x - \frac{1}{c^2}(h_t^2 + 2h_t f_t)\right\},$$ (6.406)

$$- \kappa\sigma UL = 2e^{-2f}\{- h_{xt} - h_x h_t + h_x f_t + h_t f_x\},$$ (6.407)

while equation (6.402) is

$$1 = L^2 - \frac{U^2}{c^2}.$$ (6.408)

Equation (6.405) may be used in equations (6.404) and (6.406) to express σU^2 and σL^2 in terms of the derivatives of f and h; then σ, U and L may be eliminated in turn by using equation (6.407). The result is a consistency relation which f and h must satisfy if equations (6.404) to (6.407) are to be algebraically consistent. This relation is

$$4\{h_{xt} + h_x h_t - f_t h_x - f_x h_t\}^2$$

$$= \frac{1}{c^2}\{h_{tt} - f_{tt} + c^2(h_{xx} + f_{xx} - 2f_x h_x) + 2(h_t^2 - f_t h_t)\}$$

$$\times \{h_{tt} + f_{tt} + c^2(h_{xx} - f_{xx} + 2h_x^2 - f_x h_x) - 2f_t h_t\}.$$ (6.409)

If f and h satisfy this relation, σ may be found by elimination of p, U^2, and L^2 from equations (6.405), (6.406) and (6.408), and hence ρ itself may be determined, since equation (6.405) gives p. Again equations (6.404) and (6.405) give σU^2; thus the five equations (6.404) to (6.408) are equivalent to equation (6.409), together with

$$\kappa\rho = e^{-2f}\left\{f_{xx} - h_{xx} + \frac{1}{c^2}(h_{tt} - f_{tt}) - 3h_x^2 + \frac{3}{c^2}h_t^2\right\},$$ (6.410)

$$\kappa p = e^{-2f}\{c^2(f_{xx} + h_{xx}) - (h_{tt} + f_{tt}) + c^2 h_x^2 - h_t^2\},$$ (6.411)

$$\kappa U^2 = \frac{e^{-2f}}{\sigma}\{- c^2(f_{xx} + h_{xx}) - (h_{tt} - f_{tt}) + 2c^2 f_x h_x - 2h_t^2 + 2f_t h_t\},$$ (6.412)

$$L^2 = 1 + \frac{U^2}{c^2},$$ (6.413)

where, in equation (6.412), σ may be eliminated with the help of

$$\kappa\sigma = \frac{2e^{-2f}}{c^2}\{c^2 f_{xx} - f_{tt} - c^2 h_x^2 + h_t^2\}.$$ (6.414)

These formulae are exact and we must now obtain their approximate forms when terms of order κ^3 and higher are neglected. Let

$$f = -\frac{\kappa}{2}\psi + \kappa^2 F, \qquad h = -\frac{\kappa}{2}\omega + \kappa^2 H,$$

where ψ, ω, F and H are functions of x and t, containing no terms of order c^2, and powers of κ higher than the second are to be neglected. Since the partial derivatives of f and h are then at least of order κ, it is sufficient to put

$e^{-2f} = 1 + \kappa\psi$. The consistency relation (6.409) may then be written

$$4\kappa^2\{-\tfrac{1}{2}\omega_{xt} + \kappa(H_{xt} + \tfrac{1}{4}\omega_x\omega_t - \tfrac{1}{4}\psi_t\omega_x - \tfrac{1}{4}\psi_x\omega_t)\}^2$$

$$= \kappa^2\left[+ \tfrac{1}{2}(\psi - \omega)_{tt} - \frac{c^2}{2}(\psi + \omega)_{xx} + \kappa\{c^2(H + F)_{xx}\right.$$

$$+ (H - F)_{tt} - \frac{c^2}{2}\psi_x\omega_x + \tfrac{1}{2}\omega_t^2 - \tfrac{1}{2}\psi_t\omega_t\}\bigg]$$

$$\times \left[-\frac{1}{2c^2}(\psi + \omega)_{tt} + \tfrac{1}{2}(\psi - \omega)_{xx} + \kappa\{(H - F)_{xx}\right.$$

$$+ \frac{1}{c^2}(H + F)_{tt} + \tfrac{1}{2}\omega_x^2 - \tfrac{1}{2}\psi_x\omega_x - \frac{2}{c^2}\psi_t\omega_t\}\bigg], \qquad (6.415)$$

(6.410), (6.411) and (6.407) becoming, respectively,

$$\rho = \tfrac{1}{2}(\omega - \psi)_{xx} - \frac{1}{2c^2}(\omega - \psi)_{tt} + \kappa\left\{\frac{1}{c^2}(H - F)_{tt} - (H - F)_{xx}\right.$$

$$\left. - \frac{1}{2c^2}\psi(\omega - \psi)_{tt} + \tfrac{1}{2}\psi(\omega - \psi)_{xx} - \tfrac{3}{4}\omega_x^2 + \frac{3}{4c^2}\omega_t^2\right\}, \qquad (6.416)$$

$$p = \tfrac{1}{2}(\psi + \omega)_{tt} - \frac{c^2}{2}(\psi + \omega)_{xx} + \kappa\left\{c^2(F + H)_{xx} - (F + H)_{tt}\right.$$

$$\left. - \frac{c^2}{2}\psi(\psi + \omega)_{xx} + \tfrac{1}{2}\psi(\psi + \omega)_{tt} + \tfrac{1}{4}c^2\omega_t^2 - \tfrac{1}{4}\omega_t^2\right\}, \qquad (6.417)$$

$$\sigma UL = -\omega_{xt} + \kappa(2H_{xt} - \psi\omega_{xt} + \tfrac{1}{2}\omega_x\omega_t - \tfrac{1}{2}\psi_t\omega_x - \tfrac{1}{2}\psi_x\omega_t). \qquad (6.418)$$

To pass to the Newtonian approximation we must replace c by the infinite velocity $\mathscr{C}$, and neglect all terms in $1/\mathscr{C}^2$. The result will be that f tends to zero, u^4 and L tend to unity, x and t become Newtonian distance X and Newtonian absolute time T, respectively, whilst U becomes the Newtonian velocity of the fluid. Moreover σ and ρ are now identical and equal to the Newtonian density ρ, it being assumed that the density and pressure contain no terms of order c^2. We also write

$$\omega = \frac{1}{c^2}\Psi - \psi, \qquad (6.419)$$

and we suppose that Ψ, ψ, F and H contain no terms of order c^2. Substituting in equation (6.415) and then neglecting all terms with a factor $1/\mathscr{C}^2$, we find

$$\psi_{XT}^2 = \psi_{XX}\{\psi_{TT} - \tfrac{1}{2}\Psi_{XX} + 8\pi G(\tfrac{1}{2}\psi_X^2 + H_{XX} + F_{XX})\},$$

in which the term in $8\pi G$ ($= \kappa c^2$) is now to be reckoned as a term of the second order compared with the others. Hence, equating to zero the first- and second-order terms separately, we have

$$\tfrac{1}{2}\Psi_{XX} = \psi_{TT} - \frac{\psi_{XT}^2}{\psi_{XX}}, \qquad (H + F)_{XX} = -\tfrac{1}{2}\psi_X^2. \qquad (6.420)$$

Introducing (6.419) and (6.420) into (6.416), (6.417) and (6.418) and again neglecting terms with a factor $1/\mathscr{C}^2$, there comes

$$\rho = -\psi_{XX}, \qquad p = -\psi_{TT} + \frac{\psi_{XT}^2}{\psi_{XX}} - 2\pi G\psi_X^2,$$
$$U = -\psi_{XT}/\psi_{XX}, \tag{6.421}$$

which give the Newtonian approximation to the distribution of matter described by the metric whose coefficients are (6.401). The formulae are easily interpreted through (3.201) and (3.202) with ρ, p functions of $X_1(= X)$ and T alone, $U_1 = U$ and U_2, U_3 zero, and F_2, F_3 vanishing. Direct substitution of (6.421) into (3.202) then shows that the equation of continuity is satisfied for all functions ψ, and the surviving equation of motion yields the gravitational self-attraction

$$F_1 = 4\pi G\psi_X. \tag{6.422}$$

The formulae for ρ and for F_1 thus reveal that $4\pi G\psi$ is the gravitational potential of the mass of fluid.

(ii) *Spherical symmetry.* – The isotropic form (4.416) for the metric is most suited to our purpose and therefore Einstein's equations are expressed by equations (4.419) to (4.422) and the fluid-velocity 4-vector satisfies (4.418). By an argument analogous to that employed in establishing (5.124) the velocity of the fluid relative to the coordinate-system (t, r, θ, ϕ) is

$$q = \frac{e^{\mu/2}u^1}{e^{\nu/2}u^4}. \tag{6.423}$$

The approximation to order κ^2 in Einstein's equations is carried out by writing

$$e^\mu = 1 + \kappa\psi + \kappa^2\Psi,$$
$$e^\nu = 1 + \kappa\left(\frac{2}{c^2}\omega - \psi\right) + \kappa^2 Z, \tag{6.424}$$

where ψ, Ψ, ω, Z are functions of r, t. To this order, it follows that

$$\mu = \kappa\psi + \kappa^2\xi, \qquad \nu = \kappa\left(\frac{2}{c^2}\omega - \psi\right) + \kappa^2\zeta,$$

where

$$\xi = \Psi - \tfrac{1}{2}\psi^2, \qquad \zeta = Z - \tfrac{1}{2}\left(\frac{2}{c^2}\omega - \psi\right)^2. \tag{6.425}$$

Since

$$\nabla^2 = \frac{\partial^2}{\partial r^2} + \frac{2}{r}\frac{\partial}{\partial r},$$

the equations (4.419) to (4.422) become

$$\kappa\left\{\left(\rho + \frac{p}{c^2}\right)(u^4)^2 - e^{-\nu}\frac{p}{c^2}\right\}e^\nu$$
$$= -\kappa\nabla^2\psi - \kappa^2\left(-\psi\nabla^2\psi + \nabla^2\xi + \tfrac{1}{4}\psi_r^2 - \frac{3}{4}\frac{1}{c^2}\psi_t^2\right) - \frac{\Lambda}{c^2}, \tag{6.426}$$

$$\kappa\left\{\left(\rho + \frac{p}{c^2}\right)(u^1)^2 + e^{-\mu}p\right\}e^{\mu} = \kappa\left(\frac{2}{r}\omega_r - \psi_{tt}\right)$$

$$+ \kappa^2\left\{-\frac{2}{r}\psi\omega_r + \frac{c^2}{r}(\xi + \zeta)_r + \frac{c^2}{4}\psi_r^2 + \frac{c^2}{2}\psi_r\left(\frac{2}{c^2}\omega - \psi\right)_r\right.$$

$$\left. + \left(\frac{2\omega}{c^2} - \psi\right)\psi_{tt} - \xi_{tt} - \tfrac{3}{4}\psi_t^2 + \tfrac{1}{2}\psi_t\left(\frac{2}{c^2}\omega - \psi\right)_t\right\} + \varLambda, \qquad (6.427)$$

$$\kappa p = \kappa\left(\omega_{rr} + \frac{1}{r}\omega_r - \psi_{tt}\right) + \kappa^2\left\{-\psi\left(\omega_{rr} + \frac{1}{r}\omega_r\right)\right.$$

$$+ \frac{c^2}{2}(\xi + \zeta)_{rr} + \frac{c^2}{2r}(\xi + \zeta)_r + \frac{c^2}{4}\left(\frac{2}{c^2}\omega_r - \psi_r\right)^2 + \left(\frac{2\omega}{c^2} - \psi\right)\psi_{tt}$$

$$\left. - \xi_{tt} - \tfrac{3}{4}\psi_r^2 + \tfrac{1}{2}\psi_t\left(\frac{2}{c^2}\omega - \psi\right)_t\right\} + \varLambda, \qquad (6.428)$$

$$\kappa\left(\rho + \frac{p}{c^2}\right)u^4 u^1 = \kappa\psi_{rt} + \kappa^2\left\{\xi_{rt} - \tfrac{1}{2}\psi_t\left(\frac{2}{c^2}\omega - \psi\right)_r - \frac{2\omega}{c^2}\psi_{rt}\right\}, \qquad (6.429)$$

where, of course e^{ν} and e^{μ} stand for the right-hand sides of (6.424). We now pass to the Newtonian approximation in which c is replaced by the infinite velocity $\mathscr{C}$. The time t then becomes the Newtonian absolute time T, the coordinate r becomes the radial distance from the origin in absolute Euclidean space and q becomes the Newtonian fluid velocity.

The approximation is possible provided that none of the functions ω, ψ, Z and $\varPsi$ is so large as to prevent the vanishing of every term on the right-hand sides of equations (6.424) apart from the first. In particular, this means that ω cannot be of order c^4, or higher; it may, however, be of order c^2, a possibility that will be considered in Sec. 6.5. On the assumption that q, as well as ω, ψ, Z and $\varPsi$ is not of order c^2, a small cosmical constant satisfying (6.201) must also be postulated in order that the Newtonian pressure should remain finite. The Newtonian forms of (6.426) to (6.429) therefore become

$$\rho = - \nabla^2\psi, \qquad (6.430)$$

$$\rho q^2 + p = \frac{2}{r}\omega_r - \psi_{TT} + 4\pi G\left\{\frac{2}{r}(\xi + \zeta)_r - \tfrac{1}{2}\psi_r^2\right\} + \lambda, \qquad (6.431)$$

$$p = \omega_{rr} + \frac{1}{r}\omega_r - \psi_{TT} + 4\pi G\left\{(\xi + \zeta)_{rr} + \frac{1}{r}(\xi + \zeta)_r + \tfrac{1}{2}\psi_r^2\right\} + \lambda, \qquad (6.432)$$

$$\rho q = \psi_{rT}, \qquad (6.433)$$

where p is now the Newtonian pressure. But these equations are not consistent for an arbitrary choice of the functions $\omega, (\xi + \zeta)$ and ψ because by elimination of ρ, q and p, we obtain the consistency relation

$$\omega_{rr} - \frac{1}{r}\omega_r + 4\pi G\left\{(\xi + \zeta)_{rr} - \frac{1}{r}(\xi + \zeta)_r + \psi_r^2\right\} = (\psi_{rT})^2/\nabla^2\psi, \qquad (6.434)$$

so that two of the three functions $\omega, (\xi + \zeta)$ and ψ are related to the third.

I

Thus the four equations (6.430) to (6.433) are equivalent to (6.434) together with

$$\rho = - \nabla^2\psi, \tag{6.435}$$

$$p = -\psi_{TT} + \omega_{rr} + \frac{\omega_r}{r} + 4\pi G\left\{(\xi + \zeta)_{rr} + \frac{1}{r}(\xi + \zeta)_r + \tfrac{1}{2}\psi_r^2\right\} + \lambda, \tag{6.436}$$

$$q = -\psi_{rT}/\nabla^2\psi. \tag{6.437}$$

The functions ω and $(\xi + \zeta)$ may be eliminated from (6.436) by using (6.434). Let

$$\left.\begin{array}{l} I(r, T) = \psi_{rT}^2/\nabla^2\psi, \\ \Omega = \xi + \zeta, \end{array}\right\} \tag{6.438}$$

so that (6.434) is

$$\omega_{rr} - \frac{1}{r}\omega_r = I - 4\pi G\left(\Omega_{rr} - \frac{1}{r}\Omega_r + \psi_r^2\right),$$

whence

$$\frac{1}{r}\omega_r = \int\left\{\frac{I}{r} - \frac{4\pi G}{r}\left(\Omega_{rr} - \frac{1}{r}\Omega_r + \psi_r^2\right)\right\}dr - \tfrac{1}{2}\lambda,$$

where the integration is performed as if T were a constant, and $-\tfrac{1}{2}\lambda$ is the constant of integration. But then

$$\omega_{rr} + \frac{1}{r}\omega_r = \frac{1}{r}\frac{\partial\omega_r r}{\partial r} = 2\int\left(\frac{I}{r} - \frac{4\pi G}{r}\psi_r^2\right)dr$$

$$+ I - 4\pi G\psi_r^2 - 4\pi G\left(\Omega_{rr} + \frac{1}{r}\Omega_r\right) - \lambda.$$

Thus finally equations (6.435) to (6.437) are

$$\rho = - \nabla^2\psi, \tag{6.439}$$

$$p = -\psi_{TT} + 2\int\left(\frac{I}{r} - \frac{4\pi G}{r}\psi_r^2\right)dr + I - 2\pi G\psi_r^2, \tag{6.440}$$

$$q = -\psi_{rT}/\nabla^2\psi. \tag{6.441}$$

These then are the results of reducing Einstein's equations to the Newtonian approximation for the case of spherical symmetry. Since ψ is in general a function of both r and T, density- and pressure-gradients are included in these formulae and the motion may be unsteady as well (q may be an explicit function of T).

The function ψ may be again interpreted through (3.202) and (3.201); the former is the equation of continuity which, for the case of spherical symmetry, is

$$\frac{\partial\rho}{\partial T} + \frac{1}{r^2}\frac{\partial}{\partial r}(r^2\rho q) = 0, \tag{6.442}$$

and, by (6.435) and (6.437), is identically satisfied for all functions ψ. The radial equation of motion is

$$\frac{\partial q}{\partial T} + q\frac{\partial q}{\partial r} = -\frac{1}{\rho}\frac{\partial p}{\partial r} + F,$$

where F is the radial force per unit mass of fluid, apart from the pressure-gradient force. With the help of the equation of continuity, the equation of motion may be written

$$\frac{\partial \rho q}{\partial T} + \frac{\partial}{\partial r}(\rho q^2 + p) + \frac{2}{r}\rho q^2 = \rho F. \qquad (6.443)$$

On substitution from (6.435) to (6.437), it follows that, for all functions ψ and $(\xi + \zeta)$, and for any finite value of λ,

$$F = 4\pi G \frac{\partial \psi}{\partial r}, \qquad (6.444)$$

which shows that this force is the gravitational self-attraction of the fluid.

If a higher order approximation, involving terms of order κ^3, say, were attempted in the exact equations (4.419) to (4.422), the formulae (6.439) to (6.441) would again be obtained. This is because the terms in G in (6.440) arise from those in equations (4.420) and (4.421) that are multiplied by c^2. Thus higher approximations would introduce terms multiplied by the factor $c^2\kappa^n$ where n is greater than unity. But this factor is zero when c is replaced by $\mathscr{C}$. Hence the additional terms would vanish in the Newtonian approximation.

6.5. The Cosmical Constant as a Force Parameter[2]

It was pointed out in Sec. 6.2 that there was an alternative method of performing the reduction to Newtonian theory and this will now be applied to the case of spherical symmetry. The cosmical constant will be written as the sum of two parts, viz.:

$$\Lambda = \kappa c^2 \Lambda_0 + \Lambda_1,$$

where $\kappa c^2 \Lambda_0$ is the 'large' part and Λ_1 is the 'small' cosmical constant previously postulated. The preceding sections have dealt with the case when $\Lambda_0 = 0$ and Λ_1 has then been shown to have a trivial effect in Newtonian theory. For the present purpose, Λ_1 may therefore be omitted. The surviving large cosmical constant can be counterbalanced by assuming that the function ω in (6.424) is of order c^2; if

$$\omega = \bar{\omega}c^2, \qquad \Lambda = \kappa c^2 \Lambda_0, \qquad (6.501)$$

it is evident that the terms $2\kappa\omega_r/r + \Lambda$ in (6.427) and $\kappa(\omega_{rr} + \omega_r/r) + \Lambda$ in (6.428) are of order c^2 times that of any other term in these equations. Hence these large terms must vanish identically if a Newtonian approximation is to be possible. In terms of $\bar{\omega}$ and of Λ_0 it follows that

$$\frac{2}{r}\bar{\omega}_r + \Lambda_0 = 0, \qquad \bar{\omega}_{rr} + \frac{1}{r}\bar{\omega}_r + \Lambda_0 = 0, \qquad (6.502)$$

both of which are satisfied by

$$\bar{\omega} = -\tfrac{1}{4}\Lambda_0 r^2, \qquad (6.503)$$

an equation that determines this function irrespective of what the density, pressure and velocity 4-vector of the distribution of matter may be. Using (6.501) and (6.502) in (6.426) to (6.429) and then equating to zero all terms in which a factor $1/c^2$ survives, we find the Newtonian approximation

$$\left.\begin{aligned}
\rho &= -\nabla^2 \psi - \Lambda_0, \\
\rho q^2 + p &= -\psi_{TT} + 8\pi G\left(\Lambda_0 \psi + \frac{\Omega_r}{r} - \tfrac{1}{4}\psi_r^2 - \tfrac{1}{2} r \Lambda_0 \psi_r\right), \\
p &= -\psi_{TT} + 8\pi G\left\{\Lambda_0 \psi + \tfrac{1}{2}\Omega_{rr} + \frac{1}{2r}\Omega_r + \tfrac{1}{4}(r\Lambda_0 + \psi_r)^2\right\}, \\
\rho q &= \psi_{rT},
\end{aligned}\right\} \tag{6.504}$$

where $\Omega = \xi + \zeta$. If

$$I_0 = \frac{\psi_{rT}^2}{\nabla^2 \psi + \Lambda_0},$$

elimination of p, ρ, q from the equations (6.504) gives the consistency relation

$$\Omega_{rr} - \frac{1}{r}\Omega_r = \frac{I_0}{4\pi G} - \psi_r^2 - 2\Lambda_0 r \psi_r - \tfrac{1}{2}\Lambda_0^2 r^2. \tag{6.505}$$

Evaluating the combination $\Omega_{rr} + \Omega_r/r$ in the same way as was done for $\omega_{rr} + \omega_r/r$ in Sec. 6.4 (ii), and substituting the result in the formula for p given in (6.504), we find that the four equations (6.504) are equivalent to (6.505) together with

$$\rho = -\nabla^2 \psi - \Lambda_0, \tag{6.506}$$

$$p = -\psi_{TT} + 2\int\left(\frac{I_0}{r} - \frac{4\pi G}{r}\psi_r^2\right)dr + I_0 - 2\pi G\psi_r^2$$
$$\qquad\qquad\qquad - 4\pi G\Lambda_0(2\psi + r\psi_r + \tfrac{1}{4}\Lambda_0 r^2), \tag{6.507}$$

$$q = -\psi_{rT}(\nabla^2 \psi + \Lambda_0)^{-1}. \tag{6.508}$$

The equation of continuity (6.442) is identically satisfied by the expressions (6.504) and the equation of motion (6.443) yields after some calculation

$$F = 4\pi G\left(\frac{\partial \psi}{\partial r} + \Lambda_0 r\right). \tag{6.509}$$

If a new potential function ψ_0 is introduced in place of ψ by writing $\psi = \psi + \tfrac{1}{6}\Lambda_0 r^2$, equation (6.506) takes the form $\rho = -\nabla^2 \psi_0$. Hence ψ_0 may be called the gravitational potential attributable to the matter of density ρ, on the ground that ρ and ψ_0 are connected by Poisson's equation. But now two masses within r may be defined, one corresponding to ρ, the other to an equivalent density of constant magnitude $-2\Lambda_0$, viz.:

$$M = 4\pi\int_0^r \rho r^2\, dr = -4\pi\frac{\partial \psi_0}{\partial r}r^2,$$

$$M_0 = 4\pi\int_0^r (-2\Lambda_0)r^2\, dr = -\frac{8\pi}{3}\Lambda_0 r^3.$$

Then equation (6.509) becomes

$$F = -\frac{GM}{r^2} + \frac{8\pi G}{3}\Lambda_0 r = -\frac{GM}{r^2} - \frac{GM_0}{r^2}.$$

The first of these expressions for F shows that a large cosmical constant manifests itself as a radial force proportional to distance, over and above the gravitational force due to the matter of density ρ. This radial force is a repulsion or an attraction according as Λ_0 is positive or is negative. But the second expression for F reveals that this additional force is also interpretable as the gravitational attraction due to matter having the constant equivalent density $-2\Lambda_0$. Thus the presence of a large cosmical constant in Einstein's equations produces, in the Newtonian approximation, a gravitational effect identical with that which would be produced by a universal underlying material substratum of constant (positive or negative) density. Clearly, however, this equivalent substratum cannot have a density remotely comparable in magnitude with the densities ordinarily considered in applications of Newtonian potential theory. For if this were so, this theory could not have had the success it has in fact had in the interpretation of phenomena. Now in general relativity, the only problems where a large non-zero value of the cosmical constant may be needed are cosmological (see Sec. 8.4). Thus the numerical magnitude of Λ_0 can at most be of the order of the smoothed-out density for the system of galaxies taken as a whole, i.e. some 10^{-30} to 10^{-31} gr.cm^{-3}. A large cosmical constant of this amount would obviously not reveal its presence in any ordinary physical situation.

The terms involving Λ_0 in the foregoing equations arise through those of order κ^2 in equations (6.426) to (6.429), and are therefore of the second order. Hence they would not be present if the coefficients of the metric were expanded to the first order in κ only, as was done in Sec. 6.1. Thus a large cosmical constant is similar in character to a gravitational force in Newtonian theory and does not manifest itself primarily as a pressure-gradient force.

6.6. Conclusions

The investigations of this chapter have therefore revealed the following properties of orthogonal solutions of Einstein's equations in their exact forms, at least of those solutions where the coefficients of the metric can be expanded as power-series in κ:

(1) If the cosmical constant is of order $1/c^2$, its effect is trivial; if it is of order κc^2, its influence is equivalent to the gravitational attraction of a universal underlying substratum having constant (positive or negative) density;

(2) To the first approximation in κ, whether the cosmical constant is large or small, the Newtonian approximations to the solutions of Einstein's equations give the hydrodynamical motions of a fluid, the only force being the pressure-gradient. In reaching this conclusion, it has been assumed that the fluid is perfect; and since the density is, in general, variable the fluid is identifiable with a gas;

(3) The inclusion of terms of the second order in κ introduces, in the Newtonian approximation, the self-gravitation of the fluid and, if the cosmical

constant is of order κc^2, of a universal force which produces an effect identical with that of the gravitational self-attraction of a uniform material substratum.

The difficulties which have been met in finding exact solutions of Einstein's equations are also elucidated. For what is being sought is a description of the motion of a fluid under the action of its internal stresses and of gravitational forces, based on equations far more complicated than those of classical mechanics. As a first approximation to this description is included, by way of a by-product, the solution of the equations of Newtonian gas-dynamics, one of the most formidable problems of mathematical physics. It is not therefore surprising that progress has been slow.

These conclusions also warn us that every exact solution of Einstein's equations need not correspond to a physically acceptable situation, by which is meant one in which $\rho \geqslant 0$, $p \geqslant 0$ and both the velocity and pressure are single-valued functions of position and time, except where discontinuities occur. As an illustration of a situation where these conditions are not satisfied, consider a solution that, in the Newtonian approximation, reduces to (6.421) with

$$\psi = \rho_0 \cos (X - UT) - \tfrac{1}{2} p_0 T^2,$$

where ρ_0, U, p_0 are constants. Then

$$\rho = \rho_0 \cos (X - UT), \qquad p = p_0 - 2\pi G \rho_0^2 \sin^2 (X - UT),$$

the density is thus alternatively positive and negative and vanishes when $(X - UT)$ is an odd multiple of $\pi/2$. Such a situation is obviously physically inadmissible in classical physics and there is no guarantee that the corresponding exact solution of Einstein's equations will remedy the defect. We must therefore expect that every exact solution will have to be carefully analysed before it is accepted as having a physical content.

In the next chapter, specific cases in Newtonian gas-dynamics will be discussed on the basis of the equations found in Secs. 6.2 and 6.4; but since the replacement of c by $\mathscr{C}$ will thus have already been made, these particular problems will throw no light on still another type of approximate investigation of Einstein's equations that can be carried out. We refer to solutions of the equations (6.103) wherein, though gravity is neglected, the absolute velocity is not infinite. Such problems as those of gravitational waves, or of gas-dynamics in special relativity, will be omitted and we content ourselves with pointing out that they do exist and that they well repay investigation[3].

CHAPTER 7

Special Cases in Newtonian Gas-dynamics

The results of the previous chapter point the way to a systematic classification of gas-motions in Newtonian theory. A catalogue of functions ψ may be constructed, each ψ yielding through equations such as (6.210), (6.421) or (6.439) to (6.441), a solution of the equations of motion and of continuity for a moving gas. Amongst these functions ψ will be some giving rise to flows that are adiabatic, isentropic or non-adiabatic, such sub-classes of ψ's being determined through the equation (3.208) which controls the change of entropy of unit mass. Finally, the ψ's could be further sub-classified according as they were, or were not, compatible with pre-assigned boundary conditions of different types. The compilation of such a catalogue would require a volume to itself and all that can be here attempted is to indicate the cataloguing procedure.

7.1. One-dimensional Motion

The simplest way in which a gas can move occurs when its velocity is parallel to a given straight line, and the catalogue may therefore be appropriately opened with motions of this class. Let the X_1-axis be chosen parallel to the line of motion and let distance along this line be denoted by X. Then by definition all the variables occurring in equations (6.209) and (6.210) are functions of X and T alone, a restriction which at once leads to $U_2 = 0$, $U_3 = 0$ with $U_1 = U$ alone surviving. The relation (6.209) may be satisfied by taking

$$\chi = \psi_{XT}^2/\psi_{XX}, \tag{7.101}$$

where subscripts now denote partial derivatives with respect to X and T. With the same notation, equations (6.210) become

$$U = -\psi_{XT}/\psi_{XX}, \tag{7.102}$$

$$\rho = -\psi_{XX}, \tag{7.103}$$

$$p = -\psi_{TT} + \psi_{XT}^2/\psi_{XX}. \tag{7.104}$$

In these formulae the gravitational self-attraction of the gas is neglected; but inspection of (6.421) shows that the inclusion of gravity leaves (7.102) and (7.103) unchanged but replaces (7.104) by

$$p = -\psi_{TT} + \psi_{XT}^2/\psi_{XX} - 2\pi G\psi_X^2. \tag{7.105}$$

123

Hence it is possible to use (7.102), (7.103) and (7.105) in constructing the catalogue and to sub-classify motions where gravity is neglected by simply omitting terms multiplied by G.

(a) *Linear-wave flow*. – This term is used to describe any gas-flow in which the velocity is a linear function of one spatial variable only. In one-dimensional motion the simplest flows of this type are those in which the velocity is given by

$$U = (n + 1)\left(\frac{X}{T} + \frac{nq}{n+1}\right), \tag{7.106}$$

where n is a pure number and q is a constant with the physical dimensions of velocity. Thus the catalogue may conveniently begin with the analysis of such flows. Writing $\mu = \psi_X$ and substituting from (7.106) into (7.102) it follows that μ satisfies the first order partial differential equation

$$\mu_T + (n + 1)\left(\frac{X}{T} + \frac{nq}{n+1}\right)\mu_X = 0,$$

whence

$$\mu = \psi_X = -f\left\{\left(\frac{X}{T} + q\right)T^{-n}\right\},$$

where f is an arbitrary function of its argument $(X/T + q)T^{-n}$. It then follows that

$$\psi = -T^{n+1}F\left\{\left(\frac{X}{T} + q\right)T^{-n}\right\} - \int\left\{\int P(T)dT\right\}dT, \tag{7.107}$$

where P is an arbitrary function of T and

$$F = \int f\left\{\left(\frac{X}{T} + q\right)T^{-n}\right\}T^{-(n+1)}dX, \tag{7.108}$$

T being treated as a constant in this integration. A new variable ζ defined by

$$\zeta = (X/T + q)T^{-n} \tag{7.109}$$

turns equation (7.108) into

$$F = \int f(\zeta)d\zeta.$$

By (7.109) the partial derivatives of ζ are

$$\frac{\partial\zeta}{\partial T} = -(n + 1)XT^{-(n+2)} - nqT^{-(n+1)},$$

$$\frac{\partial^2\zeta}{\partial T^2} = (n + 1)\{(n + 2)XT^{-(n+3)} + nqT^{-(n+2)}\},$$

$$\frac{\partial\zeta}{\partial X} = T^{-(n+1)}, \qquad \frac{\partial^2\zeta}{\partial X\partial T} = -(n + 1)T^{-(n+2)},$$

and those of ψ are, by (7.107),

$$\psi_{TT} = -n(n + 1)T^{n-1}F - \left\{2(n + 1)\frac{\partial\zeta}{\partial T} + T\frac{\partial^2\zeta}{\partial T^2}\right\}T^nF_\zeta - T^{n+1}\left(\frac{\partial\zeta}{\partial T}\right)^2F_{\zeta\zeta},$$

$$\psi_{TX} = -\frac{\partial\zeta}{\partial T}F_{\zeta\zeta},$$

$$\psi_{XX} = -T^{-(n+1)}F_{\zeta\zeta}.$$

These results convert equations (7.102), (7.103) and (7.105) into

$$U = (n + 1)\left\{\zeta T^n - \frac{q}{n + 1}\right\},$$

$$\rho = T^{-(n+1)}F_{\zeta\zeta},$$

$$p = P - n(n + 1)T^{n-1}\zeta^2(F/\zeta)_\zeta - 2\pi GF_\zeta^2. \qquad (7.110)$$

Obviously a physically acceptable case must have $\rho > 0$, i.e. F must be such that $F_{\zeta\zeta} > 0$ for all values of ζ corresponding to the region of space occupied by the moving gas, and for the relevant times; and the pressure p must also be positive. Hence F, P and n must be chosen so as to fulfil these requirements. Proceeding with the cataloguing, bearing these points in mind, the next step is to evaluate the rate of change of entropy by means of (3.208). The operator d/dT is now $\dfrac{\partial}{\partial T} + U\dfrac{\partial}{\partial X}$ and it is easy to show from (7.106) and (7.109) that

$$\frac{d\zeta}{dT} = 0.$$

This result, and the expressions for p and ρ given by (7.110), turn (3.208) into

$$\frac{dS}{dT} = \frac{n + 1}{pT}\left[\frac{TP_T}{n + 1} + \gamma P\right.$$

$$\left. - n\{n - 1 + \gamma(n + 1)\}T^{n-1}\zeta^2(F/\zeta)_\zeta - 2\pi G\gamma F_\zeta^2\right]. \quad (7.111)$$

The first two terms in the square bracket are functions of T alone, the others involve ζ. This expression for dS/dT shows that linear-wave flows with arbitrary functions $P(T)$ and $F(\zeta)$ are in general non-adiabatic, the rate of change of entropy of unit mass of gas, following its motion, being calculated from (7.111). If the rate of loss of energy in ergs per sec per cm³ is dE/dT then by (3.205) and the definition of S we have

$$\frac{dE}{dT} = \mathscr{J}\rho\frac{dQ}{dT} = -\frac{\mathscr{R}\rho\mathscr{T}}{\gamma - 1}\frac{dS}{dT} = -\frac{p}{\gamma - 1}\frac{dS}{dT}, \qquad (7.112)$$

where dS/dT is given by (7.111). This energy is, of course, lost entirely to the gas, for example, by the emission of radiation.

The sub-class of *adiabatic* flows is of particular interest and corresponds to functions P and F chosen so that

$$\frac{TP_T}{n + 1} + \gamma P = n\{(n - 1) + \gamma(n + 1)\}T^{n-1}\zeta^2(F/\zeta)_\zeta + 2\pi G\gamma F_\zeta^2. \quad (7.113)$$

(i) Consider first the case when the gravitational self-attraction of the gas is neglected and the motion therefore takes place under the action of the pressure-gradient alone. This situation corresponds to neglecting terms in G in the preceding formulae and therefore (7.113) may be satisfied for arbitrary F by

$$(n - 1) + \gamma(n + 1) = 0, \qquad \frac{TP_T}{n + 1} + \gamma P = 0,$$

whence

$$n = -\frac{\gamma - 1}{\gamma + 1}, \qquad P = p_0\left(\frac{T}{T_0}\right)^{-\frac{2\gamma}{\gamma+1}}, \qquad (7.114)$$

where p_0, T_0 are constants of integration. Hence we obtain, through (7.110) and (7.114) with $G \equiv 0$, the following theorem: any one-dimensional gas flow in which the velocity, density and pressure of the gas are given by

$$\left.\begin{aligned}
U &= \frac{2}{\gamma + 1}\left\{\frac{X}{T} - \tfrac{1}{2}(\gamma - 1)q\right\}, \\
\rho &= T^{-\frac{2}{\gamma+1}}F_{\zeta\zeta}, \\
p &= p_0\left(\frac{T}{T_0}\right)^{-\frac{2\gamma}{\gamma+1}} + \frac{2(\gamma - 1)}{(\gamma + 1)^2}T^{-\frac{2\gamma}{\gamma+1}}\zeta^2(F/\zeta)_\zeta,
\end{aligned}\right\} \qquad (7.115)$$

where F is an arbitrary function of $\zeta = (X/T + q)T^{(\gamma-1)/(\gamma+1)}$, is an adiabatic flow. For physical acceptability, of course, F must be selected so that $F_{\zeta\zeta} > 0$ and $p > 0$ throughout the region occupied by the flow.

The sub-class of adiabatic flows which are *isentropic* is characterized by $p = \eta\rho^\gamma$ where η is a constant. Hence using (7.115) we have

$$p_0 T_0^{\frac{2\gamma}{\gamma+1}} + 2\frac{\gamma - 1}{(\gamma + 1)^2}\zeta^2 F_{\zeta\zeta} = \eta F_{\zeta\zeta}^\gamma, \qquad (7.116)$$

which is an equation determining the function F in isentropic flow. The well-known particular case of simple waves is obtained by assuming that

$$F = A\zeta^\lambda$$

where A is a positive constant and λ is a constant to be determined. Substituting into (7.116) and equating powers of ζ, we find that

$$p_0 \equiv 0, \qquad \lambda = \frac{2\gamma}{\gamma - 1},$$

and therefore (7.115) reduces to

$$\left.\begin{aligned}
U &= \frac{2}{\gamma + 1}\frac{X}{T} - \frac{\gamma - 1}{\gamma + 1}q, \\
\rho &= \frac{2\gamma(\gamma + 1)}{(\gamma - 1)^2}A\left(\frac{X}{T} + q\right)^{\frac{2}{\gamma-1}}, \\
p &= \frac{2A}{\gamma + 1}\left(\frac{X}{T} + q\right)^{\frac{2\gamma}{\gamma-1}}.
\end{aligned}\right\} \qquad (7.117)$$

This solution of the equations of Newtonian gas-dynamics has been used in the theory of the expansion into a vacuum of the face (assumed plane and of infinite extent) of an initially uniform interstellar gas-cloud[1]. It can be shown that the constant q is identifiable with $-2a_0(\gamma + 1)$ where a_0 is the velocity of sound in the as yet undisturbed part of the gas.

(ii) When the gravitational self-attraction of the gas is taken into account, the situation with regard to adiabatic flow is fundamentally altered. The equation (7.113) must now be satisfied taking the term in G into account. Since the left-hand side is a function of T alone, the right-hand side must be independent of ζ. There are only two possible ways of securing this: in the first way, we have $F_\zeta = constant$, which means that $\rho = 0$ and therefore the solution is physically trivial; in the second, $n = 1$ and

$$\tfrac{1}{2}TP_T + \gamma P = constant.$$

But this reduces (7.113) to

$$\zeta^2(F/\zeta)_\zeta + \pi GF_\zeta^2 = constant,$$

and differentiation of this equation with respect to ζ leads to one or other of the alternatives

$$F_{\zeta\zeta} = 0 \qquad \text{or} \qquad F_\zeta = -\frac{\zeta}{2\pi G}\;.$$

In the first case $\rho = 0$; in the second $\rho = -(2\pi GT^2)^{-1}$, both of which are physically trivial. The conclusion is therefore that there are no non-trivial adiabatic linear-wave flows when the gravitational self-attraction and the pressure-gradient force together control the motion of the gas.

But since any adiabatic or isentropic flow of the kind considered in (i) above satisfies

$$\frac{TP_T}{n+1} + \gamma P = n\{(n-1) + \gamma(n+1)\}T^{n-1}\zeta^2(F/\zeta)_\zeta,$$

it follows from (7.113) and (7.111) that such a flow is possible in the gravitational case provided that there is a change of entropy, following the motion of unit mass, given by

$$\frac{dS}{dT} = -\frac{\gamma(n+1)}{pT}2\pi GF_\zeta^2.$$

Hence by (7.112) the loss of energy per sec per cm³ is

$$\frac{dE}{dT} = \frac{\gamma(n+1)}{\gamma-1}\frac{2\pi G}{T}F_\zeta^2,$$

and, in particular, for the simple wave isentropic flow (7.117), in which $F = A\zeta^{2\gamma/(\gamma-1)}$ and $n = -(\gamma-1)/(\gamma+1)$,

$$\frac{dE}{dT} = \frac{16\pi GA^2}{\gamma+1}\left(\frac{\gamma}{\gamma-1}\right)^3\left(\frac{X}{T}+q\right)^{2\frac{\gamma+1}{\gamma-1}}T.$$

Thus it would appear that a linear-wave gas-flow is a constrained motion when gravitation is taken into account, the gas having to lose energy in a particular way in order that the motion should be maintained.

The detailed classification of the various possible functions P and F will not be pursued further here. To do so would bring in considerations of boundary conditions and this would lead too far afield into the theory of shock waves and of other types of boundaries that can limit a gas-flow. We proceed instead to a short sketch of another chapter of the catalogue of one-dimensional flows in which, by way of illustration, a certain simple kind of boundary condition will be used.

(b) *Gas-velocity independent of position.* – This kind of motion, which includes the isentropic flow sometimes called that of sound waves of finite amplitude, is defined by

$$\psi = - \int f(\zeta)\, d\zeta - \int\{\int P(T)dT\}dT, \qquad (7.118)$$

where f and P are arbitrary functions of their arguments, and

$$\zeta = X - \int v(T)\, dT, \qquad (7.119)$$

the function v also being arbitrary. By (7.102), (7.103) and (7.104) there comes

$$U = v(T), \qquad \rho = f_\zeta, \qquad p = P - v_T f - 2\pi G f^2, \qquad (7.120)$$

which shows that U is a function of the time alone, all portions of the gas moving with the same speed at any given time. Since $d\zeta/dT = 0$, the formula for the rate of change of entropy, (3.208), becomes

$$\frac{dS}{dT} = \frac{P_T - f v_{TT}}{P - f v_T - 2\pi G f^2}. \qquad (7.121)$$

The definition of adiabatic flows is again

$$P_T = 0, \qquad v_{TT} = 0,$$

and therefore

$$P = \Pi, \qquad v = \alpha t + \beta, \qquad (7.122)$$

where Π, α, β are constants. Hence in the sub-class of adiabatic flows, the velocity, density and pressure are, respectively,

$$U = \alpha t + \beta, \qquad \rho = f_\zeta, \qquad p = \Pi - \alpha f - 2\pi G f^2. \qquad (7.123)$$

A simple physical situation, from the point of view of boundary conditions, is obtained when the gas is envisaged as a slab of infinite extent perpendicular to the X-axis, of permanent width L, the region outside the slab being occupied by a vacuum. At any time T, the gas occupies a range of values of X which, by (7.119) and (7.122) is

$$0 \leqslant X - (\tfrac{1}{2}\alpha T^2 + \beta T) \leqslant L.$$

Thus the boundaries of the slab are defined by $\zeta = 0$ and $\zeta = L$, and ρ, p must be zero at each boundary. The vanishing of ρ means that $f_\zeta(0) = 0$, $f_\zeta(L) = 0$, the density, of course, being positive in $0 \leqslant \zeta \leqslant L$. Hence there must be a maximum of ρ, say ρ_m, at $\zeta = l$, where $0 < l < L$. Again the vanishing of the pressure at the boundaries gives

$$\left.\begin{array}{l} 0 = \Pi - \alpha f(0) - 2\pi G f^2(0), \\ 0 = \Pi - \alpha f(L) - 2\pi G f^2(L), \end{array}\right\} \qquad (7.124)$$

and, since $p > 0$ within the slab, f must be so chosen that

$$0 < \Pi - \alpha f(\zeta) - 2\pi G f^2(\zeta), \qquad (0 < \zeta < L).$$

The reader may verify that the functions

$$f = - \rho_m \frac{L}{\pi} \cos \frac{\pi \zeta}{L} \quad \text{or} \quad f = \frac{4\rho_m}{L^2}(\tfrac{1}{2}L\zeta^2 - \tfrac{1}{3}\zeta^3) + \mu,$$

where μ is a constant, satisfy the foregoing conditions. For any appropriate function f, certain general conclusions may be drawn. If it happens that $f(0) = - f(L) \neq 0$, then by (7.124), $\alpha = 0$ and $\Pi = 2\pi G f^2(L)$. Thus by (7.123) the velocity of the gas is a constant in all such motions. Alternatively, if $f(0) \neq \pm f(L)$, and one at least is not equal to zero, then

$$\alpha = - 2\pi G\{f(0) + f(L)\},$$
$$\Pi = - 2\pi G\{f(0)f(L)\},$$

the motion of the gas now being subject to a constant acceleration α. In either case, the width of the slab, L, is determinable in terms of the density and the pressure or the temperature at $\zeta = l$. For example, if $\alpha = 0$,

$$p_m = 2\pi G\{f^2(L) - f^2(l)\} \tag{7.125}$$

But since $\rho_m = f_\zeta(l)$ and f is a known function of ζ it is possible to express f as a function of f_ζ and therefore

$$f(l) = g(\rho_m), \text{ say.}$$

Also $p_m = \mathcal{R}\rho_m \mathcal{T}_m$, and therefore (7.125) is

$$f(L) = \left\{ \frac{\mathcal{R}\rho_m \mathcal{T}_m + 2\pi G g^2(\rho_m)}{2\pi G} \right\}^{\frac{1}{2}},$$

which determines L in terms of ρ_m, $\mathcal{T}_m$. A similar treatment applies when $\alpha \neq 0$. The calculation of L is, however, a consequence of the presence of the terms in G in equations (7.123); in other words, if the slab is to have a finite width, its gravitational self-attraction must be there in order to hold the gas together.

Though the idealization of an interstellar gas-cloud as a slab of gas of this type may seem extreme, it is of interest to note that the theory gives widths that range from 45 to 1/3 parsecs², according to the densities and temperatures postulated at $\zeta = l$, the densest portion of the cloud. Such widths are in rough agreement with observation.

7.2. Spherical Symmetry and Linear-waves

The mathematical complexity of spherically symmetric gas-flows, as compared with one-dimensional motions, arises because, in the equations (6.439) to (6.441), there is still an integration with respect to r to be performed. The compilation of the catalogue of those spherically symmetric motions that are expressible in finite form is thus more difficult. Attention will therefore be restricted to the case of linear-waves, not only because the analysis is then the simplest possible under the circumstances of spherical symmetry, but because certain of the results obtained are of some interest in cosmology.

By a linear-wave flow will now be meant one in which the radial velocity has the form

$$q = \frac{f_T}{f}r, \qquad (7.201)$$

where f is an arbitrary function of T. This rule for the velocity has the following interesting property: Let O be the origin from which r is measured and let P be a typical element of the moving fluid. Then, in vector notation, $\overrightarrow{OP} = \mathbf{r}$ and the velocity of P relative to O is

$$\dot{\mathbf{r}} = \mathbf{q} = \frac{f_T}{f}\mathbf{r}.$$

The gas-element at O itself has, of course, zero velocity relative to O. Now suppose that O' is a second origin located at an element of the gas and moving with this element. If $\overrightarrow{O'P} = \mathbf{r}'$ and $\overrightarrow{OO'} = \mathbf{a}$ then the velocity of P relative to O' is

$$\dot{\mathbf{r}}' = \dot{\mathbf{r}} - \dot{\mathbf{a}} = \frac{f_T}{f}(\mathbf{r} - \mathbf{a}) = \frac{f_T}{f}\mathbf{r}',$$

the velocity of the fluid element at O' being again zero relative to O'. Hence the form of the velocity law (7.201) is independent of the choice of origin, provided that this point be chosen to move with an element of the fluid. An observer accompanying any fluid element 'sees' the fluid moving in a spherically symmetric fashion about him, every fluid element receding from (or approaching) him with a speed proportional to its distance.

If $\mu = \psi_r$ in (6.441), the differential equation for μ is

$$r\mu_r + \frac{f\mu_T}{f_T} + 2\mu = 0,$$

and therefore

$$\mu = -\frac{1}{f^2}h(rf^{-1}),$$

where h is an arbitrary function of rf^{-1}. Thus a partial integration with respect to r yields the required expression for ψ, viz.:

$$\psi = -\frac{1}{f^2}\int h(rf^{-1})dr - \int\{\int P(T)dT\}dT, \qquad (7.202)$$

or, in terms of the variable

$$\zeta = rf^{-1}, \qquad (7.203)$$

$$\psi = -\frac{1}{f}\int h(\zeta)d\zeta - \int\{\int P(T)dT\}dT. \qquad (7.204)$$

The derivatives and integrals which are needed to evaluate p and ρ through formulae (6.440) and (6.439) respectively, are the following:

$$\zeta_r = 1/f, \qquad \zeta_T = -\frac{f_T}{f^2}r = -\frac{f_T}{f}\zeta,$$

$$\psi_r = -\frac{h}{f^2}, \qquad \psi_{rr} = -\frac{h_\zeta}{f^3}, \qquad \nabla^2\psi = -\frac{1}{\zeta^2}\frac{1}{f^3}(\zeta^2 h)_\zeta$$

$$\psi_{rT} = \frac{f_T}{f^3}\frac{1}{\zeta}(\zeta^2 h)_\zeta,$$

$$\psi_T = -\int P(T)dT + \frac{f_T}{f^2}(\int hd\zeta + h\zeta),$$

$$\psi_{TT} = -P + \left(\frac{f_{TT}}{f^2} - \frac{2f_T^2}{f^3}\right)(\int hd\zeta + h\zeta) - \frac{f_T^2}{f^3}(\zeta^2 h)_\zeta,$$

$$I = \frac{\psi_{rT}^2}{\nabla^2\psi} = -\frac{f_T^2}{f^3}(\zeta^2 h)_\zeta,$$

$$\int\frac{I}{r}dr = -\frac{f_T^2}{f^3}(\int hd\zeta + h\zeta),$$

$$\int\frac{\psi_r^2}{r}dr = \frac{1}{f^4}\int\frac{h^2}{\zeta}d\zeta.$$

$$\left.\begin{array}{c}\\\\\\\\\\\\\\\\\\\\\\\\\\\\end{array}\right\} \quad (7.205)$$

Hence

$$p = P(T) - \frac{f_{TT}}{f^2}(\int hd\zeta + h\zeta) - \frac{8\pi G}{f^4}\left(\int\frac{h^2}{\zeta}d\zeta + \tfrac{1}{4}h^2\right), \qquad (7.206)$$

$$\rho = \frac{1}{f^3}\left(h_\zeta + \frac{2h}{\zeta}\right). \qquad (7.207)$$

The computation of the rate of change of the entropy function S is simplified by introducing the symbols

$$\left.\begin{array}{l}H(\zeta) = \int hd\zeta + h\zeta,\\[2mm] J(\zeta) = \displaystyle\int\frac{h^2}{\zeta}d\zeta + \tfrac{1}{4}h^2.\end{array}\right\} \qquad (7.208)$$

Noticing also that (7.201) and (7.203) imply

$$\frac{d\zeta}{dT} = 0,$$

we obtain after some calculation from (3.208) with $d/dT = \partial/\partial T + q(\partial/\partial r)$

$$\frac{dS}{dT} = \frac{1}{p}\left[\left\{P_T + 3\gamma\frac{f_T}{f}P\right\} - \left\{\left(\frac{f_{TT}}{f^2}\right)_T + 3\gamma\frac{f_T}{f}\frac{f_{TT}}{f^2}\right\}H\right.$$
$$\left. + 8\pi G(4 - 3\gamma)\frac{f_T}{f^5}J\right]. \qquad (7.209)$$

Hence the sub-class of adiabatic linear-wave flows is characterized by functions $P(T), f(T)$ and $h(\zeta)$ which satisfy

$$P_T + 3\gamma\frac{f_T}{f}P = \left\{\left(\frac{f_{TT}}{f^2}\right)_T + 3\gamma\frac{f_T}{f}\frac{f_{TT}}{f^2}\right\}H(\zeta) - 8\pi G(4 - 3\gamma)\frac{f_T}{f^5}J(\zeta), \qquad (7.210)$$

an equation whose left-hand side is a function of T alone, so that its right-hand side cannot involve ζ. Considerations of space again preclude an exhaustive listing of all possible adiabatic motions[3]; but two specific illustrations will be given in the next and following sections.

7.3. Linear-wave Expansion of a Finite Sphere of Gas

The method applied in one-dimensional motion suggests that it is advisable to begin by neglecting the gravitational self-attraction of the gaseous mass. This means that the pressure-gradient is the effective force controlling the motion, gravitation being regarded as negligible in comparison. Equations (7.206), (7.207) and (7.210) become

$$p = P(T) - \frac{f_{TT}}{f^2}H(\zeta), \tag{7.301}$$

$$\rho = \frac{1}{f^3}\left(h_\zeta + \frac{2h}{\zeta}\right), \tag{7.302}$$

$$P_T + 3\gamma\frac{f_T}{f}P = \left\{\left(\frac{f_{TT}}{f^2}\right)_T + 3\gamma\frac{f_T}{f}\left(\frac{f_{TT}}{f^2}\right)\right\}H(\zeta). \tag{7.303}$$

The boundary conditions which will be employed are: (a) the pressure and density must be finite and positive everywhere within the sphere of gas, in particular, at the centre $r = 0$; (b) outside the sphere, there is effectively a vacuum, so that, on the boundary, $p = 0$, $\rho = 0$. If the radius of the sphere at time T is $r_b(T)$, then

$$\frac{dr_b}{dT} = (q)_{r=r_b} = \frac{f_T}{f}r_b.$$

Hence

$$r_b(T) = f(T)$$

and the function f is therefore identifiable with the outer radius of the gas sphere. It is then obvious from (7.203) that $\zeta = 0$ at the centre, and $\zeta = 1$ at the outer boundary of the mass.

Let the subscript zero denote the values of f and its derivatives at some pre-selected instant T_0 and let ρ_{0c}, p_{0c} be the density and pressure (assumed finite) at the centre of the gas-sphere at this same instant. The assumption that P is proportional to f_{TT}/f^2 will also make the functions of T in (7.303) proportional to one another, and this equation is then satisfied for an arbitrary function $h(\zeta)$ if

$$P = \rho_{0c}f_0^3\frac{f_{TT}}{f^2}, \tag{7.304}$$

$$P_T + 3\gamma\frac{f_T}{f}P = 0. \tag{7.305}$$

The solution of (7.305) is

$$P = \rho_{0c}\left(\frac{f_0}{f}\right)^{3\gamma}, \tag{7.306}$$

and this can then be used in (7.304) to give a differential equation for f, viz.:

$$\frac{d^2f}{dT^2} = \frac{p_{0c}}{\rho_{0c}} f_0^{3(\gamma-1)} f^{2-3\gamma}.$$

If f_T has the value v_0 at $T = T_0$, the integral of this equation is

$$\left(\frac{df}{dT}\right)^2 - v_0^2 = \alpha^2 v_0^2 (f_0^{3(1-\gamma)} - f^{3(1-\gamma)}), \qquad (7.307)$$

where, using also the equation of state (3.204),

$$\alpha^2 = \frac{2p_{0c}}{3(\gamma - 1)\rho_{0c}v_0^2} f_0^{3(\gamma-1)} = \frac{2\mathscr{R}\mathscr{T}_{0c}}{3(\gamma - 1)v_0^2} f_0^{3(\gamma-1)}.$$

Thus if

$$\beta^2 = \alpha^2(1 + \alpha^2 f_0^{3(1-\gamma)})^{-1}, \qquad x^2 = f^{3(\gamma-1)} - \beta^2,$$

equation (7.307) may be integrated as

$$v_0(T - T_0) = \frac{2\beta}{3(\gamma - 1)\alpha} \int_{x_0}^{x} (x^2 + \beta^2)^{\frac{5-3\gamma}{6(\gamma-1)}} dx, \qquad (7.308)$$

where

$$x_0^2 = f_0^{3(\gamma-1)} - \beta^2$$
$$= \frac{3(\gamma - 1)\rho_{0c}v_0^2 f_0^{3(\gamma-1)}}{2p_{0c} + 3(\gamma - 1)\rho_{0c}v_0^2}.$$

A specific example illustrates the meaning of these formulae. If the gas is monatomic, consisting, say, of hydrogen, then $\gamma = 5/3$ and (7.308) may be integrated to give

$$v_0(T - T_0) = \frac{\beta}{\alpha}(x - x_0).$$

Clearly there is no loss of generality in setting $T_0 = 0$. Thus the formula for f is

$$f^2 = f_0^2 + 2\frac{\alpha}{\beta}x_0 v_0 T + \frac{\alpha^2}{\beta^2}v_0^2 T^2,$$

and therefore by (7.201) the velocity is

$$q = \frac{\alpha}{\beta}v_0 \frac{x_0 + \alpha v_0 T/\beta}{f_0^2 + 2\alpha x_0 v_0 T/\beta + \alpha^2 v_0^2 T^2/\beta^2} r.$$

If q is real, x_0^2 cannot be negative, and this is true because

$$x_0^2 = \frac{p_{0c}v_0^2 f_0^2}{p_{0c} + \rho_{0c}v_0^2} = \frac{v_0^2}{\mathscr{R}\mathscr{T}_{0c} + v_0^2} f_0^2 > 0.$$

Hence q is always real. Clearly also as T becomes large, $f \to \alpha v_0 T/\beta$ and the boundary thus eventually increases linearly with the time whereas the gas-velocity tends to the simple form r/T. If γ does not have the particular value 5/3, the integration of (7.308) is more complex but it can be proved that eventually f will again increase linearly with T.

After f has been found from (7.308), it is still necessary to choose the function $h(\zeta)$ so that the boundary conditions are satisfied. It will be proved that any polynomial with constant coefficients,

$$h = \sum_{j=1}^{n} a_j \zeta^j, \qquad (7.309)$$

where a_1, a_2 and a_3, at least, are non-zero, is an appropriate form for h. For the pressure and the density are, by (7.208), (7.301), (7.302), (7.304) and (7.306),

$$p = p_{0c}\left(\frac{f_0}{f}\right)^{3\gamma}\left(1 - \frac{1}{\rho_{0c}f_0^3}\sum_{j=1}^{n}\frac{j+2}{j+1}a_j\zeta^{j+1}\right),$$

$$\rho = \frac{1}{f^3}\sum_{j=1}^{n}(j+2)a_j\zeta^{j-1}.$$

Now at the centre $\zeta = 0$ and therefore the central pressure and density at any time T are

$$p_c = p_{0c}\left(\frac{f_0}{f}\right)^{3\gamma}, \qquad \rho_c = \frac{3a_1}{f^3} = \rho_{0c}\left(\frac{f_0}{f}\right)^3.$$

Thus $a_1 = \frac{1}{3}\rho_{0c}f_0^3$ and since $\rho_c > 0$, a_1 must be positive. At the outer boundary $\zeta = 1$ and $p = 0$, $\rho = 0$, so that the constants a_j must be chosen to satisfy

$$\rho_{0c}f_0^3 = \sum_{j=1}^{n}\frac{j+2}{j+1}a_j,$$

$$0 = \sum_{j=1}^{n}(j+2)a_j,$$

and this can always be done. The reader will easily verify that the last two conditions are fulfilled by

$$a_1 = \frac{1}{3}\rho_{0c}f_0^3, \qquad a_2 = \frac{9}{4}\rho_{0c}f_0^3, \qquad a_3 = -2\rho_{0c}f_0^3,$$

$$a_j = 0, \qquad (j = 4, 5, \ldots, n),$$

in which case, remembering that $\zeta = rf^{-1}$,

$$\left.\begin{array}{l} p = p_{0c}\left(\dfrac{f_0}{f}\right)^{3\gamma}\left\{1 - \frac{1}{2}\left(\dfrac{r}{f}\right)^2 - 3\left(\dfrac{r}{f}\right)^3 + 5\left(\dfrac{r}{f}\right)^4\right\}, \\[4mm] \rho = \rho_{0c}\left(\dfrac{f_0}{f}\right)^3\left\{1 + 9\left(\dfrac{r}{f}\right) - 10\left(\dfrac{r}{f}\right)^2\right\}. \end{array}\right\} \qquad (7.310)$$

Hence at any given instant T, the maximum of p occurs at the centre, and the minimum of p, at the outer boundary, of the gas sphere. The density increases up to $r = 9f/20$ and then decreases to zero at $r = f$.

As in the case of one-dimensional motion, the inclusion of gravity greatly reduces the possibilities for adiabatic flow. To satisfy equation (7.210) it is now necessary to assume that

$$H(\zeta) = 2AJ(\zeta),$$

where A is an arbitrary constant. This equation leads to either $h = \zeta/A$ or $h = B\zeta^{-2}$, where B is a constant of integration. In the first case, $\rho = 3/(Af^3)$, which means that boundary condition (b) cannot be satisfied; and in the second, $\rho = 0$, which is trivial. In general, therefore, spherically symmetric linear-wave gravitational flows that satisfy the boundary conditions (a) and (b) are non-adiabatic. Another way of expressing this conclusion is to say that if a linear-wave flow were to be started by some means in the gas sphere, the motion would break down unless every unit mass of gas gained or lost energy in a particular way. It should be noticed, however, that, in any gravitational motion in which P, f are given by (7.306), (7.308), respectively, and h is determined so as to satisfy the boundary conditions, the loss of energy per sec per cm^3 reduces to

$$\frac{dE}{dT} = 8\pi G \frac{3\gamma - 4}{\gamma - 1} \frac{f_T}{f^5} J,$$

as may be verified from (7.112) and (7.209). At any instant during the motion, the total rate of loss of energy from the entire sphere is

$$4\pi f^3 \int_0^1 \frac{dE}{dT} \zeta^2 d\zeta = 32\pi^2 G \frac{3\gamma - 4}{\gamma - 1} \frac{f_T}{f^2} \int_0^1 J \zeta^2 d\zeta.$$

If the sphere is expanding, $f_T/f > 0$, and obviously $f > 0$. Moreover, by (7.208), the integral of $J\zeta^2$ over the limits 0 to 1 in ζ is also positive. The conclusion is therefore: if a gas sphere expands gravitationally with a linear-wave motion, there must be emission of energy to maintain the motion, provided that $\gamma > 4/3$ which is certainly true for real gases. But if the gas is, for example, the idealized 'rough spherical molecule' gas[4] in which $\gamma = 4/3$, the motion can be maintained without loss or gain of energy.

A nova or supernova explosion presumably takes place in a more complicated manner than is here being discussed, the motion following some more elaborate law than that of the linear-wave. Nevertheless, it is of interest to note that even the linear-wave expansion occurs with the *emission* of energy – presumably in the form of radiation – and does not require the absorption of energy by the gas sphere.

7.4. Linear-waves in a Uniform Gas

There is a particular case of linear-wave flow which is of interest because it provides, in Newtonian mechanics, the analogue of the cosmology of general relativity. If, in equation (7.207), it is assumed that ρ is independent of r, the function h satisfies

$$h_\zeta + \frac{2h}{\zeta} = \rho_0 f_0^3,$$

where ρ_0, f_0 are constants. Hence

$$h = \tfrac{1}{3}\rho_0 f_0^3 \zeta + \frac{A}{\zeta^2}, \tag{7.401}$$

where A is a constant of integration. Substitution into (7.206) and evaluation of the integrals gives

$$p = P(T) - \tfrac{1}{2}\rho_0 f_0^3 \left(\frac{f_{TT}}{f^2} + \frac{4\pi G}{3} \rho_0 \frac{f_0^3}{f^4} \right) \zeta^2 + 4\pi G \frac{A\rho_0 f_0^3}{f^4 \zeta},$$

and therefore, if it is also assumed that p is independent of r, we must have $A = 0$ and

$$f_{TT} + \frac{4\pi G}{3} \rho_0 \frac{f_0^3}{f^2} = 0. \qquad (7.402)$$

A first integral of this equation is

$$\frac{f_T^2}{f^2} = \frac{8\pi G}{3} \rho_0 f_0^3 \left(\frac{1}{f^3} - \frac{k_n}{f_0 f^2} \right), \qquad (7.403)$$

where k_n/f_0 is the constant integration, k_n being a pure number. A further integration gives

$$\left(\frac{8\pi G}{3} \rho_0 k_n^3 \right)^{\frac{1}{2}} (T - T_0) = \sin^{-1} \left(\frac{k_n f}{f_0} \right)^{\frac{1}{2}} - \left(\frac{k_n f}{f_0} \right)^{\frac{1}{2}} \left(1 - \frac{k_n f}{f_0} \right)^{\frac{1}{2}}$$

$$- \sin^{-1} k_n^{\frac{1}{2}} + k_n^{\frac{1}{2}}(1 - k_n)^{\frac{1}{2}}, \qquad (k_n \neq 0), \qquad (7.404)$$

and

$$f = (6\pi G \rho_0 f_0^3)^{\frac{1}{3}} (T - T_0)^{\frac{2}{3}}, \qquad (k_n = 0), \qquad (7.405)$$

where T_0 is the second constant of integration. Thus if f is given by either (7.404) or (7.405) the density, pressure and radial velocity of the gas are, respectively,

$$\rho = \rho_0 \frac{f_0^3}{f^3}, \qquad p = P(T), \qquad q = \frac{f_T}{f} r. \qquad (7.406)$$

The density and pressure being independent of position, it is legitimate to describe the gas as *uniform*, its physical state being the same at all points in space at any given instant T. The density and velocity are related to the extent that the same function f appears in both. But the pressure is independent of the density and of the velocity also. Thus the pressure plays no part in the determination of the motion, the reason, of course, being that the spatial pressure-gradient is zero. However, thermodynamical considerations destroy this independence of the pressure. If, for example, the flow is to be adiabatic, then by (3.208) it easily follows that

$$P = P_0 \left(\frac{f_0}{f} \right)^{3\gamma},$$

and thus P now also depends on f and so is no longer independent of ρ and q.

It was shown in Section 7.2 that the linear-wave velocity law had the same form relative to any gas-element selected as origin, and a corresponding result follows for the gravitational force obtained by combining (6.444), (7.204) and

(7.401) with $A = 0$. In vector notation, this force at the typical gas-element P is

$$\mathbf{F} = -\frac{4\pi G}{3}\rho_0\left(\frac{f_0}{f}\right)^3\mathbf{r},$$

relative to the origin O. Hence the force at O' is

$$\mathbf{F}_0 = -\frac{4\pi G}{3}\rho_0\left(\frac{f_0}{f}\right)^3\mathbf{a}.$$

But the gravitational force on P relative to the origin O' is

$$\mathbf{F'} = \mathbf{F} - \mathbf{F}_0 = -\frac{4\pi G}{3}\rho_0\left(\frac{f_0}{f}\right)^3(\mathbf{r} - \mathbf{a})$$

$$= -\frac{4\pi G}{3}\rho_0\left(\frac{f_0}{f}\right)^3\mathbf{r'},$$

and therefore there is no change of form when O' replaces O as origin. Hence, whatever gas-element is selected as origin, the remainder of the gas will appear to move radially with respect to that element, and the gravitational force acting at any point of the gas will be the attraction of the material internal to the sphere centred at the origin and passing through the point in question[5].

CHAPTER 8

Theory of Uniform Model Universes

Reference has already been made in Chapter 1 to the expanding universe theory, the second of the main applications of general relativity in its exact form. Nowadays the term cosmology – the study of the universe taken as a whole – has replaced the earlier term, though it must be remembered that cosmology in this sense refers only to the investigation of the universe that is revealed to us by astronomical instruments. Those aspects of the universe which form the subject-matter of the biological sciences, of philosophy or of religion, are automatically excluded from the enquiry. The remainder of this book will therefore be devoted to an exposition of this astronomical cosmology[1].

8.1. Sketch of the Observational Data

During the present century, a major achievement in astronomy has been the construction of a world-picture in which the distribution of stars and of interstellar gas-clouds in space is not continuous. Rather are these objects regarded as forming vast agglomerations, called galaxies, each galaxy being separated from the next by regions in which matter has not been demonstrated to occur in appreciable quantity and wherein the radiation emitted by galaxies alone pursues its journey. The shapes of galaxies vary from almost spherical, through a variety of elliptical forms to flattened systems with trailing spiral arms of stars and gas-clouds. But in addition to these regular systems there are numerous galaxies of irregular shapes. The instrument that made this world-picture possible was the 100-inch telescope of the Mount Wilson Observatory which first resolved individual stars in galaxies of the greatest apparent brightness. Instruments of larger aperture, or of alternative design, such as the Schmidt cameras, have helped to complete the picture without, up to the present, qualitatively altering its general character. The Sun itself is a member of a large galaxy of spiral type, called the Galaxy, whose obscuring interstellar clouds are an obstacle to the study of the system of galaxies as a whole. Happily these clouds are mostly concentrated near the plane of the Milky Way, and therefore by looking in different directions at an angle to this plane, the effects of obscuration can be detected and allowed for. Photographs of portions of the celestial sphere in non-obscured directions reveal the following characteristics: (*a*) plates of the same exposure time show a qualitatively similar picture in different directions, provided that galaxies of apparent magnitude 17 or so, and fainter, are recorded; (*b*) however powerful the instrument, there does not seem to be a lower limit to the apparent magnitudes of galaxies, images increasing in numbers on the plates with each successive decrease in apparent luminosity; (*c*) the distribution of images on the plates is not regular, the galaxies forming small-scale groupings called clusters.

With apparent magnitude as a rough guide to the distance of a galaxy, property (*a*) indicates that the system of galaxies has spherical symmetry about the point of observation, which is the Earth. Property (*b*) suggests that the whole system is not within the range of our most powerful telescopes and that a portion only of some larger system is being observed. The increase in the numbers of galaxies with decreasing brightness also suggests that, in some sense, the large-scale spatial distribution is uniform. But property (*c*) indicates that on a smaller scale this distribution is irregular. While the total number of galaxies that can be observed with the largest telescopes probably runs into scores of millions, clusters contain some 200 members, with the largest ones having some thousands of members. The distance in parsecs (1 pc = $3 \cdot 0857 \times 10^{18}$ cm) of a galaxy is determined through a formula of type[2]

$$\log_{10} D = 0 \cdot 2(m - M) + 1, \qquad (8.101)$$

where *m* is the apparent, and *M*, the absolute, magnitude of the object. An important feature of the underlying theory of this equation is that the intensity of a light-source must fall off as the inverse square of *D*. Absolute magnitudes of galaxies are estimated by first identifying, where possible, objects in the galaxies such as Cepheid and other variable stars, globular star-clusters, novae, etc., whose intrinsic luminosities are known from criteria independent of distance[3]. These objects thus give *D* for the galaxy in which they are embedded and thus from the apparent magnitude of the galaxy as a whole, its absolute magnitude is found. Individual stellar objects can only be identified in galaxies with relatively small values of *m*, but these reveal that the absolute magnitudes of galaxies tend to lie on a roughly Gaussian distribution curve. Hence in a very faint cluster of galaxies it may be presumed that the brighter members will be comparable in absolute magnitude with the brighter nearby galaxies. The well-known galaxy in Andromeda, M31, is one such nearby giant system and has a value of *D* equal to about 7×10^5 pc. At the other end of the scale, the 200-inch telescope can probably 'see' galaxies at some 10^9 pc distance.

The spectra of galaxies possess a remarkable property in that, on the average, the fainter the apparent magnitude, the more the lines in the spectrum are shifted towards the red. If the displacement of a line of laboratory wave-length λ is $d\lambda$, then $z = d\lambda/\lambda$ is constant for all lines in the spectrum of a given galaxy. In classical theory, such a shift would be attributed to a velocity of recession of the galaxy relative to the observer, and this interpretation is taken over in general relativity. The velocities of recession classically equivalent to the observed red-shifts are high, ranging, for example, from 1,000 km/sec at apparent magnitude about 8 to 61,000 km/sec at apparent magnitude 18. The red-shifts for galaxies in a given cluster are not all equal, however; these individual motions over and above the general recession for the cluster as a whole providing one means of determining the mass of a galaxy. Masses found by this and other methods[4] range from 10^9 to 10^{12} solar masses.

Another over-all type of datum having cosmological interest is the galaxy-count. Areas of the celestial sphere that are regarded as typical are photographed to various successive limits of apparent magnitude and the numbers of galaxies to each limit are counted. Extrapolation yields the numbers over the whole celestial sphere. Such data are necessarily very rough, partly because of the difficulty of assigning the limiting magnitudes, and partly because of the disturbing effect of the clustering. However, it does turn out that, as a very crude first approximation, the number of galaxies increases as D^3, an indication that spatial uniformity of distribution may be a hypothesis worth investigating.

All galaxies emit radio waves, but some of them do so in a very vigorous fashion. Indeed many are known to emit as much power in the radio spectrum as they do in the optical. The study of radio galaxies, and particularly of their distribution in space, is likely to throw considerable light in the future on the nature of the universe and has already presented astronomers with interesting problems that will be discussed in due course.

Certain other types of observational data are also available in cosmology, and these will be described as the theory of the relevant phenomena is developed in this and the succeeding chapter. Enough has perhaps been said to indicate that cosmology in general relativity is concerned in the first instance with the mechanics of the system of galaxies taken as a whole and not with such questions as the evolution of the various constituents of a galaxy, the changes of shape that a galaxy may undergo during its history, etc. And it is necessary to emphasize once again that the whole of the observed system is not accessible to us for study, but a part only. The cosmological theory to be developed therefore provides a range of acceptable possibilities rather than a single unique answer. All the alternatives found have, however, one feature in common, namely, they are consistent with the available data provided by the accessible region of the observed universe.

8.2. Uniform Model Universes

If the system of galaxies is regarded as a collection of discrete masses in relative motion, its representative space-time would presumably be some modification of the Schwarzschild space-time, containing moving singularities separated by empty regions. Very little progress has been made towards solving this problem (see Sec. 8.9) owing to the extreme mathematical difficulties encountered. These difficulties, however, can be avoided if, instead of discrete masses, a continuous distribution of matter is substituted for the system of galaxies. The gravitational field, and the motion, of this continuous matter are to be selected so as to mimic as closely as possible the observed facts. The material will be envisaged as a perfect fluid and the physical data described in the preceding section suggest that the fluid should exhibit spherical symmetry about the point of observation, the Earth. Obviously an idealization of this kind can only serve as a rough approximation to the observed system since it ignores not only the discrete character of the galaxies themselves but also their tendency to form clusters. Ultimately, therefore, the picture will have to be modified to take these characteristics into account.

The Earth is imagined to be located at the point $r = 0$ in a spherically symmetric space-time whose metric is

$$ds^2 = e^\nu \, dt^2 - \frac{e^\mu}{c^2}(dr^2 + r^2 \, d\theta^2 + r^2 \sin^2 \theta \, d\phi^2), \qquad (8.201)$$

where ν and μ are functions of r and t. The velocity 4-vector of the fluid reduces to (see page 74)

$$u^4 \neq 0, \qquad u^1 \neq 0, \qquad u^2 = 0, \qquad u^3 = 0. \qquad (8.202)$$

The surviving Einstein equations are (4.419) to (4.422), and the last of these indicates that there is a sub-class of space-times (8.201) in which $u^1 = 0$. It will be shown presently that this condition does not necessarily imply that the fluid is at rest relative to an observer at $r = 0$; it is, in fact, a limitation on the coordinate-system which makes it *co-moving*, i.e. the coordinates r and t are so adjusted that the 'spherical surface' $r = constant$ moves with the material lying on its surface. Co-moving coordinates are present if ν and μ satisfy, by (4.422), the partial differential equation

$$\mu_{rt} = \tfrac{1}{2}\mu_t \nu_r,$$

and, integrating partially with respect to r, treating t as a constant, there comes

$$\log \mu_t = \tfrac{1}{2}\nu + \log \frac{2R'}{R},$$

where $R(t)$ is an arbitrary function of t, whose derivative with respect to t is written R'. Integrating partially with respect to t, treating r this time as a constant, we obtain

$$\mu = \chi(r) + 2\int \frac{R'}{R}e^{\frac{1}{2}\nu}dt, \qquad (8.203)$$

where $\chi(r)$ is an arbitrary function of r. Thus co-moving coordinates exist if μ and ν are related by this equation.

The condition $u^1 = 0$ introduced into (4.420) and (4.421) gives two expressions for p that are identical if

$$\tfrac{1}{2}(\mu + \nu)_{rr} + \frac{1}{2}\frac{1}{r}(\mu + \nu)_r + \tfrac{1}{4}\nu_r^2 = \frac{1}{r}(\mu + \nu)_r + \tfrac{1}{4}\mu_r^2 + \tfrac{1}{2}\mu_r\nu_r, \qquad (8.204)$$

and this therefore is the consistency relation for the problem. Consider now the sub-class of space-times in which (a) co-moving coordinates exist, and (b) the function ν is zero. By (8.203) it follows that

$$\mu = \chi(r) + 2 \log R, \qquad (8.205)$$

and then (8.204) reduces to the ordinary differential equation for χ,

$$\frac{d^2\chi}{dr^2} = \frac{1}{r}\frac{d\chi}{dr} + \frac{1}{2}\left(\frac{d\chi}{dr}\right)^2.$$

The substitution $\dfrac{1}{r}\dfrac{d\chi}{dr} = w$ gives

$$\frac{1}{w^2}\frac{dw}{dr} = \tfrac{1}{2}r,$$

whose integral is

$$w = \frac{1}{r}\frac{d\chi}{dr} = -\frac{k}{1 + kr^2/4},$$

where k is the constant of integration; and a further integration then yields

$$\chi = -2 \log (1 + kr^2/4), \qquad (8.206)$$

where the constant of integration is of the nature of a scale factor and can be taken to be zero. Thus the space-times (8.201) in which $\nu = 0$ and μ is given by (8.205) and (8.206) have metrics

$$ds^2 = dt^2 - \frac{R^2(t)}{c^2}\left\{\frac{dr^2 + r^2\, d\theta^2 + r^2 \sin^2 \theta\, d\phi^2}{(1 + kr^2/4)^2}\right\}, \qquad (8.207)$$

where R is an arbitrary function of t, which will be called the *scale-factor*, and k is an undetermined constant. Unlike the general case (8.201), a space-time (8.207) has the property of being homogeneous[5], i.e. if a different point were chosen for the origin $r = 0$, the mathematical form of the metric would be preserved and a coordinate-transformation would exist between the original, and the new, coordinate-systems. This property is also reflected in the values of the density and pressure of the distribution of matter which are obtained from (4.419), (4.421) by putting

$$\nu = 0, \qquad \mu = \log \{R^2(1 + kr^2/4)^{-2}\}, \qquad u^4 = 1 \qquad (8.208)$$

and they are, since $\kappa = 8\pi G/c^2$,

$$8\pi G\rho = \frac{3}{R^2}(kc^2 + R'^2) - \Lambda, \qquad (8.209)$$

$$\frac{8\pi G}{c^2}p = -\frac{2R''}{R} - \frac{R'^2}{R^2} - \frac{kc^2}{R^2} + \Lambda. \qquad (8.210)$$

Hence both the pressure and the density are *independent of the spatial co-ordinates r, θ, φ and are functions of the time t alone*. Thus the distribution of matter described by (8.207) is a perfect fluid whose pressure is, of course, isotropic, and in which, at any instant *t*, the density and pressure each have the same value at all points of space. For this reason the distribution of matter will be described as being *uniform* and the class of space-times with metrics of the form (8.207) will be said to represent *uniform model universes*.

This definition of the term 'uniformity' is very important. Any property of the model universe that depends on *t* alone and is independent of *r, θ, φ* will be said to be uniform. Uniformity in this sense does not imply that the variable describing the property *has the same value* at different instants *t*; but only that, at any instant *t*, the variable in question has the same value at *all points of space*. Such a variable, for example, is the density *ρ* given by (8.209).

It follows from (8.209) and (8.210) that

$$8\pi G \frac{d}{dt}(\rho R^3) = 3R'R^2\left(\frac{2R''}{R} + \frac{R'^2}{R^2} + \frac{kc^2}{R^2} - \Lambda\right))$$
$$= -3R'R^2(8\pi G p/c^2),$$

and therefore

$$\frac{d}{dt}(\rho R^3) + \frac{p}{c^2}\frac{dR^3}{dt} = 0, \tag{8.211}$$

is a relation valid in all uniform models of the universe.

Before proceeding, it is advantageous to discuss some of the properties of the space-times (8.207) and we may begin with the question of the physical dimensions of the coordinates and of the scale-factor *R*. If *s* and *t* are assigned the dimensions of time and *c* those of velocity, it is permissible to say that *r*, like *θ* and *φ*, is of zero physical dimensions. Thus *k* must also be a pure number, and *R* must have the physical dimensions of length. The coordinates *r, θ, φ* may then be replaced by dimensionless coordinates (*x, y, z*) through

$$x = r \sin\theta \cos\phi, \qquad y = r \sin\theta \sin\phi, \qquad z = r\cos\theta, \tag{8.212}$$

and (8.207) takes the equivalent form

$$ds^2 = dt^2 - \frac{R^2(t)}{c^2}\left\{\frac{dx^2 + dy^2 + dz^2}{(1 + kr^2/4)^2}\right\}. \tag{8.213}$$

Again, by a suitable adjustment of the unit in which *r* is measured the values of the *space-curvature constant k* may be taken to be

$$k = 1, 0, \text{ or } -1. \tag{8.214}$$

The physical interpretation of this constant will be considered in detail in Sec. 8.7. We note here only that space is said to be spherical, flat (or Euclidean) or hyperbolic according as $k = +1, 0$ or -1.

Another form of (8.207) is

$$ds^2 = dt^2 - \frac{R^2(t)}{c^2}\{d\omega^2 + \mathscr{S}_k^2(\omega)(d\theta^2 + \sin^2\theta \, d\phi^2)\}, \tag{8.215}$$

where

$$
\left.
\begin{aligned}
&\text{if } k = +1: \quad r = 2\tan\frac{\omega}{2} \quad \text{and } \mathscr{S}_{+1} = \sin\omega;\\
&\text{if } k = 0: \quad\quad r = \omega \quad\quad\quad \text{and } \mathscr{S}_0 = \omega;\\
&\text{if } k = -1: \quad r = 2\tanh\frac{\omega}{2} \text{ and } \mathscr{S}_{-1} = \sinh\omega.
\end{aligned}
\right\}
\tag{8.216}
$$

Associated with $\mathscr{S}_k$ is the function

$$
\mathscr{C}_k = \frac{d\mathscr{S}_k}{d\omega} =
\begin{cases}
\cos\omega & \text{if } k = +1,\\
1 & \text{if } k = 0,\\
\cosh\omega & \text{if } k = -1
\end{cases}.
\tag{8.217}
$$

It is important to notice that

$$
\mathscr{S}_k(\omega) = \omega - \tfrac{1}{6}k\omega^3 + \ldots,
$$

and therefore $\mathscr{S}_k = \omega$ so long as the *cube* and higher powers of ω are regarded as negligible.

Two additional forms of (8.207) arise as follows: let $t = t^*$ be a preselected instant and let $R(t^*)$ be denoted by R^*. Let the radial coordinates u and U be defined, respectively, by

$$
u = \frac{R^* r}{1 + kr^2/4} = R^* \mathscr{S}_k(\omega),
\tag{8.218}
$$

$$
U = R^* \int_0^r \frac{dr}{1 + kr^2/4} = R^*\omega.
\tag{8.219}
$$

Then if R^* is treated as a constant

$$
d\omega = \frac{1}{R^*}\frac{du}{\mathscr{C}_k} = \frac{1}{R^*}\frac{du}{(1 - ku^2/R^{*2})^{1/2}},
$$

and

$$
d\omega = dU/R^*.
$$

Then (8.207) becomes, in the two cases respectively,

$$
ds^2 = dt^2 - \frac{1}{c^2}\left(\frac{R}{R^*}\right)^2 \left\{\frac{du^2}{1 - ku^2/R^{*2}} + u^2(d\theta^2 + \sin^2\theta\, d\phi^2)\right\},
\tag{8.220}
$$

$$
ds^2 = dt^2 - \frac{1}{c^2}\left(\frac{R}{R^*}\right)^2 \{dU^2 + \mathscr{S}_k^2(U/R^*)(d\theta^2 + \sin^2\theta\, d\phi^2)\}.
\tag{8.221}
$$

Clearly t^* could be employed as the unit of time. If t is measured in this unit a function $g(t)$ may be defined by

$$
e^{g(t)} = (R/R^*)^2,
$$

with

$$
g(1) = 0.
$$

Moreover R^* may be employed as the unit for u and for U. Then (8.220), (8.221) take the forms

$$
ds^2 = dt^2 - \frac{e^g}{c^2}\left\{\frac{du^2}{1 - ku^2} + u^2(d\theta^2 + \sin^2\theta\, d\phi^2)\right\},
\tag{8.222}
$$

$$
ds^2 = dt^2 - \frac{e^g}{c^2}\{dU^2 + \mathscr{S}_k^2(U)(d\theta^2 + \sin^2\theta\, d\phi^2)\}.
\tag{8.223}
$$

8.3. The Red-shift

The first step in the analysis of the space-times (8.207) must be to determine whether or not they can give a representation of the red-shift observed in the spectral lines of galaxies. It will be useful to introduce the term *source* to describe any emitter of radiation in the universe. This is an object such as a galaxy which emits light, or radio-waves, or gamma-rays, or any other type of electromagnetic radiation. A source, of course, may also emit all such radiations simultaneously. The problem of the red-shift of spectral lines may be attacked by a consideration of the geodesics and null-geodesics of the space-times. Since the metric is orthogonal, the geodesic equations (2.807) may be used, and it is also convenient to take the metric in the equivalent form (8.213) with the coordinate identification

$$t = x^4, \qquad x = x^1, \qquad y = x^2, \qquad z = x^3.$$

The geodesic equations are therefore

$$\frac{d^2x^4}{ds^2} + \frac{RR'}{c^2(1 + kr^2/4)^2} \sum_{j=1}^{3} \left(\frac{dx^j}{ds}\right)^2 = 0, \tag{8.301}$$

$$\frac{d}{ds}\left(\frac{R^2}{c^2(1 + kr^2/4)^2} \frac{dx^i}{ds}\right)$$

$$+ \frac{kR^2x^i}{2c^2(1 + kr^2/4)^3} \sum_{j=1}^{3} \left(\frac{dx^j}{ds}\right)^2 = 0, \qquad (i = 1, 2, 3), \tag{8.302}$$

and it is obvious by inspection that, for all three values of k and for any function R, a class of solutions of these equations is

$$x^4 = s + s_0, \qquad x^i = x^i_0, \qquad (i = 1, 2, 3) \tag{8.303}$$

where the three x^i_0 and s_0 are constants of integration.

These solutions of the geodesic equations will be said to define *special world-lines*; they are clearly not the most general solutions of the geodesic equations because they contain only four constants of integration instead of the seven independent constants which would otherwise be present. Nevertheless it will be postulated that every source of radiation in the model universe has a special world-line. In addition the observer, permanently located at the origin of spatial coordinates, also has a special world-line. When presently the scale-factor comes to be determined (see Sec. 8.4) it will be found that there is always a mathematically obvious definition of the initial instant of the history of a model universe. Matters may then be so arranged that the proper-time s along every special world-line has the same zero value at the initial instant. Thus a common time for all special world-lines is introduced and (8.303) shows that it can also be identified with x^4 or t.

Since a source now has fixed coordinates (x, y, z), it must also have fixed coordinates (r, θ, ϕ), if the metric is expressed by (8.207). Consider then one of these sources located at the point P_i, coordinates (r_i, θ_i, ϕ_i), which emits radiation that is observed at the point O, coordinates $(0, 0, 0)$. The motion of the radiation is described by a null-geodesic passing through P_i and O, whose equations are identical in form with (8.301) and (8.302) except that a non-zero parameter μ replaces s. It is first necessary to show that the null-geodesic is radial, i.e. that $\theta = \theta_i$, $\phi = \phi_i$ along it. Assume this to be the case; then for any point along the null-geodesic between P_i and O,

$$x = \alpha^1 r, \qquad y = \alpha^2 r, \qquad z = \alpha^3 r,$$

where $(\alpha^1, \alpha^2, \alpha^3)$ are constants which, by (8.212), are expressible in terms of θ_i, ϕ_i by $\alpha^1 = \sin \theta_i \cos \phi_i$, $\alpha^2 = \sin \theta_i \sin \phi_i$, $\alpha^3 = \cos \theta_i$, and therefore

$$(\alpha^1)^2 + (\alpha^2)^2 + (\alpha^3)^2 = 1.$$

Hence the equation corresponding to (8.301) is

$$\frac{d^2 t}{d\mu^2} + \frac{1}{2c^2(1 + kr^2/4)^2} \frac{dR^2}{d\mu} \cdot \frac{d\mu}{dt} \left(\frac{dr}{d\mu}\right)^2 = 0$$

or

$$\frac{1}{2} \frac{d}{d\mu} \left\{ \left(\frac{dt}{d\mu}\right)^2 \right\} + \frac{1}{2c^2(1 + kr^2/4)^2} \frac{dR^2}{d\mu} \left(\frac{dr}{d\mu}\right)^2 = 0. \qquad (8.304)$$

Next, substituting $x^i = \alpha^i r$ in each of the three equations corresponding to (8.302), the single equation

$$\frac{d}{d\mu} \left\{ \frac{R^2}{c^2(1 + kr^2/4)^2} \frac{dr}{d\mu} \right\} + \frac{kR^2 r}{2c^2(1 + kr^2/4)^3} \left(\frac{dr}{d\mu}\right)^2 = 0$$

is obtained. Hence

$$\frac{dr}{d\mu} \frac{d}{d\mu} \left\{ \frac{R^2}{c^2(1 + kr^2/4)^2} \frac{dr}{d\mu} \right\} - \frac{R^2}{2} \left(\frac{dr}{d\mu}\right)^2 \frac{d}{d\mu} \left\{ \frac{1}{c^2(1 + kr^2/4)^2} \right\} = 0. \quad (8.305)$$

If now equation (8.305) is subtracted from (8.304) and the terms are rearranged, the result is

$$\frac{d}{d\mu} \left\{ \left(\frac{dt}{d\mu}\right)^2 - \frac{R^2}{c^2(1 + kr^2/4)^2} \left(\frac{dr}{d\mu}\right)^2 \right\} = 0. \qquad (8.306)$$

But the expression in curly brackets is known to be zero, when θ, ϕ are constants, from the integral (2.809) applied to (8.207), viz.:

$$\left(\frac{dt}{d\mu}\right)^2 - \frac{R^2}{c^2(1 + kr^2/4)^2} \left(\frac{dr}{d\mu}\right)^2 = 0. \qquad (8.307)$$

Hence the assumption that the motion of the radiation travelling from P_i to O is described by a radial null-geodesic is verified, since (8.306) is an identity.

If equation (8.307) is divided throughout by $(dt/d\mu)^2$, it becomes

$$\left(\frac{dr}{dt}\right)^2 = \frac{c^2(1 + kr^2/4)^2}{R^2}.$$

Since we are interested in radiation proceeding from P_i towards O, i.e. from larger to smaller values of r as t increases, the equation governing the motion of the radiation is

$$\frac{dr}{dt} = - \frac{c(1 + kr^2/4)}{R}. \qquad (8.308)$$

This is a very important equation for all our further developments. The first application which will be given is to the derivation of the red-shift formula and the method of Sec. 5.4 will be employed. Let the emission of a photon of radiation be defined by the pair of events $E_e(t_e, r_i, \theta_i, \phi_i)$ and $E'_e(t_e + dt_e, r_i, \theta_i, \phi_i)$, and its receipt at O by the pair of events $E_0(t_0, 0, 0, 0)$ and $E_0(t_0 + dt_0, 0, 0, 0)$. The pairs of events E_e, E_0 and E'_e, E'_0 both lie on the null-geodesic whose equation is (8.308). Hence

$$c\int_{t_e}^{t_0} \frac{dt}{R(t)} = - \int_{r_i}^{0} \frac{dr}{1 + kr^2/4}, \qquad (8.309)$$

and

$$c\int_{t_e + dt_e}^{t_0 + dt_0} \frac{dt}{R(t)} = - \int_{r_i}^{0} \frac{dr}{1 + kr^2/4}, \qquad (8.310)$$

since the r-coordinates of P_i and O are both fixed. But

$$\int_{t_e + dt_e}^{t_0 + dt_0} \frac{dt}{R} = \left\{ \int_{t_e + dt_e}^{t_e} + \int_{t_e}^{t_0} + \int_{t_0}^{t_0 + dt_0} \right\} \frac{dt}{R}$$

$$= - \frac{dt_e}{R(t_e)} + \int_{t_e}^{t_0} \frac{dt}{R} + \frac{dt_0}{R(t_0)}.$$

Hence subtracting (8.310) and (8.309), and using this result, it follows that

$$\frac{dt_e}{R(t_e)} = \frac{dt_0}{R(t_0)}, \qquad (8.311)$$

and therefore dt_0 and dt_e are *unequal* except when R is a constant.

The events E_e, E'_e are separated by the invariant time-interval

$$ds_e = dt_e \qquad (8.312)$$

and the events E_0, E'_0 by

$$ds_0 = dt_0. \qquad (8.313)$$

Hence by a similar argument to that employed in Sec. 5.4 the wave-length and frequency of the emitted wave are, respectively,

$$\lambda_e = cds_e, \qquad \nu_e = \frac{1}{ds_e},$$

and they are also, by definition, equal to the wave-length and the frequency of the comparison wave in the laboratory at O. For the arriving wave, we have

$$\lambda_e + d\lambda_e = cds_0, \qquad \nu_e + d\nu_e = \frac{1}{ds_0}.$$

Hence, by (8.311) to (8.313), there comes, dropping the suffix e

$$\left(1 + \frac{dv}{v}\right)^{-1} = 1 + \frac{d\lambda}{\lambda} = \frac{R(t_0)}{R(t)} = \frac{R_0}{R}, \tag{8.314}$$

a formula showing that the fractional change of wave-length, $d\lambda/\lambda$, depends only on the values of R at $t = t_e$ and $t = t_0$ and is the same for all wave-lengths λ. Hence it is of the nature of a Doppler effect and, as will be shown presently, can be connected with the rate of change of distance between O and P_i. For the moment, we observe that $d\lambda/\lambda$ is positive, i.e. there is a red-shift of the spectral lines of P_i observed at O, if $R_0 > R$. But the theory of uniform models of the universe does not guarantee this, since the function $R(t)$ is un-determined. Indeed, uniformity could equally well be associated with the alternative possibility of negative displacements; or with displacements some of which were positive, while others were negative. Identification of the point O with an observer on Earth and the instant $t = t_0$ with the present moment, together with the fact that all galaxies *hitherto observed* have $d\lambda/\lambda > 0$, imply that the function R must satisfy

$$R_0 > R \tag{8.315}$$

for all relevant instants of emission t.

The instant $t(= t_e)$ at which the radiation must leave the typical source P_i in order to arrive at O at the instant t_0, will be called the *departure-time*. The instant t_0 will, correspondingly, be the *arrival-time*. The time interval $\tau = t_0 - t$ will be referred to as the *travel-time* of the radiation. The fraction

$$z = \frac{d\lambda}{\lambda} = \frac{R_0}{R} - 1, \tag{8.316}$$

is called the *red-shift*† of the source P_i observed at O at the arrival-time t_0.

In (8.314) and (8.316) the symbols v and λ stand for v_e and λ_e, the frequency and wave-length of the radiation at the instant of emission. It is often advan-tageous however to employ v and λ for the frequency and wave-length of the arriving wave at O. In this case

$$\left.\begin{array}{c} \lambda = \lambda_e + d\lambda_e = (1 + z)\lambda_e, \\[2mm] v = v_e + dv_e = \dfrac{v_e}{1 + z}. \end{array}\right\} \tag{8.317}$$

Thus bandwidths $d\lambda_e$, dv_e at emission become $d\lambda$, dv on arrival of the radiation at O where

$$d\lambda = (1 + z)d\lambda_e, \qquad dv = \frac{dv_e}{1 + z}. \tag{8.318}$$

There are three important functions of the arrival-time which can be deduced from (8.316). Let it be assumed that the function R possesses a

---

† In the first edition of this book I attempted to introduce the symbol δ for the red-shift but this suggestion has not found favour among other writers. The traditional symbol z has therefore been adopted in spite of the fact that z normally stands for a coordinate, as in formulae (8.301) and (8.302) above.

Taylor expansion around t_0. Let $R(t)$, where t is the departure-time, be regarded as a function of the travel-time τ so that

$$R(t) = R(t_0 - \tau).$$

Then the Taylor expansion of $1/R$ is

$$\frac{1}{R} = \frac{1}{R_0} + \tau\left(\frac{R_0'}{R_0^2}\right) + \frac{\tau^2}{2}\left(-\frac{R_0''}{R_0^2} + 2\frac{R_0'^2}{R_0^3}\right) + \ldots,$$

where a suffix zero means, of course, that the function in question is evaluated at $t = t_0$. The three functions of t_0 are then:

The Hubble parameter, or Hubble 'constant',

$$h_1 = R_0'/R_0; \tag{8.319}$$

the acceleration parameter

$$h_2 = R_0''/R_0; \tag{8.320}$$

and the acceleration factor

$$q_0 = -\frac{R_0''}{R_0}\left(\frac{R_0}{R_0'}\right)^2. \tag{8.321}$$

These functions also occur in the expression for the red-shift as a power series in the travel-time. One finds, by (8.316) and the series for $1/R$, that

$$z = h_1\tau + h_1^2(2 + q_0)\frac{\tau^2}{2} + \ldots \tag{8.322}$$

It has become customary to call the Hubble parameter the Hubble constant and this practice will be followed here, self-contradictory though the term may be. In fact h_1 varies with the time t_0, as will presently be shown (see Sec. 8.6). The physical dimensions of h_1 are those of the reciprocal of a time and therefore

$$T_0 = \frac{1}{h_1} = \frac{R_0}{R_0'}, \tag{8.323}$$

is a time-interval which may be expressed in seconds or in years. Another expression for the Hubble constant is obtained by employing the second as unit of time in calculating h_1 and remembering that one megaparsec (mpc) equals $3 \cdot 086 \times 10^{19}$ km. Therefore the quantity

$$H = \frac{(1\ \text{km} \times h_1\ \text{sec}^{-1}) \times 3 \cdot 086 \times 10^{19}}{1\ \text{mpc}}$$

$$= 3 \cdot 086 \times 10^{19}\, h_1,$$

has the physical dimensions of km/sec per megaparsec which will be written for brevity as km/sec/mpc. We also have

$$\left.\begin{array}{l} H = \dfrac{3 \cdot 086 \times 10^{19}}{T_0} \quad (T_0\ \text{in seconds}) \\[2mm] = \dfrac{9 \cdot 778 \times 10^{11}}{T_0} \quad (T_0\ \text{in years}). \end{array}\right\} \tag{8.324}$$

The acceleration parameter h_2 is the reciprocal of the square of a time and the acceleration factor q_0 is a pure number.

L

8.4. Solutions of Einstein's equations. Age of the model universe

It is obvious that if the scale-factor R were known for all values of t and if k and Λ were also known, the Einstein equations (8.209) and (8.210) would give the density and pressure of the material content of the model universe. Moreover the formula (8.316) would then also provide a specific expression for the red-shift in terms of the departure-time and of the arrival-time. One method of finding R, approximately at least, is to develop series expansions for observable quantities such as the red-shift and then, by an appeal to observation, to estimate the values of the successive derivatives of R at the instant t_0. This method of expansion was adequate so long as galaxies with red-shifts no greater than 0·2 were included in the available data. But as soon as larger red-shifts began to be measured the method of expansions became so laborious as to be effectively useless.

The alternative procedure is to find R by solving the Einstein equations themselves. But these equations are two in number and yet contain three unknown functions, ρ, p and R. They are therefore indeterminate unless some additional hypothesis is introduced. It will be shown when, in the next chapter, the observational data are considered, that a useful assumption to make is

$$\frac{p}{c^2} = 0.$$

It defines a class of models which will be called *zero-pressure models*. However, in order to show that the assumption is not unique, models in which p/c^2 is proportional to a power of the density will also be briefly considered.

In solving the Einstein equations, we shall bear in mind that our ultimate object is to compare the theory with observation. Let us identify the human astronomer with the observer O located at the origin $r = 0$ of the space-time (8.207). The travel-time of radiation received from any galaxy is believed to be immensely long compared with the entire history of astronomy. Hence it is sufficient to assume that the observer makes all his observations at a single instant t_0.

At the instant t_0, equations (8.209) and (8.210) may be written, with the aid of (8.319), (8.321) and (8.323),

$$\left. \begin{array}{l} 8\pi G \rho_0 = \dfrac{3}{T_0^2} + \dfrac{3kc^2}{R_0^2} - \Lambda, \\[2ex] 8\pi G \dfrac{p_0}{c^2} = \dfrac{2q_0 - 1}{T_0^2} - \dfrac{kc^2}{R_0^2} + \Lambda. \end{array} \right\} \qquad (8.401)$$

Introduce the *density parameter*, σ_0, and the *pressure parameter*, ε_0, by

$$\left. \begin{array}{l} \sigma_0 = \dfrac{4\pi G}{3} \rho_0 T_0^2 = \dfrac{4\pi G}{3} \dfrac{\rho_0}{h_1^2}, \\[2ex] \varepsilon_0 = \dfrac{p_0/c^2}{\rho_0}. \end{array} \right\} \qquad (8.402)$$

These parameters are pure numbers and physical considerations make it clear that both are positive. Otherwise it would be necessary to interpret either the density or the pressure as negative quantities. Then (8.401) may be written

$$\left. \begin{aligned} \varLambda &= -3\{q_0 - (1 + 3\varepsilon_0)\sigma_0\}T_0^{-2}, \\ k\left(\frac{cT_0}{R_0}\right)^2 &= -\{q_0 + 1 - 3(1 + \varepsilon_0)\sigma_0\}. \end{aligned} \right\} \tag{8.403}$$

In zero-pressure models, ε_0 is zero and the last pair of equations becomes

$$\varLambda T_0^2 = -3(q_0 - \sigma_0), \tag{8.404}$$

$$k\left(\frac{cT_0}{R_0}\right)^2 = -(q_0 + 1 - 3\sigma_0). \tag{8.405}$$

The zero-pressure models are relatively simpler to deal with and they will be considered first. We regard q_0, σ_0 and T_0 as having known numerical values for reasons which will appear in the next chapter. In a zero-pressure model (8.211) may be integrated to give

$$\rho R^3 = \rho_0 R_0^3 = \frac{3}{4\pi G}C^3, \tag{8.406}$$

where C is a constant of integration. Since (8.211) can replace (8.210) there is only (8.209) left to integrate. Substituting $\rho = \rho_0(R_0/R)^3$ and using (8.402), (8.404), (8.405) also, one finds that (8.209) becomes

$$\frac{2\sigma_0}{T_0^2}\left(\frac{R_0}{R}\right)^3 = \left(\frac{R'}{R}\right)^2 - \frac{q_0 + 1 - 3\sigma_0}{T_0^2}\left(\frac{R_0}{R}\right)^2 + \frac{q_0 - \sigma_0}{T_0^2}.$$

Introduce the dimensionless variables

$$Y = R/R_0, \qquad X = t/T_0 \tag{8.407}$$

and the differential equation becomes

$$\left. \begin{aligned} \frac{dY}{dX} &= \frac{1}{Z(Y)}, \\ Z^2(Y) &= \frac{Y}{2\sigma_0 + (q_0 + 1 - 3\sigma_0)Y - (q_0 - \sigma_0)Y^3}. \end{aligned} \right\} \tag{8.408}$$

Thus all zero-pressure models are obtained from (8.408) by giving different numerical values to q_0 and σ_0. However, it must be borne in mind that the relation between R and t deduced from (8.407) and (8.408) will involve R_0, T_0, q_0 and σ_0, none of which is, in general, a constant in the sense of being independent of t_0 as are $\varLambda$, k and the C of (8·406). Notice also that when k is $+1$ or -1, R_0 is expressible in terms of T_0, q_0 and σ_0 by (8.405). This is however impossible when $k = 0$. In these models, by (8.402) and (8.406), we may use instead

$$R_0 = C(T_0^2/\sigma_0)^{1/3}. \tag{8.409}$$

Since $Y = 1$ at $t = t_0$, the solution of (8.408) may be written

$$t_0 - t = T_0(X_0 - X) = T_0\int_Y^1 Z\,dY = T_0 W(Y). \tag{8.410}$$

Another form of the solution is obtained by the introduction of the initial value of R. Let $t = t_i$ be the initial instant and let X_i and Y_i (< 1) be the associated values of X and Y. Then

$$X - X_i = \int_{Y_i}^{Y} Z dY = W(Y_i) - W(Y). \tag{8.411}$$

The evaluation of the integral W involves elliptic functions in general. In practice, with specific values of q_0 and σ_0, W can be rapidly computed numerically and this is almost certainly the best method to employ. However, there are certain degenerate cases in which W is always expressible in terms of elementary functions. These are described in Categories A1 to A3 below. The reduction to standard elliptic integrals may also prove useful to some readers. The first steps in this reduction are described under Category A3; the rest of the reduction may be carried out by following the procedures found in the standard textbooks[6].

The important function is the cubic polynomial $P(Y) = Y/Z^2$ where

$$P(Y) = 2\sigma_0 + (q_0 + 1 - 3\sigma_0)Y - (q_0 - \sigma_0)Y^3, \tag{8.412}$$

and the equation $P(Y) = 0$ necessarily has at least one real root $Y = \eta$. The other two roots may be real or complex and will be denoted by η_1 and η_2.

Category A1. This is defined by $q_0 = \sigma_0$ so that the cosmical constant is zero. The polynomial $P(Y)$ reduces to the linear function

$$P(Y) = 2q_0 + (1 - 2q_0)Y. \tag{8.413}$$

The integral W is expressible in terms of elementary functions and the various possibilities are listed in the Appendix.

Category A2. These are empty models defined by $\sigma_0 = 0$ and then

$$P(Y) = Y\{q_0 + 1 - q_0Y^2\}. \tag{8.414}$$

The integral W is again expressible in terms of elementary functions, and these cases are listed in the Appendix. Categories A1 and A2 have a model in common, namely, $q_0 = 0$, $\sigma_0 = 0$.

Category A3. This is the general case in which $q_0 \neq \sigma_0$, $\sigma_0 > 0$. When Λ is negative, so that $q_0 > \sigma_0$, we have $P(-\infty) > 0$, $P(0) = 2\sigma_0 > 0$, $P(1) = 1 > 0$ and $P(\infty) < 0$. Thus the root η is greater than unity. When Λ is positive, so that $q_0 < \sigma_0$, we have $P(-\infty) < 0$, $P(0) = 2\sigma_0 > 0$ and $P(\infty) > 0$. Hence $\eta < 0$ in this case. When $\Lambda < 0$ we may write

$$P(Y) = (q_0 - \sigma_0)(\eta - Y)(\eta_1 + Y)(\eta_2 + Y), \tag{8.415}$$

and for $\Lambda > 0$,

$$P(Y) = (\sigma_0 - q_0)(Y - \eta)(\eta_1 + Y)(\eta_2 + Y), \tag{8.416}$$

where, in both cases

$$q_0 = \frac{1}{\eta^2 - 1}\left\{1 + \frac{(\eta - 1)^2(\eta + 2)}{\eta}\sigma_0\right\}, \tag{8.417}$$

and

$$\eta_1 = \frac{\eta}{2}(1 - \zeta), \qquad \eta_2 = \frac{\eta}{2}(1 + \zeta),$$

$$\left. \zeta = \left\{ 1 - \frac{2(\eta - 1)(\eta + 2)^2}{\eta^3}\sigma_0 \right\}^{1/2} \left\{ 1 - \frac{2(\eta - 1)}{\eta}\sigma_0 \right\}^{-1/2}. \right\} \qquad (8.418)$$

It also follows that

$$\varDelta T_0^2 = -3(q_0 - \sigma_0) = -\frac{3}{\eta^2 - 1}\left\{ 1 - \frac{2(\eta - 1)}{\eta}\sigma_0 \right\}, \qquad (8.419)$$

and

$$q_0 + 1 - 3\sigma_0 = \frac{\eta^2}{\eta^2 - 1}\left\{ 1 - \frac{2(\eta^3 - 1)}{\eta^3}\sigma_0 \right\}. \qquad (8.420)$$

The quantities q_0, η and σ_0 are necessarily real but ζ may be imaginary so that η_1, η_2 may be conjugate complex numbers. In practice it is q_0 and σ_0 that are determined from observation. Though neither is known exactly, it does appear to be the case that $q_0 > \sigma_0$. Thus (8.415) is applicable and, as an aid to the determination of η for a given pair (q_0, σ_0), we write (8.417) in the form $q_0 = a + b\sigma_0$ and then list a and b for a number of η values in Table V.

TABLE V

η	a	b	η	a	b
1·1	4·762	0·134	1·6	0·641	0·519
1·15	3·101	0·191	1·7	0·529	0·564
1·2	2·273	0·242	1·8	0·446	0·603
1·3	1·449	0·331	1·9	0·383	0·637
1·4	1·042	0·405	2·0	0·333	0·667
1·5	0·800	0·467	3·0	0·125	0·833
			4·0	0·067	0·900

Since W may be written in the case (8.415) as

$$W = \frac{1}{(q_0 - \sigma_0)^{1/2}}\int_Y^1 \frac{Y\,dY}{\{Y(\eta - Y)(\eta_1 + Y)(\eta_2 + Y)\}^{1/2}},$$

the reduction to standard elliptic integrals follows from the methods given in the textbooks, the roots of the quartic in the denominator now being known. A corresponding integral, of course, arises for (8.416). When $\zeta = 0$, the roots η_1, and η_2 of $P(Y) = 0$ are equal and W is again expressible in terms of elementary functions (models vii–a and vii–b of the Appendix).

Examination of the specific cases of the three categories listed in the Appendix shows that the initial value of R may be taken to be zero in many models. These are the *point-source zero-pressure models*. But models also exist in which R is infinite at $t = -\infty$, decreases to a non-zero minimum value and then increases to infinity at $t = +\infty$. In certain point-source models R increases indefinitely with t, in others R starts from zero, increases to a finite maximum value and then decreases to zero again, the cycle occupying a finite span of time.

Category B. The two Einstein equations (8.209) and (8.210) will now be made determinate by postulating that a polytropic relation exists between the pressure and density of the material content of the model universe, namely,

$$\frac{p}{c^2} = \varepsilon_0 \rho_0 \left(\frac{\rho}{\rho_0}\right)^{1+\frac{1}{n}}, \tag{8.421}$$

where $n(> 0)$ is a constant and ε_0 is defined by the second of equations (8.402). The solution of (8.211) with $\rho = \rho_0$ when $R = R_0$ is

$$\frac{\rho}{\rho_0} = \left\{(1 + \varepsilon_0)\left(\frac{R}{R_0}\right)^{3/n} - \varepsilon_0\right\}^{-n}. \tag{8.422}$$

If this expression is used to replace ρ in (8.209) and (8.403), (8.407) are also employed, there comes

$$\left.\begin{aligned}
\frac{dY}{dX} &= \frac{1}{Z(Y)}, \\
Z^2(Y) &= Y[2\sigma_0 Y^3\{(1 + \varepsilon_0)Y^{3/n} - \varepsilon_0\}^{-n} + \{q_0 + 1 - 3(1 + \varepsilon_0)\sigma_0\}Y \\
&\quad - \{q_0 - (1 + 3\varepsilon_0)\sigma_0\}Y^3]^{-1}.
\end{aligned}\right\} \tag{8.423}$$

The solution of this equation may be written

$$t_0 - t = T_0(X_0 - X) = T_0 \int_Y^1 Z dY = T_0 W(Y), \tag{8.424}$$

and it differs from (8.410) only in that Z is now given by (8.423) instead of by (8.408). Clearly, with so complicated a formula for Z, resort should be had at once to numerical integration. However, a couple of special cases, in which W can be expressed in terms of elementary functions, are given in the Appendix.

Age of model universe

An immediate deduction from these solutions of Einstein's equations is the age of the model universe. Let $t = t_i$ be the initial instant. Then, whether (8.410) or (8.424) is used, the lapse of time from the initial instant to the moment, t_0, at which the observer is making his observations, is

$$t_0 - t_i = AT_0, \tag{8.425}$$

where the age factor is

$$A = \int_{Y_i}^1 Z dY. \tag{8.426}$$

The time AT_0 is called the age of the model universe.

In point-source zero-pressure models one may choose $t_i = 0$ at $Y_i = 0$, i.e. at the instant when the scale-factor R has the value zero. The age of any such model will be greater than, equal to, or less than, the time-interval T_0, which is the reciprocal of the Hubble constant, according as $A \gtreqless 1$. The question may be discussed by considering a (Z, Y) diagram as in Fig. 6. The derivative of Z with respect to Y is also needed. By (8.408) it is

$$\frac{dZ}{dY} = \frac{1}{Y^{1/2}} \cdot \frac{\sigma_0 + (q_0 - \sigma_0) Y^3}{\{2\sigma_0 + (q_0 + 1 - 3\sigma_0) Y - (q_0 - \sigma_0) Y^3\}^{3/2}}. \qquad (8.427)$$

The model $q_0 = 0$, $\sigma_0 = 0$ has $Z(Y) = 1$ and thus its value of A is also unity, since we may choose $t_i = 0$ for the initial instant at which $Y_i = 0$. Consider also, for example, those models for which $q_0 > \sigma_0 > 0$. In the (Z, Y) diagram the value of A for the $q_0 = 0$, $\sigma_0 = 0$ model is represented by the area of the square of unit side, $OLMN$ in Fig. 6. Now by (8.427) any point-source zero-pressure model for which $q_0 > \sigma_0 > 0$ has an infinite value of dZ/dY at

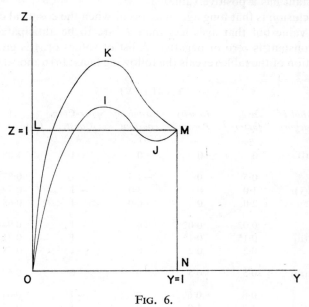

FIG. 6.

$Y = 0$. Again at $Y = 1$, dZ/dY is positive. The (Z, Y) curve for the model therefore has ON for initial tangent line and its slope is positive at M, as shown for the curve $OIJM$. Now if $A > 1$ in a $q_0 > \sigma_0 > 0$ model the area under the curve $OIJM$ must exceed the area of the square $OLMN$. The curve must therefore intersect MN not only at M but at two (or more) other points in $0 < Y < 1$ as well. Hence dZ/dY must vanish at two points at least, such as I and J. Therefore by (8.427) there must be at least two values of Y in $0 < Y < 1$ which satisfy

$$\sigma_0 + (q_0 - \sigma_0) Y^3 = 0. \qquad (8.428)$$

But this is impossible if $q_0 > \sigma_0 > 0$ since both terms on the left side of the equation are positive. Thus the points I and J do not exist and the curve

$OIJM$ must lie entirely within the square $OLMN$. Hence $A < 1$ and $t_0 < T_0$ for a $q_0 > \sigma_0 > 0$ model. Reference to (8.404) shows that these models have a negative cosmical constant. Clearly (8.428) also has no solution when $\varLambda = 0$, because then $q_0 = \sigma_0$.

But for a point-source zero-pressure model in which $q_0 < 0$ and $\sigma_0 > 0$, dZ/dY is negative at M and the (Z, Y) curve could look like OKM in Fig. 6. Moreover (8.428) would now have a real root in $0 < Y < 1$. Therefore the area under OKM might be greater than unity and therefore the value of A for the model would exceed unity. Thus the age of the model would exceed T_0. Referring again to (8.404) we observe that $q_0 < 0$, $\sigma_0 > 0$ means that the cosmical constant has a positive value.

The conclusion is that long ages may occur when the cosmical constant has a positive value but that ages less than T_0 are to be anticipated when the cosmical constant is zero or negative. A list of values of A is given in Table VI. Inspection of the table reveals the following facts: (a) a model with $\varLambda = 0$

TABLE VI

Model Category	Acc. factor q_0	Density Param. σ_0	Cosmical constant $\varLambda T_0^2$	Space-Curv. Const. k	A (Age $= AT_0$)
A1(i)	0	0	0	-1	1·00
	0·5	0	$-1·5$	-1	0·87
A2(v)	1·0	0	$-3·0$	-1	0·79
	2·0	0	$-6·0$	-1	0·68
	0·02	0·02	0	-1	0·94
A1(ii)	0·15	0·15	0	-1	0·81
	0·2	0·2	0	-1	0·78
A1(iii)	0·5	0·5	0	0	0·67
	0·6	0·6	0	$+1$	0·64
A1(iv)	1·0	1·0	0	$+1$	0·57
	2·0	2·0	0	$+1$	0·47
	0·2	0·02	$-0·54$	-1	0·89
	0·5	0·02	$-1·44$	-1	0·84
	0·65	0·15	$-1·5$	-1	0·73
	1·02	0·02	$-3·0$	-1	0·76
A3	1·15	0·15	$-3·0$	-1	0·68
	2·02	0·02	$-6·0$	-1	0·66
	2·15	0·15	$-6·0$	-1	0·61
	1·0	0·8	$-0·6$	$+1$	0·59
	0·15	0·35	$+0·6$	-1	0·73
	0	0·33	$+1·0$	0	0·76
A2(vi-c)	$-0·9$	0	$+2·7$	-1	1·92
A2(vi-b)	$-1·0$	0	$+3$	0	∞

does not necessarily have a greater age than one with $\Lambda < 0$; (b) the condition $q_0 = 0$ by itself fails to guarantee $A = 1$; (c) a positive cosmical constant does not necessarily imply a long age. It is the simultaneous smallness of both q_0 and σ_0 that makes for a long age[7].

8.5. Travel-time. The radial coordinate. Horizons

Let the departure-time of the radiation emitted by a source be t, at which moment the scale-factor has the value $R(t)$. Let the arrival-time be t_0, the value of R then being $R(t_0)$. Therefore the travel-time $t_0 - t$ of the radiation is given by either of the equations (8.410) or (8.424). Moreover, since $t_0 > t$, it follows that $R(t_0) > R(t)$ and therefore the lower limit, Y, in (8.410) or (8.424) must be less than unity. Since the red-shift of the source, observed from $r = 0$ at $t = t_0$ is given by (8.316), it follows that

$$1 + z = 1/Y, \quad (Y \le 1). \tag{8.501}$$

Thus, when $X \le X_0$, (8.408) and (8.423) may be converted into (z, X) equations and then integrated. For the zero-pressure models, the travel-time is

$$\left. \begin{aligned} t_0 - t &= T_0 \int_0^z \frac{Z(z)dz}{(1 + z)^2}, \\ Z^2(z) &= \frac{(1 + z)^2}{1 + 2(q_0 + 1)z + (q_0 + 1 + 3\sigma_0)z^2 + 2\sigma_0 z^3} \end{aligned} \right\} \tag{8.502}$$

If the red-shift of a source is known and the model universe is also known, the travel-time is easily obtained from (8.502) either by numerical integration or by analytical means if the values of (q_0, σ_0) which define the model permit it.

The travel-time in models with pressure is still given by (8.502) but $Z(z)$ is now obtained from (8.424) with Y replaced by $(1 + z)^{-1}$. The expansion of Z as a power series in z has, for its first three terms,

$$Z = 1 - q_0 z + \frac{3}{2}\left\{ q_0^2 + q_0 - \sigma_0\left(1 + \frac{3 + 4n}{n}\varepsilon_0 + \frac{3(n + 1)}{n}\varepsilon_0^2\right)\right\} z^2, \tag{8.503}$$

and it is easy to verify that the series in zero-pressure models follows by setting $\varepsilon_0 = 0$ in (8.503). If the series for Z is introduced into (8.502) and term by term integration is employed, it follows that

$$t_0 - t = T_0 z \left[1 - \frac{q_0 + 2}{2} z \right.$$

$$\left. + \left\{ 1 + \frac{1}{2}q_0^2 + \frac{7}{6}q_0 - \frac{\sigma_0}{2}\left(1 + \frac{3 + 4n}{n}\varepsilon_0 + \frac{3(n + 1)}{n}\varepsilon_0^2\right)\right\} z^2 \right]. \tag{8.504}$$

This formula shows that, if z is small enough for its cube to be negligible compared with unity, the travel-time depends only on T_0 and q_0. To this order, the travel-time in a zero-pressure model is the same as in a model with pressure having the same q_0 and T_0 as the first model had.

Consider next the radial coordinate of a source which is connected with the departure-time and the arrival-time by (8.309). It is convenient to replace the r-coordinate by ω through (8.216) and to denote, in (8.309), the departure-time by t. Then

$$\omega = c \int_t^{t_0} \frac{dt}{R(t)},$$

which becomes by (8.407)

$$\omega = \frac{cT_0}{R_0} \int_X^{X_0} \frac{dX}{Y}.$$

Again, each value of Y in the integrand is connected with X by the equations (8.408) in zero-pressure models or by (8.423) in models with pressure. Thus

$$\omega = \frac{cT_0}{R_0} \int_Y^1 \frac{Z(Y)}{Y} dY, \qquad (8.505)$$

and, on conversion to an integration with respect to z, we obtain

$$\omega = \frac{cT_0}{R_0} I(Y) = \frac{cT_0}{R_0} I(z), \qquad (8.506)$$

where

$$I(Y) = \int_Y^1 \frac{Z(Y)}{Y} dY, \qquad (8.507)$$

$$I(z) = \int_0^z \frac{Z(z)}{1+z} dz. \qquad (8.508)$$

The integral I is of basic importance in what follows. Its value can most rapidly and conveniently be found by numerical computation, for a given q_0, σ_0, and ε_0. In zero-pressure models it takes the form, by (8.408) and (8.502),

$$I(Y) = \int_Y^1 \frac{dY}{\{2\sigma_0 Y + (q_0 + 1 - 3\sigma_0)Y^2 - (q_0 - \sigma_0)Y^4\}^{1/2}}, \qquad (8.509)$$

or

$$I(z) = \int_0^z \frac{dz}{\{1 + 2(q_0 + 1)z + (q_0 + 1 + 3\sigma_0)z^2 + 2\sigma_0 z^3\}^{1/2}}. \qquad (8.510)$$

Of course, these two expressions for I are equivalent and the choice between them is to be made solely on the basis of convenience in computation. If (8.509) is employed, the conversion to z in place of Y can be made through (8.501) after the integration has been performed.

It is noteworthy that the integral (8.509) reduces to a simpler elliptic integral than does the corresponding integral for $W(Y)$. If the $P(Y)$ of (8.412) is given by (8.415), for example, we have

$$I(Y) = \frac{1}{(q_0 - \sigma_0)^{1/2}} \int_Y^1 \frac{dY}{\{Y(\eta - Y)(\eta_1 + Y)(\eta_2 + Y)\}^{1/2}},$$

and the substitution

$$\frac{1}{Y} = \frac{1}{\eta} + \frac{\eta + \eta_2}{\eta\eta_2} \tan^2 \vartheta,$$

transforms I into

$$I = \frac{2}{\{(q_0 - \sigma_0)\eta_2(\eta + \eta_1)\}^{1/2}} \{F(\psi, l) - F(\psi_0, l)\}, \qquad (8.511)$$

where F is the incomplete elliptic integral of the first kind

$$F(\psi, l) = \int_0^{\psi} \frac{d\vartheta}{(1 - l^2 \sin^2 \vartheta)^{1/2}},$$

with

$$l^2 = 1 - \frac{\eta_1}{\eta_2}\left(\frac{\eta + \eta_2}{\eta + \eta_1}\right) = 1 + \frac{(\zeta - 1)(3 + \zeta)}{(\zeta + 1)(3 - \zeta)},$$

$$\tan^2 \psi = \frac{\eta\eta_2}{\eta + \eta_2}\left(\frac{1}{Y} - \frac{1}{\eta}\right) = \frac{\eta\eta_2}{\eta + \eta_2}\left(1 + z - \frac{1}{\eta}\right),$$

$$\tan^2 \psi_0 = \frac{\eta\eta_2}{\eta + \eta_2}\left(1 - \frac{1}{\eta}\right).$$

Clearly these formulae are most easily used when η_1, η_2 and l are all real.†

When z is small compared with unity, the integrand in (8.510) may be expanded as a power series in z. Term by term integration then determines $I(z)$ and the result may be introduced into (8.506). Thus, for zero-pressure models,

$$\omega = \frac{cT_0}{R_0}z\{1 - \tfrac{1}{2}(q_0 + 1)z + \tfrac{1}{6}(3q_0^2 + 5q_0 + 2 - 3\sigma_0)z^2 + \ldots\}, \qquad (8.512)$$

and for models with pressure,

$$\omega = \frac{cT_0}{R_0}z\left[1 - \tfrac{1}{2}(q_0 + 1)z + \tfrac{1}{6}\left\{3q_0^2 + 5q_0 + 2 - 3\sigma_0\left(1 + \frac{3 + 4n}{n}\varepsilon_0 + \frac{3(n + 1)}{n}\varepsilon_0^2\right)\right\}z^2 + \ldots\right]. \qquad (8.513)$$

We may briefly consider here the question of horizons[8] in model universes and, to fix ideas, we shall deal with point-source zero-pressure models. In such models, the minimum value of Y is zero and this corresponds to an infinite value of z. Now it may happen that the function $I(z)$ is such that $I(\infty)$ is finite. Therefore at the instant t_0, the radiation arriving from a source whose ω-coordinate is

$$\omega_m = \frac{cT_0}{R_0}I(\infty) \qquad (8.514)$$

would exhibit an infinitely large red-shift and therefore presumably be undetectable. Sources whose ω-coordinates exceed ω_m could not be observed at all. Therefore ω_m defines a 'horizon' between sources that can be detected, and

† For example, if $\eta = 1\cdot4$ and $q_0 = 1\cdot123$, $\sigma_0 = 0\cdot2$, then $\zeta = 0\cdot607$, $l = 0\cdot794$.

those which cannot be observed, at the instant t_0, by an observer at the origin $\omega = 0$. The radiation emitted at the initial instant by a source lying beyond the horizon has not yet reached the observer at the instant t_0. But it may do so at some later instant as may be exemplified by the model A1(iii), the Einstein–de Sitter universe. In this model the horizon at time t_0 is defined by

$$\omega_m = \frac{6^{1/3}c}{C}t_0^{1/3}.$$

Thus at a later time of observation t'_0 ($> t_0$) the new horizon lies at

$$\omega'_m = (t'_0/t_0)^{1/3}\omega_m > \omega_m.$$

Hence a source which lay on the horizon at time $t = t_0$, lies within it at time t'_0 because the source has a special world-line and therefore its ω always has the same value. A theoretical criterion for the visibility of a source by the observer is that the source's red-shift shall be finite. The example just given demonstrates that sources do not disappear over the observer's horizon as time proceeds. On the contrary, sources previously undetectable come into the oberver's ken as time goes on.

It is also clear that all the models in which η_1, η_2 and l are real and I is given by (8.511) possess horizons because the value of ψ at $z = \infty$ is $\psi = \pi/2$. Thus $I(\infty)$ is proportional to the difference between the complete elliptic integral $F(\tfrac{1}{2}\pi, l)$ and $F(\psi_0, l)$. Both of these are finite except in the special case where $l = 1$.

The expressions for ω_m for various models will be found in the Appendix.

8.6. Distance and the Velocity of Recession

The problem of distance is a complicated one in cosmology largely because astronomers in their ordinary work are accustomed to using classical theories in which a Newtonian absolute distance is pre-supposed. For example, celestial mechanics or the dynamics of stellar systems in the Galaxy are discussed in terms of Newtonian mechanics with its absolute time and absolute space. In these theories, a unique meaning can be assigned, at any instant of absolute time, to the distance between two celestial bodies by saying that it is the Euclidean distance between the points of absolute space occupied by the bodies at the instant in question. Distance thus comes to be identified with an absolute and unique quantity intrinsically associated with the two bodies at each instant of absolute time. It is also taken for granted that all internally self-consistent methods of measuring the distance must give the same result. In contrast to this state of affairs, relativity theory abandons the notion of absolute distance. It is therefore necessary to specify carefully what is to be meant by the distance between two celestial bodies, in particular, between the observer at the origin and a source with a special world-line. Two procedures are possible, the first of which amounts to choosing a 'distance' which is mathematically the most obvious. The second procedure however is to associate the definition of distance with the operational method by which the distance is measured. In this fashion distance is associated with a clear sequence of observational steps. Different mathematical definitions, or different operational procedures, are found to lead to distances which are not equal to one another. But since distance has no absolute meaning, there is no way of asserting that one type of distance is the 'correct' one. We proceed to define a few of the distances that have been used in uniform models of the universe.

(*i*) *Mathematical distances.* Suppose that in (8.218) and (8.219) we set $t^* = t_0$ so that

$$u = R_0 \mathscr{S}_k(\omega), \qquad U = R_0 \omega. \tag{8.601}$$

The metric would then be expressed either by (8.220) or by (8.221). Moreover the coordinates u and U both have the physical dimensions of length. In addition, the U-coordinate of a source is proportional to ω and u is a simple function thereof. Therefore, by (8.506), it could be asserted that either

$$u = R_0 \mathscr{S}_k \left\{ \frac{cT_0}{R_0} I(z) \right\}, \tag{8.602}$$

or

$$U = cT_0 I(z), \tag{8.603}$$

was the distance from the observer to the source (whose radiation exhibited a red-shift z) at the instant of observation t_0. There seems to be nothing except mathematical simplicity to choose between them. They are equal only if $k = 0$. Since no description of the method of measurement of either u or U has been given, it is impossible to say whether or not they correspond to the distances measured by astronomers in the observed universe.

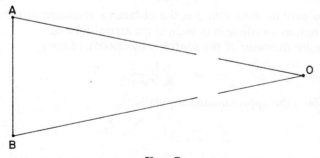

FIG. 7.

(*ii*) *Distance by apparent size.* We turn to the first example of a distance whose definition is tied to a specified operation of measurement. Suppose that the source has a small finite extension on the celestial sphere. Let AB in Fig. 7 be a diameter of the source and let the (fixed) coordinates of A be (r_i, θ_i, ϕ_i) those of B being $(r_i, \theta_i + d\theta_i, \phi_i)$. Let the departure-time of the radiation from

A be t. Then the null-geodesic AO passes through the events $(t, r_i, \theta_i, \phi_i)$ and $(t_0, 0, 0, 0)$ and it is a radial null-geodesic. Similarly the radial null-geodesic BO is defined by the events $(t, r_i, \theta_i + d\theta_i, \phi_i)$ and $(t_0, 0, 0, 0)$. The two emission events are therefore separated by the local distance

$$l = icds = \frac{R(t)r_i}{1 + kr_i^2/4}d\theta_i,$$

and since the null-geodesics are radial the angle between them at O is also $d\theta_i$. The *distance by apparent size* of the source for departure-time t and arrival-time t_0 is defined to be

$$\xi = \frac{R(t)r_i}{1 + kr_i^2/4}, \tag{8.604}$$

and its angular diameter a ($= d\theta_i$) is

$$a = \frac{l}{\xi}. \tag{8.605}$$

In (8.604), r_i must be expressed in terms of t_0 and t by the fundamental equation (8.309). However an equivalent expression in terms of the red-shift is possible. With the aid of (8.216) and of (8.314) we obtain

$$\xi = \frac{R_0}{1 + z}\mathscr{S}_k(\omega). \tag{8.606}$$

Since $\mathscr{S}_k(\omega)$ differs from ω only by powers of ω greater than the second, the first two terms in the series (8.512) may be used to express ξ, in zero-pressure models, correct to the order z^2, as

$$\xi = cT_0 z\left\{1 - \frac{q_0 + 3}{2}z\right\}. \tag{8.607}$$

It is also easy to show that ξ is the distance u *evaluated at the departure-time t* and not, as was done in (8.602), at the arrival-time t_0.

The angular diameter of the source is by (8.605), (8.606)

$$a = \frac{l}{R_0}\frac{1 + z}{\mathscr{S}_k(\omega)}, \tag{8.608}$$

and by (8.607) the approximate formula is

$$a = \frac{l}{cT_0}\frac{1}{z}\left\{1 + \frac{q_0 + 3}{2}z\right\}. \tag{8.609}$$

The distance ξ possesses an interesting property in many models, namely, it can attain a maximum value before the horizon is reached. Thereafter, ξ decreases again. To show this in zero-pressure models, (8.606) is differentiated with respect to z and (8.506) and (8.510) are also employed to give

$$\frac{d\xi}{dz} = R_0\left\{\frac{cT_0}{R_0}\frac{\mathscr{C}_k(\omega)}{(1 + z)P^{1/2}(z)} - \frac{\mathscr{S}_k(\omega)}{(1 + z)^2}\right\}, \tag{8.610}$$

where $P(z)$ stands for the cubic polynomial in the denominator of the integrand of (8.510). For small z, with the aid of (8.607), we obtain

$$\frac{d\xi}{dz} = cT_0\{1 - (q_0 + 3)z\} > 0.$$

Hence at first ξ increases with z as would be expected, and this, of course, implies that the angular diameters of sources with the same l decrease as their remoteness from the observer increases. However, when z is very large, we have from (8.610) for $\sigma_0 > 0$,

$$\frac{d\xi}{dz}\begin{cases} = -\dfrac{R_0}{2}\dfrac{e^\omega}{z^2}\left\{1 - \dfrac{cT_0}{R_0}\dfrac{1}{(2\sigma_0 z)^{1/2}}\right\} & k = -1, \\[2ex] = -\dfrac{R_0}{z^2}\left\{\omega - \dfrac{cT_0}{R_0}\dfrac{1}{(2\sigma_0 z)^{1/2}}\right\}, & k = 0, \\[2ex] = -\dfrac{R_0}{z^2}\left\{\sin\omega - \dfrac{cT_0}{R_0}\dfrac{\cos\omega}{(2\sigma_0 z)^{1/2}}\right\}, & k = +1. \end{cases}$$

If there is a horizon at a finite value of ω, then obviously $d\xi/dz < 0$ near the horizon when $k = 0$ and $k = -1$. If $k = +1$ and the horizon occurs for $\omega < \pi$ (i.e. before r becomes infinite) then again $d\xi/dz$ is negative. Thus in such models ξ is decreasing when z is large. Conversely the angular diameters of sources with a given l are then increasing with z. The minimum of a occurs for the value of z which makes the right-hand side of (8.610) vanish and some examples are given in the Appendix.

A different situation occurs in empty models in which $\sigma_0 = 0$. For large z, the polynomial $P(z)$ has the following values:

$$P(z) = (q_0 + 1)z^2, \quad q_0 \neq -1,$$
$$= 1, \quad q_0 = -1.$$

It then follows that, for large z,

$$\frac{d\xi}{dz}\begin{cases} = R_0\left\{\dfrac{cT_0}{R_0}\dfrac{\mathscr{C}_k(\omega)}{(q_0 + 1)^{1/2}z^{3/2}} - \dfrac{\mathscr{S}_k(\omega)}{z^2}\right\}, & q_0 \neq -1, \\[2ex] = R_0\left\{\dfrac{cT_0}{R_0}\dfrac{\mathscr{C}_k(\omega)}{z} - \dfrac{\mathscr{S}_k(\omega)}{z^2}\right\}, & q_0 = -1, \end{cases}$$

and therefore $d\xi/dz > 0$ as z tends to infinity. Therefore the reversal of the diminution of angular diameter with distance before the horizon is reached is absent in the models defined by $\sigma_0 = 0$. These are A1(i) and those of category A2. As z increases to infinity, or to its finite maximum in the models A2(vi–a), the angular diameter now simply decreases to a finite minimum value. These minima are listed in the Appendix.

(iii) *Luminosity-distance.* The distance D used in practice to define the distances of galaxies is, as has been mentioned in Sec. 8.1, characterized by the property that the intensity of a light-source falls off inversely as the square of D. This kind of distance is called *luminosity-distance* and the formula for D

valid in any one of the space-times (8.207) may be obtained in the following manner: Consider again the source P_i and let it be a point-source of radiation. The departure-time is t_e, the arrival-time t_0, the r-coordinate of P_i has the fixed value r_i and that of the observer O, the equally fixed value $r = 0$. It will be assumed, because of the homogeneity of the space-time (8.207), that the relationships will remain unaltered if the observer is placed at $r = r_i$ and the source at $r = 0$, the departure-time and arrival-time being unchanged. The assumption will be justified by showing that D depends only on t_0, t_e and r_i.

If h is Planck's constant, then a photon of wave-length λ_e at emission has an energy hc/λ_e. When this photon reaches O its energy has become

$$\frac{hc}{\lambda_e(1 + z)},$$

because of the red-shift. This is Hubble's *energy-effect* for the transmission of individual photons. Suppose next that P_i emits n photons in time Δt_e without preferential direction. The rate of emission of photons by P_i is therefore

$$\frac{n}{\Delta t_e}.$$

But since a null-geodesic joining P_i and O represents the motion of a photon, and both these points have fixed (r, θ, ϕ) coordinates, the argument by which (8.311) was derived from (8.309) and (8.310) may again be used to show that the time-interval Δt_e has become Δt_0 at O where

$$\Delta t_0 = (1 + z)\Delta t_e.$$

Thus the rate of arrival of photons at O (Hubble's *number-effect*) is

$$\frac{n}{\Delta t_0} = \frac{n}{(1 + z)\Delta t_e}.$$

Lastly, O lies on the pseudo-sphere $r_i = constant$ and the photons reach this observer at time t_0 when the scale-factor has the value R_0. The area of this pseudo-sphere is

$$S_0 = \frac{R_0^2 r_i^2}{(1 + kr_i^2/4)^2} \int_0^\pi \int_0^{2\pi} \sin\theta \, d\theta d\phi$$

$$= \frac{4\pi R_0^2 r_i^2}{(1 + kr_i^2/4)^2}.$$

Hence the average flow of energy per unit time through unit area at O held normal to the flow of energy, is

$$dh_i = \left\{\frac{hc}{(1 + z)\lambda_e}\right\}\left\{\frac{n}{(1 + z)\Delta t_e}\right\}\frac{1}{S_0}$$

$$= \left\{\frac{hc}{4\pi\lambda_e}\frac{n}{\Delta t_e}\right\}\left\{\frac{R_0(1 + z)r_i}{1 + kr_i^2/4}\right\}^{-2}.$$

Now

$$P_e = \frac{hc}{\lambda_e}\frac{n}{\Delta t_e}, \qquad (8.611)$$

is the total power emitted by P_i in the form of photons of wave-length λ_e. If we write

$$D = \frac{R_0(1 + z)r_i}{1 + kr_i^2/4}, \tag{8.612}$$

we have

$$dh_i = \frac{P_e}{4\pi D^2}, \tag{8.613}$$

the familiar classical formula for the rate of arrival of radiative energy at unit area at the observer. The distance D is the *luminosity-distance* of the source and it plays the same role as does the classical distance when the luminosities (or the flux-densities) of sources are in question. Since by (8.316) we may also write

$$D = \frac{R^2(t_0)}{R(t_e)} \frac{r}{1 + kr_i^2/4}, \tag{8.614}$$

it follows that D depends only on t_0, t_e and r_i. Thus, if the observer is returned to $r = 0$ and the source is replaced at $r = r_i$, the times t_0 and t_e being kept unchanged, it follows that D is also the luminosity-distance of the source in its actual position.

The luminosity-distance of a source at r, the departure-time being t, may be expressed in a variety of ways. With the aid of (8.216) and (8.506) the formula (8.612) becomes

$$D = cT_0\mathscr{D},$$

$$\mathscr{D} = \frac{R_0}{cT_0}(1 + z)\mathscr{S}_k(\omega) = \frac{R_0}{cT_0}(1 + z)\mathscr{S}_k\left\{\frac{cT_0}{R_0}I(z)\right\}. \tag{8.615}$$

In zero-pressure models, the expression (8.512) for ω in terms of z may be used to express $\mathscr{D}$ as a power series in the red-shift. When the cube and higher powers of z are neglected,

$$\mathscr{D} = z\{1 - \tfrac{1}{2}(q_0 - 1)z\}. \tag{8.616}$$

The relations between D and the distances u, U and ξ are, by (8.601) and (8.606),

$$D = (1 + z)^2\xi = (1 + z)u = R_0(1 + z)\mathscr{S}_k(U/R_0). \tag{8.617}$$

Clearly, if the square of z is negligible, it follows that

$$D = \xi = U = u = cT_0z. \tag{8.618}$$

The factor $(1 + z)$ in $\mathscr{D}$ is, in general, only apparently present because $\mathscr{S}_k$ may contain a factor $(1 + z)^{-1}$. Examples are found in models A1(i), (ii), (iii), (iv) of the Appendix.

(*iv*) *Velocity of Recession*. It was mentioned in Sec. 8.2 that the condition $u^1 = 0$ was insufficient to ensure that the distribution of matter was at rest, a statement that can now be justified by showing that the source P_i possesses a velocity, according to an observer stationed at O. It will be assumed that (8.315) is true and that all spectral displacements are thus towards the red.

M

Then a naïve definition is obtained by appealing to the classical theory of the Doppler effect and defining the velocity of recession of P_i to be

$$V_c = cz. \tag{8.619}$$

But the term velocity, if it means anything at all, presumably means the rate of change of distance with time. It has been shown that there are at least four definitions of the distance of the source from the observer. Therefore it is necessary to find the rate of change of each of these distances with respect to time before the corresponding velocity of recession of the source can be defined. The solution of this problem is most easily reached if the rate of change with respect to t of the red-shift z of a given source is first evaluated at the instant t_0. Since the r-coordinate of the source is fixed, the radiation that left the source at the departure-time $t + dt$ reaches the observer at time $t_0 + dt_0$. Therefore the new red-shift is

$$z + dz = \frac{R(t_0 + dt_0)}{R(t + dt)} - 1.$$

Thus

$$dz = \frac{R_0 + R_0'dt_0}{R + R'dt} - \frac{R_0}{R}$$

$$= \frac{R_0}{R}\left(\frac{R_0'}{R_0} - \frac{R'}{R}\frac{dt}{dt_0}\right)dt_0.$$

But the constancy of the r-coordinate of the source means that the argument which established (8.311) may be used again to show that

$$\frac{dt}{dt_0} = \frac{R}{R_0}.$$

Hence if z' denotes the derivative of z at the instant t_0 we have

$$z' = \frac{R_0}{R}\left(\frac{R_0'}{R_0} - \frac{R'}{R_0}\right).$$

With the aid of (8.316), (8.323) and (8.407) one finds

$$z' = \frac{1 + z}{T_0}\left(1 - \frac{dY}{dX}\right)$$

$$= \frac{1 + z}{T_0}(1 - Z^{-1}), \tag{8.620}$$

a result valid in all uniform models.

Consider next the rate of change with time of the luminosity-distance. By the definition (8.612), only z and R_0 can vary with the time. Logarithmic differentiation of this formula yields at once, for the time rate of change of D at the instant t_0,

$$D_0' = \left(\frac{z'}{1 + z} + \frac{R_0'}{R_0}\right)D$$

$$= \frac{2D}{T_0}\left\{1 - \frac{1}{2}\frac{1}{Z(Y)}\right\}. \tag{8.621}$$

For zero-pressure models, Z is expressed in terms of z by (8.503) with $\varepsilon_0 = 0$ and thence Z^{-1} is easily obtained as a power series in z. Combining this series with (8.615) and (8.616) one finds

$$D_0' = cz\left(1 + \frac{q_0 + 1}{2}z + \ldots\right). \tag{8.622}$$

Each model of the universe has its own exact Doppler formula connecting D'_0 with the red-shift. Thus in model† A1(i) the Doppler formula is

$$D_0' = cz(1 + \tfrac{1}{2}z),$$

whereas in model A2(vi–b), it is

$$D_0' = cz(1 + 2z).$$

The rates of change of the distances ξ, u and U are obtained by similar methods. In the following formulae, the exact relation is given first, followed by the first two terms of the series expansion in z for zero-pressure models. We have

$$\xi_0' = \frac{\xi}{T_0}\frac{dY}{dX} = cz\left(1 + \frac{q_0 - 3}{2}z + \ldots\right), \tag{8.623}$$

$$U_0' = \frac{U}{T_0} = cz\left(1 - \frac{q_0 + 1}{2}z + \ldots\right), \tag{8.624}$$

$$u_0' = \frac{u}{T_0} = cz\left(1 - \frac{{}_0q + 1}{2}z + \ldots\right). \tag{8.625}$$

The term 'velocity of recession' of a source is therefore ambiguous unless the type of distance is first specified. Each kind of distance has its own Doppler formula and none of these agrees with the classical formula (8.619) even for relatively small red-shifts. But clearly, if z is so small that its square may be neglected compared with unity, then

$$D_0' = \xi_0' = U_0' = u_0' = V_e = cz. \tag{8.626}$$

It is also obvious that, if the hypothesis of the proportionality of the velocity of recession to the distance of the source is accepted, then 'distance' must be defined as either U or u. This point will be examined in more detail in Sec. 9.1.

Another question which can be elucidated by the formula (8.620) for z' concerns the physical meaning of q_0. Consider the sources which are in the immediate neighbourhood of the observer. Their red-shifts are small and therefore the velocity of recession of any one of them is uniquely defined by (8.626) to be

$$V_e = cz.$$

† It is easy to prove that the q of the special relativity Doppler formula (5.410) is

$$q = u/t = \tanh \omega.$$

In any model, (8.503) reduces, for small z, to

$$Z^{-1} = 1 + q_0 z,$$

and therefore (8.620) yields

$$\left(\frac{dV_c}{dt}\right)_0 = -q_0 \left(\frac{V_c}{T_0}\right). \tag{8.627}$$

Hence at the instant t_0 the character of the acceleration of the expansion in the immediate neighbourhood of the observer depends on the sign and magnitude of q_0. It is for this reason that q_0 has been named the acceleration factor.

We conclude this section with a remark on the rates of change of the fundamental parameters h_1 and T_0, h_2, q_0 and σ_0 in zero-pressure models. The equation (8.210) with $p/c^2 = 0$ may be differentiated once again with respect to t and this gives, at the instant t_0,

$$\left(\frac{R'''}{R}\right)_0 = -(q_0 - 3\sigma_0)T_0^{-3}.$$

Using this result wherever it is needed, we find, from (8.319) to (8.321), (8.323) and (8.402),

$$\left(\frac{dh_1}{dt}\right)_0 = -\frac{1 + q_0}{T_0^2},$$

$$\left(\frac{dT_0}{dt}\right)_0 = 1 + q_0,$$

$$\left(\frac{dh_2}{dt}\right)_0 = \frac{3\sigma_0}{T_0^3},$$

$$\left(\frac{dq_0}{dt}\right)_0 = \frac{2q_0^2 + 2q_0 - 3\sigma_0}{T_0}.$$

$$\left(\frac{d\sigma_0}{dt}\right)_0 = \frac{(2q_0 - 1)\sigma_0}{T_0}.$$

It will be noticed that the Hubble 'constant' h_1 is in fact a constant only if $q_0 = -1$ and $\sigma_0 = 0$, i.e. only in model A2(vi–b). For all other combinations of the values of q_0 and σ_0, it is a time-variable.

8.7. Volume. Number of Sources

The metric of a model universe is expressed orthogonally in terms of the coordinates (r, θ, ϕ) of (8.207). Thus at the instant t, the three mutually perpendicular infinitesimal distances which define an element of volume are

$$\frac{R(t)dr}{1 + kr^2/4}, \qquad \frac{R(t)rd\theta}{1 + kr^2/4}, \qquad \frac{R(t)r \sin\theta \, d\phi}{1 + kr^2/4},$$

respectively. The volume element at this instant is therefore

$$\frac{R^3(t)r^2 \sin\theta \, d\theta d\phi dr}{(1 + kr^2/4)^3}.$$

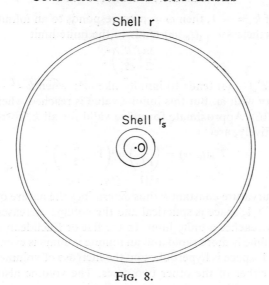

Shell r

Shell r_s

·O

FIG. 8.

Fig. 8 shows the cross-sections of two typical shells centred at the observer O and the volume of Shell r at the instant t is obtained by integrating the last expression with respect to θ from 0 to π and with respect to ϕ from 0 to 2π. The volume is

$$dV_k(t,r) = \frac{4\pi R^3(t)r^2 dr}{(1 + kr^2/4)^3} = 4\pi R^3(t)\mathscr{S}_k^2(\omega)d\omega. \tag{8.701}$$

With this expression for the volume of a shell, it is possible to develop two alternative definitions of the volume within radius r – or equivalently ω – which might be set up by the observer at $r = 0$. In the first place, the instantaneous volume at the instant t_0 may be defined to be

$$V_k(t_0, \omega) = 4\pi R_0^3 \int_0^\omega \mathscr{S}_k^2(\omega)d\omega, \tag{8.702}$$

which can also be written

$$V_k(t_0, \omega) = \frac{4\pi}{3}(cT_0)^3 \mathscr{V}_k(t_0, \omega), \tag{8.703}$$

where $\mathscr{V}_k$ is the dimensionless function of t_0 and ω

$$\left. \begin{aligned} \mathscr{V}_k &= \frac{3}{2}\left(\frac{R_0}{cT_0}\right)^3 \{k\omega - \tfrac{1}{2}k\mathscr{S}_k(2\omega)\}, \quad k = \pm 1, \\ &= \left(\frac{R_0}{cT_0}\right)^3 \omega^3, \quad k = 0. \end{aligned} \right\} \tag{8.704}$$

Since ω may be replaced by z through (8.506) these formulae are convertible to $\mathscr{V}_k(t_0, z)$. If $k = +1$, then $\omega = \pi$ corresponds to an infinitely large value of r. But nevertheless $\mathscr{V}_{+1}(t_0, \omega)$ tends to the finite limit

$$\frac{3\pi}{2}\left(\frac{R_0}{cT_0}\right)^3.$$

When $k = 0$, $\mathscr{V}_0(t_0, \omega)$ tends to infinity like ω^3; when $k = -1$, $\mathscr{V}_{-1}$ again tends to infinity with ω. But this infinite value is reached when $r = 2$, by the definition (8.216). Approximate formulae valid for all k, correct to order ω^5 and z^4, respectively, are

$$\left.\begin{aligned}\mathscr{V}_k(t_0, \omega) &= \left(\frac{R_0}{cT_0}\right)^3\omega^3\left(1 - \frac{k}{5}\omega^2\right)\\&= z^3\{1 - \tfrac{3}{2}(q_0 + 1)z\}.\end{aligned}\right\} \qquad (8.705)$$

The space-curvature constant k thus determines the nature of the volume of space. If $k = +1$, space is spherical and the volume increases slowly with ω and eventually reaches a finite limit. In the flat or Euclidean case $k = 0$, the increase of volume is more rapid and an infinite volume is eventually attained. When $k = -1$, space is hyperbolic and the increase of volume with ω is more rapid than in either of the other two cases. The volume also attains an infinite value as ω tends to infinity.

The reader should notice that the preceding results are purely mathematical however because they imply that the observer can 'see' the whole of space instantaneously. In many models there is a finite *observable volume* at each instant t_0; it is given by $\mathscr{V}_k(t_0, \omega_m)$ where ω_m is the horizon value of ω. Models with finite observable volumes are, for example, the group A1(ii), whereas in A1(i) and A2(v) the observable volume is infinite.

The second way of defining the volume within radius r around $r = 0$ is to sum the volumes of successive shells from $r = 0$ outwards. Since (8.701) may also be written

$$dV_k = 4\pi R_0^3\left(\frac{R}{R_0}\right)^3\mathscr{S}_k^2(\omega)d\omega,$$

this kind of volume is

$$\bar{V}_k(t_0, \omega) = 4\pi(cT_0)^3\left(\frac{R_0}{cT_0}\right)^3\int_0^\omega Y^3\mathscr{S}_k^2(\omega)d\omega, \qquad (8.706)$$

and this by the derivative of (8.505) is also

$$\bar{V}_k(t_0, Y) = 4\pi(cT_0)^3\left(\frac{R_0}{cT_0}\right)^2\int_Y^1 ZY^2\mathscr{S}_k^2(\omega)dY, \qquad (8.707)$$

where, of course, the ω in the integrand is to be replaced by the function of Y given by (8.505).

As an example of the difference between V_k and $\bar{V}_k$ consider the model A2(vi–b) in which $Z = Y^{-1}$ and $\omega = (cT_0/R_0)z$. We have from (8.703) and (8.704)

$$V_0(t_0, z) = \frac{4\pi}{3}(cT_0)^3z^3, \qquad (8.708)$$

and from (8.707), after evaluation of the integral and substitution of $Y = (1 + z)^{-1}$,

$$\left. \begin{aligned} \bar{V}_0(t_0, z) &= \frac{4\pi}{3}(cT_0)^3 \left\{ \ln(1 + z) - \frac{z(2 + 3z)}{2(1 + z)^2} \right\} \\ &= \frac{4\pi}{3}(cT_0)^3 z^3 \left(1 - \frac{9}{4}z + \dots \right). \end{aligned} \right\} \quad (8.709)$$

Thus V_0 tends to infinity like z^3 but $\bar{V}_0$ proceeds like $\ln z$ and so more slowly. Clearly $\bar{V}_0$ increases more slowly with z than does V_0 for small z also.

The theory of spatial volume is closely related to that of the number of sources per unit volume, or the *number-density* of sources. Consider those sources whose (r, θ, ϕ) coordinates lie in the coordinate volume

$$dv = \frac{r^2 dr \sin\theta \, d\theta d\phi}{(1 + kr^2/4)^3}.$$

Since the sources have special world-lines their coordinates are fixed, and the sources remain inside dv throughout their lifetimes. Consider now two coordinate volumes dv_1 and dv_2 which are equal to one another. The first one, dv_1, lies so close to the observer O that the departure-times for the sources within it are essentially t_0; the second coordinate volume dv_2, lies in Shell r of Fig. 8 and the departure-time for the sources within it is t. Suppose firstly that there is the same number, $\mathcal{N}$, of sources at all times in both dv_1 and dv_2. The physical volumes corresponding to dv_1 and dv_2, as observed at O, are $R_0^3 dv_1$ and $R^3 dv_2$, respectively. Thus the number-densities of sources in the two (physical) volumes are, respectively,

$$n_0 = \frac{\mathcal{N}}{R_0^3 dv_1}, \qquad n = \frac{\mathcal{N}}{R^3 dv_2}, \qquad (8.710)$$

so that

$$n = \left(\frac{R_0}{R} \right)^3 n_0. \qquad (8.711)$$

Secondly, suppose that the number of sources in dv_1 and dv_2 is the same at the same instant of time t but differs from one instant to the next. This case would arise if the sources had relatively short lifetimes and were formed out of previously non-radiating material, lasted for a time and then ceased to radiate. Such a situation can be allowed for by assuming that $\mathcal{N}$ is a function of t; a little consideration will show that $\mathcal{N}$ could not also be a function of r for this would destroy the assumed homogeneity and isotropy conditions on which the uniform models are based. We may write, since R is a function of t and $Y = R/R_0$,

$$\mathcal{N}(t) = \alpha(Y)\mathcal{N}(t_0),$$

where α is a function of Y such that $\alpha(1) = 1$. Then in place of (8.710) we should have

$$n_0 = \frac{\mathcal{N}(t_0)}{R_0^3 dv_1}, \qquad n = \frac{\alpha(Y)\mathcal{N}(t_0)}{R^3 dv_2},$$

so that

$$n = \alpha(Y)\left(\frac{R_0}{R}\right)^3 n_0 = \frac{\alpha(Y)}{Y^3} n_0. \tag{8.712}$$

Clearly (8.712) includes (8.711) as the special case in which α is a constant equal to unity.

We apply these ideas to the calculation of the total number of sources observed by O as being within radius r (or ω). By (8.701) and (8.712), these are

$$N(t_0, \omega) = 4\pi \int_0^\omega n R^3 \mathscr{S}_k^2(\omega) d\omega$$

$$= 4\pi n_0 R_0^3 \int_0^\omega \alpha(Y) \mathscr{S}_k^2(\omega) d\omega, \tag{8.713}$$

where, in the integrand, Y is given as a function of ω by (8.505). It is immediately obvious from (8.702) that, when α is a constant equal to unity,

$$N(t_0, \omega) = n_0 V_k(t_0, \omega). \tag{8.714}$$

This is the case which most closely approximates to sources evenly distributed and at relative rest in the Euclidean space of classical physics. For it corresponds to sources which persist throughout the history of the model universe and whose numbers in equal coordinate volumes never vary. This is the assumption made in general relativity with regard to the galaxies regarded as sources of optical radiation. However, among other possibilities is the one in which n is always equal to n_0 so that the number-density of sources is constant.† There must therefore be some process for bringing new sources into play at a rate just sufficient to compensate for the effect of the expansion in enlarging every volume. The condition for a constant number-density is $\alpha(Y) = Y^3 = R^3/R_0^3$. Then (8.713) gives

$$\bar{N}(t_0, \omega) = 4\pi R_0^3 n_0 \int_0^\omega Y^3 \mathscr{S}_k^2(\omega) d\omega$$

$$= n_0 \bar{V}_k(t_0, \omega). \tag{8.715}$$

Clearly many other possibilities may occur according to the assumed form of the dependence of $\alpha(Y)$ on Y.

The differential form of (8.713) may be written, with the aid of (8.506), (8.508) in the form

$$\frac{dN}{dz} = 4\pi n_0 R_0^2 (cT_0) \alpha(z) \mathscr{S}_k^2(\omega) \frac{Z(z)}{1+z}, \tag{8.716}$$

where $\alpha(z)$ is the result of replacing Y by $(1+z)^{-1}$ in the function $\alpha(Y)$.

---

† This is the hypothesis made in the steady-state theory which also employs model A2(vi–b). The results (8.708) and (8.709) indicate that $N > \bar{N}$ for any given instant of observation t_0.

8.8. The Measurement of Radiation

A very important type of measurement made by the observer at O in Fig. 8 is the determination of the apparent brightness of a source. The theory of observations of this kind must now be considered and, to simplify the problem, let us first suppose that each source is a point-source of radiation.

(*i*) *Optical sources*. Consider a point-source of radiation in Shell r of Fig. 8 the departure-time being t and the arrival-time t_0. Suppose that the source radiates isotropically in the bandwidth $d\lambda_e$ centred on λ_e at a rate

$$B(t, \lambda_e)d\lambda_e \text{ watts.} \tag{8.801}$$

On arrival at the observer, this flux of electromagnetic energy becomes, by (8.317) and (8.318)

$$B(t, \lambda Y)Yd\lambda \tag{8.802}$$

where $Y = (1 + z)^{-1}$ and the bandwidth at receipt is $d\lambda$ centred on wavelength λ. Moreover, by (8.410) or (8.424)

$$t = t_0 - T_0 W(Y). \tag{8.803}$$

The recording apparatus at O records only a fraction $\sigma(\lambda)$ of the arriving energy, where $\sigma(\lambda)$ is the extinction function. It differs from zero in a restricted band of wave-length λ_1 to λ_2, say. Moreover the flow of energy (8.802) impinges on the inner surface of a pseudo-sphere of radius D, the luminosity-distance of the source in Shell r. Hence the (optical) luminosity of the source is

$$L = \frac{1}{4\pi D^2} Y \int_{\lambda_1}^{\lambda_2} \sigma(\lambda)B(t, \lambda Y)d\lambda \quad \text{W.cm}^{-2}, \tag{8.804}$$

where t, of course, is defined by (8.803). A similar standard source in Shell r_s is defined to be one which has the same function B as the source in Shell r but which is so near to O that $t \simeq t_0$ and $Y \simeq 1$. If suffix s refers to this standard source one has

$$L_s = \frac{1}{4\pi D_s^2} \int_{\lambda_1}^{\lambda_2} \sigma(\lambda)B(t_0, \lambda)d\lambda \quad \text{W.cm}^{-2}. \tag{8.805}$$

The optical apparent magnitudes of the two sources are defined to be the pure numbers m and m_s, respectively, where

$$m_s - m = \frac{5}{2}\log\frac{L}{L_s}. \tag{8.806}$$

However, the standard source is usually defined as the source in Shell r transported in our imagination to a distance of 10 pc from the observer. Thus $D_s = 10$ pc in (8.805) and then M is written for m_s in (8.806). It is called the *absolute magnitude* of the source. Thus (8.804) to (8.806) give

$$M - m = -5\log D + 5 + \frac{5}{2}\log\left\{\frac{Y\int_{\lambda_1}^{\lambda_2}\sigma(\lambda)B(t, \lambda Y)d\lambda}{\int_{\lambda_1}^{\lambda_2}\sigma(\lambda)B(t_0,\lambda)d\lambda}\right\}.$$

This formula leads to the introduction of the *K-correction* namely,

$$K(t_0, z) = -\frac{5}{2} \log \left\{ \frac{Y \int_{\lambda_1}^{\lambda_2} \sigma(\lambda) B(t, \lambda Y) d\lambda}{\int_{\lambda_1}^{\lambda_2} \sigma(\lambda) B(t_0, \lambda) d\lambda} \right\}, \tag{8.807}$$

where it has been assumed that t, Y have been expressed in terms of z through (8.803) and the definition $Y = (1 + z)^{-1}$. Hence the relation between m and D becomes

$$\log D = 0 \cdot 2\{m - K(t_0, z) - M\} + 1. \tag{8.808}$$

The bolometric apparent and absolute magnitudes of a source, m_b and M_b, are defined by assuming that $\sigma(\lambda) = 1$ at all wave-lengths. The bolometric *K*-correction is therefore

$$K_b(t_0, z) = -\frac{5}{2} \log \left\{ \frac{\int_0^\infty B(t, x) dx}{\int_0^\infty B(t_0, x) dx} \right\}, \tag{8.809}$$

where $x = \lambda Y$ in the integral in the numerator and $x = \lambda$ in the integral in the denominator. Thus (8.808) is also

$$\log D = 0 \cdot 2\{m_b - K_b(t_0, z) - M_b\} + 1, \tag{8.810}$$

and it is obvious that, if B is independent of the departure-time, the bolometric *K*-correction is zero. Magnitudes of other kinds (photographic, photovisual, etc.) are each defined by a specific function $\sigma(\lambda)$. In principle a corrected apparent magnitude can be defined by

$$m_c = m - K(t_0, z). \tag{8.811}$$

Then (8.808) and (8.810) yield, by elimination of D,

$$m_c = m_b - K_b(t_0, z) + M - M_b. \tag{8.812}$$

When B is independent of the departure-time, so that $K_b = 0$, m_c and m_b differ only because of the difference between M and M_b.

In the general case, (8.811), (8.808) and (8.615) may be combined to give either

$$m = (5 \log cT_0 + M - 5) + K + 5 \log \mathcal{D}, \tag{8.813}$$

or, alternatively,

$$m_c = (5 \log cT_0 + M - 5) + 5 \log \mathcal{D}. \tag{8.814}$$

An approximate expression for the *K*-correction, valid to order z, may be derived as follows: write

$$B_t = \left(\frac{\partial B}{\partial t}\right)_0, \qquad B_\lambda = \left(\frac{\partial B}{\partial \lambda}\right)_0,$$

and

$$I_0 = \int_{\lambda_1}^{\lambda_2} \sigma(\lambda)B(t_0, \lambda)d\lambda,$$

$$I_0' = \int_{\lambda_1}^{\lambda_2} \sigma(\lambda)\lambda B_\lambda d\lambda,$$

$$J_0' = \int_{\lambda_1}^{\lambda_2} \sigma(\lambda)B_t d\lambda,$$

and then employ (8.502) and (8.503) instead of (8.803) to find the departure-time t. One obtains

$$t = t_0 - T_0 z. \tag{8.815}$$

To the same order of approximation $Y = 1 - z$ and therefore (8.807) is

$$K(t_0, z) = -\frac{5}{2}\log\left[\frac{(1-z)\int_{\lambda_1}^{\lambda_2}\sigma(\lambda)B\{t_0 - T_0 z, \lambda(1-z)\}d\lambda}{\int_{\lambda_1}^{\lambda_2}\sigma(\lambda)B(t_0, \lambda)d\lambda}\right].$$

Appropriate expansions to order z then yield

$$K(t_0, z) = (K_1 + W_1)z, \tag{8.816}$$

where K_1, W_1 are constants defined by

$$\left.\begin{aligned}
K_1 &= \frac{5}{2E}\left(1 + \frac{I_0'}{I_0}\right), \\
W_1 &= \frac{5}{2E}T_0\frac{J_0'}{I_0},
\end{aligned}\right\} \tag{8.817}$$

and

$$E = \ln 10 = 2{\cdot}303. \tag{8.818}$$

To this order of approximation formula (8.808) may be – but of course, need not be! – written

$$\log D = 0{\cdot}2\{(m - K_1 z) - (M + W_1 z)\} + 1. \tag{8.819}$$

In this way the part $K_1 z$ of the K-correction is associated with the apparent magnitude of the source and the corrected apparent magnitude is

$$m_c = m - K_1 z.$$

On the other hand, the part $W_1 z$ is regarded as belonging to the absolute magnitude of the source. It arises only when B is a function of the departure-time and corresponds to the fact that the intrinsic power output of the source at the departure-time was different from the intrinsic power output of the standard source at the later time t_0.

In addition to the apparent and absolute magnitudes of the source, its colour-index may also be measured. A two-colour-index is obtained from the differential forms of (8.804) and (8.806). Let dL and dL^* be the flux of energy received, respectively, in the bandwidths $d\lambda$ and $d\lambda^*$. Then the two-colour-index of the source in Shell r is defined to be

$$C(\lambda, \lambda^*) = \frac{5}{2} \log \frac{dL}{dL^*} = \frac{5}{2} \log \frac{\sigma(\lambda)d\lambda}{\sigma(\lambda^*)d\lambda^*} + \frac{5}{2} \log \frac{B(t, \lambda Y)}{B(t, \lambda^* Y)}.$$

Similarly for the nearby standard source, we have

$$C_s(\lambda, \lambda^*) = \frac{5}{2} \log \frac{\sigma(\lambda)d\lambda}{\sigma(\lambda^*)d\lambda^*} + \frac{5}{2} \log \frac{B(t_0, \lambda)}{B(t_0, \lambda^*)}.$$

Thus the difference of the indices of the two sources is

$$C - C_s = \frac{5}{2} \log \left\{ \frac{B(t, \lambda Y)}{B(t_0, \lambda)} \cdot \frac{B(t_0, \lambda^*)}{B(t, \lambda^* Y)} \right\}. \tag{8.820}$$

To the first order in z this gives

$$C - C_s = -\frac{5}{2E} \left[\left\{ \frac{\lambda B_\lambda(t_0, \lambda)}{B(t_0, \lambda)} - \frac{\lambda^* B_\lambda(t_0, \lambda^*)}{B(t_0, \lambda^*)} \right\} \right.$$
$$\left. - T_0 \left\{ \frac{B_t(t_0, \lambda)}{B(t_0, \lambda)} - \frac{B_t(t_0, \lambda^*)}{B(t_0, \lambda^*)} \right\} \right] z. \tag{8.821}$$

The first pair of terms on the right is always present; the second pair occurs only if B is a function of the departure-time.

(ii) *Radio sources.* The emission of radio waves by external galaxies follows the rule that the emitted energy per unit time is proportional to a power of the emitted frequency. For a point-source in Shell r in Fig. 8 the emission at frequency ν_e centred in bandwidth $d\nu_e$ may be written

$$B_0(\nu_e/\nu_0)^x d\nu_e \qquad \text{watts}, \tag{8.822}$$

an expression which replaces the equation (8.801) of the optical case. Here ν_0 is a frequency selected by the observer and is the same for all the sources he observes. The exponent x is called the *spectral index*. Examination of 242 extragalactic radio sources[9] shows that their spectral indices cluster sharply around the value -0.77, with fifty per cent in the range -0.70 to -0.85. None has been found with a spectral index less than -1.23 and the maximum of x is about -0.2. Moreover the sources fall into two classes: in one class the spectral index has a constant value for each source, in the other, the spectral index decreases with increasing frequency. The second class includes objects that are estimated to be intrinsically very powerful emitters of radio waves, like Cygnus A or 3C48. We begin with the consideration of sources of constant x and for definiteness we shall suppose that $-1.1 \leq x \leq -0.2$. The quantity B_0 in (8.822) contains any normalizing factors; we shall also assume that it is a function of the departure-time t of the radiation. On arrival at the observer (8.822) is transformed with the aid of (8.317) and (8.318) to

$$B_0(t)(\nu/\nu_0)^x (1 + z)^{x+1} d\nu.$$

If the luminosity-distance D is expressed for the moment in metres, the flux-density received by the observer is

$$S(\nu) = \frac{B_0(t)(\nu/\nu_0)^x(1 + z)^{x+1}}{4\pi D^2} \qquad \text{W.m}^{-2}(\text{c/s})^{-1}. \qquad (8.823)$$

When B_0 is in fact independent of t, this constant may be conveniently eliminated by considering a 'similar' comparison source. This has the same values of B_0 and of x as the given source; its luminosity-distance is D_s and its red-shift z_s. We then have

$$\frac{S(\nu)}{S_s(\nu)} = \frac{(1 + z)^{x+1}}{(1 + z_s)^{x+1}} \frac{D_s^2}{D^2}, \qquad (8.824)$$

and, of course, D_s and D may now both be expressed in parsec.

Another way of eliminating B_0 is to use the apparent and absolute radio magnitudes and the method applies equally well whether B_0 is constant or not. These magnitudes have been defined by studying nearby 'ordinary' radio galaxies and the original observations[10] were made at 158 Mcs. The apparent radio magnitude, m_r, of a source whose flux-density at 158 Mcs is $S(158)$ is defined by the empirical equation

$$m_r = - 53 \cdot 4 - \frac{5}{2} \log S(158). \qquad (8.825)$$

If ν_0 is identified with 158 Mcs, it follows from (8.823) and (8.825) that

$$m_r = - 53 \cdot 4 - \frac{5}{2} \log \{B_0/4\pi\} + 5 \log D - \frac{5}{2}(1 + x) \log (1 + z).$$

The absolute radio magnitude M_r is defined by transporting the given source in our imagination to a distance of 10 pc. At such a distance its red-shift would be zero. We shall still suppose, however, that this imaginary translation of the source is performed without alteration of the value of $B_0(t)$. Thus

$$M_r(t) = - 53 \cdot 4 - \frac{5}{2} \log \{B_0(t)/4\pi\} + 5,$$

and therefore

$$m_r - M_r(t) = 5 \log D - 5 - \frac{5}{2}(1 + x) \log (1 + z),$$

or

$$\log D = 0 \cdot 2\{m_r - K_r - M_r(z)\} + 1, \qquad (8.826)$$

where K_r is the radio K-correction

$$K_r = - \frac{5}{2}(1 + x) \log (1 + z), \qquad (8.827)$$

and, since t is a function of z, we regard M_r as a function of the red-shift of the source instead of as a function of the departure-time.

The equation (8.826) may also be written in a form analogous to (8.814), namely,

$$m_r - K_r = (5 \log cT_0 + M_r(z) - 5) + 5 \log \mathscr{D}, \qquad (8.828)$$

where $m_r - K_r$ is the corrected apparent radio magnitude.

When the flux-density of the source is measured at a frequency of ν Mcs, different from $\nu_0 = 158$ Mcs, the radio magnitude is calculated from

$$m_r = -53\cdot4 - \frac{5}{2}\log S(\nu) + \frac{5}{2}\log \frac{S(\nu)}{S(158)}.$$

But since for a given source $S(\nu)/S(158) = (\nu/158)^x$ we have

$$m_r = -53\cdot4 + \frac{5x}{2}\log \frac{\nu}{158} - \frac{5}{2}\log S(\nu). \qquad (8.829)$$

Ryle and his co-workers at Cambridge employ a method which avoids the initial specification of the detailed law (8.822) of energy emission. Suppose that the isotropic emission of the source, in watts $(c/s)^{-1}$ ster^{-1} at frequency ν_e in the bandwidth $d\nu_e$, is P. Then P is presumably a function of ν_e and it may also be a function of the departure-time t. The total emission of the source is therefore

$$4\pi P(\nu_e, t)d\nu_e \qquad \text{watts.}$$

On arrival at the observer this is reckoned to be radiation of frequency ν in the bandwidth $d\nu$ and amounts to

$$4\pi(1 + z)P\{\nu(1 + z), t\}d\nu \qquad \text{watts.}$$

Therefore the flux-density is

$$S(\nu) = \frac{(1 + z)P\{\nu(1 + z), t\}}{D^2} \qquad \text{W.m}^{-2}\text{ (c/s)}^{-1}, \qquad (8.830)$$

where D is again converted to metres. A set of sources which are all similar in the sense that each one has the same function P, will therefore have different numerators in the fraction on the right-hand side of (8.830) if their red-shifts are appreciable. This is true even if P is independent of the departure-time. However if the source is imagined transported to 10 pc, keeping its rate of emission as it was at the departure-time, the resulting $P(\nu, t)$ can be related to the absolute radio magnitude of the source. In fact, by (8.829) and (8.830) with $D = 3\cdot086 \times 10^{17}$m, we have

$$M_r(t) = 34\cdot05 - \frac{5}{2}\log P(\nu, t) + \frac{5x}{2}\log \frac{\nu}{158}. \qquad (8.831)$$

Ryle's method is also useful when spectral indices that vary with frequency are in question (see Sec. 9.2).

(iii) *Extended sources of radiation.* The classical theory of radiation, when the source and observer are at relative rest, is relatively simple and symmetrical because of the existence of an absolute distance. In the uniform models of the universe the theory is complicated by the fact that distance by apparent size is different from luminosity-distance. We shall not attempt to reconstruct the analogue, in its most general form, of the classical theory but shall content ourselves with a particular case. Let the source lie in Shell r of Fig. 8 and, in Fig. 9, let LMN be the physical boundary of the source, the

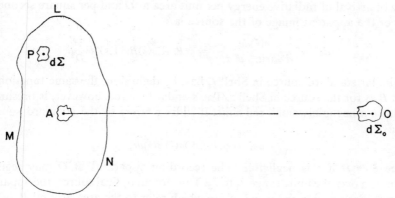

FIG. 9.

observer being at O. We assume that the most luminous portion of the source lies around the point A and that the entire area of the source may be regarded as being perpendicular to OA. The angular size of the source as viewed from O is small, though finite. The area $d\Sigma_0$ at O is also perpendicular to OA.

For simplicity, consider a source whose radiative output is constant in time. Let $d\Sigma$ be an element of area centred on a point P in LMN, whose co-ordinates are (r, θ, ϕ) according to O who, as usual, is at $r = 0$. We shall say that the rate of emission by $d\Sigma$ of radiative energy of wave-length λ_e in the bandwidth $d\lambda_e$ is

$$\gamma(P, A)B(\lambda_e)d\lambda_e d\Sigma,$$

where $B(\lambda_e)$ now refers to the emission at A and $\gamma(P, A)$ gives the fraction of the emission at P relative to that at A. If the appropriate solid angle of the target area $d\Sigma_0$ is $d\Omega_0$, then the rate of passage of radiative energy through $d\Sigma_0$ is

$$\gamma(P, A)B(\lambda_e)d\lambda_e d\Sigma d\Omega_0,$$

or, with due allowance for the change of wave-length and of bandwidth,

$$de = \gamma(P, A)B(\lambda Y)Yd\lambda d\Sigma d\Omega_0.$$

Let $d\Sigma$ be defined by increments $d\theta$ and $d\phi$ of the coordinates so that

$$d\Sigma = \xi^2 \sin \theta \, d\theta d\phi,$$

where ξ is the distance by apparent size of the source. Moreover, for the motion of the radiation towards the target $d\Sigma_0$, the appropriate distance is the luminosity-distance D and therefore

$$d\Omega_0 = d\Sigma_0/D^2.$$

The factor $\sin \theta \, d\theta d\phi$ may be equated, from the observer's viewpoint, with one square second of arc. Hence if $\sigma(\lambda)$ is the extinction function, the registered rate of arrival of radiative energy per unit area at O and per square second of arc of the apparent image of the source is

$$de'' = \frac{\sigma(\lambda)de}{d\Sigma_0(\sin\theta\, d\theta d\phi)} = \gamma(P, A)\sigma(\lambda)B(\lambda Y)Yd\lambda\frac{\xi^2}{D^2}.$$

A similar standard source in Shell r_s has, by definition, the same functions γ and B as for the source in Shell r. The standard source, however, is presumed to have a negligibly small red-shift. If suffix s refers to the standard source, then

$$de''_s = \gamma(P_s, A_s)\sigma(\lambda)B(\lambda)d\lambda,$$

since $\xi = D$ if z is negligible. The recording apparatus at O may register radiation over the finite range λ_1 to λ_2. Thus for an optical source, the apparent magnitudes per square second of arc which refer to the area around P_s in the standard source and to P in the source in Shell r, are defined by

$$m''_s - m'' = \frac{5}{2}\log\left(\frac{\int_{\lambda_1}^{\lambda_2} de''}{\int_{\lambda_1}^{\lambda_2} de''_s}\right).$$

Now $\xi^2/D^2 = Y^4$ and therefore

$$m''_s - m'' = \frac{5}{2}\log\left\{\frac{\gamma(P, A)}{\gamma(P_s, A_s)}Y^4\right\} + \frac{5}{2}\log\left\{\frac{Y\int_{\lambda_1}^{\lambda_2}\sigma(\lambda)B(\lambda Y)d\lambda}{\int_{\lambda_1}^{\lambda_2}\sigma(\lambda)B(\lambda)d\lambda}\right\}.$$

Reference to (8.807) shows that the second term on the right is the K-correction for the case when the emission of the source is independent of the departure-time. Therefore, since $Y = (1 + z)^{-1}$,

$$m_s - m'' = \frac{5}{2}\log\left\{\frac{\gamma(P, A)}{\gamma(P_s, A_s)}\frac{1}{(1 + z)^4}\right\} - K(z), \qquad (8.832)$$

a formula which will be discussed further from the empirical point of view in Sec. 9.3. Suffice it to say for the moment that the calculation of m'' from the red-shift of the source and a measurement of m''_s involves not only a knowledge of the function γ but also of the K-correction.

If the source in Shell r is a radio source which has a small angular extent relative to the beam-width of the radio telescope at O, we may proceed in the following way. Let S be the total flux density received by the observer from the source and let each element of area $d\Sigma$ contribute equally to the total flux-density. Let dS be the contribution from $d\Sigma$; then the *brightness* of this element of area of the source is b where

$$dS = bd\Omega,$$

and $d\Omega$ is the solid angle subtended at O by $d\Sigma$. Hence $d\Omega = d\Sigma/\xi^2$ and so for the whole physical area of the source

$$S = \frac{b\Sigma}{\xi^2}.$$

Consideration of a similar source in Shell r_s would give the result that

$$\frac{S}{S_s} = \frac{b}{b_s}\frac{\xi_s^2}{\xi^2},$$

and so with the aid of (8.824) and (8.617)

$$\frac{b}{b_s} = \frac{(1 + z_s)^{3-x}}{(1 + z)^{3-x}}. \tag{8.833}$$

If the flux-density is measured at frequency ν, the *brightness temperature* $\mathscr{T}$ of a source of brightness b is defined by

$$\mathscr{T} = \frac{c^2}{\nu^2}\frac{b}{2k},$$

where k is now Boltzmann's constant. Hence (8.833) is also expressible as

$$\frac{\mathscr{T}}{\mathscr{T}_s} = \frac{(1 + z_s)^{3-x}}{(1 + z)^{3-x}}. \tag{8.834}$$

Another expression for the brightness temperature that can easily be derived from the foregoing formulae is

$$\mathscr{T} = \left(\frac{c^2}{2k\nu^2}\frac{1}{\Sigma}\right)S\xi^2. \tag{8.835}$$

8.9. Non-uniform Models

In the uniform models of the universe, the observed distribution of matter is replaced by a uniform representative gas. The next stage in the construction of a realistic model of the observed universe would be to find the metric of a space-time in which each individual galaxy was represented by a condensation of matter having a density greater than that of its surroundings. Numerous attempts to solve this problem have been made[11]. One of the earliest[12], in the form of an exact solution of the equations (4.419) to (4.422), corresponds to a single condensation centred at $r = 0$ and surrounded by an ambient perfect fluid. The metric of space-time is

$$ds^2 = A\,dt^2 - B(dr^2 + r^2 d\theta^2 + r^2 \sin^2\theta\, d\phi^2)/c^2,$$

where

$$A^{1/2} = \frac{1 - \dfrac{me^{-g/2}}{2R_0 r}\left(1 + \dfrac{kr^2}{4}\right)^{1/2}}{1 + \dfrac{me^{-g/2}}{2R_0 r}\left(1 + \dfrac{kr^2}{4}\right)^{1/2}},$$

$$B = \frac{\left\{1 + \dfrac{me^{-g/2}}{2R_0 r}\left(1 + \dfrac{kr^2}{4}\right)^{1/2}\right\}^4}{\left(1 + \dfrac{kr^2}{4}\right)^2}R_0^2 e^g,$$

N

m, R_0 are constants and g is a function of t. Thus, if $m = 0$ and $R = R_0 e^{g/2}$, the metric (8.207) is recovered; but if g has the constant value zero and $k = 0$, the Schwarzschild metric (5.123) is obtained by writing $\bar{r} = R_0 r$.

When there is more than one condensation of matter – each galaxy being represented by a condensation – an approximate form of the metric can be established[13]. The hypothesis is made that each condensation is spherically symmetric. As a guide, consider the approximate solution (4.226) of Einstein's equations, viz.:

$$ds^2 = (1 - \kappa\psi)(dx^4)^2 - \frac{1 + \kappa\psi}{c^2}\{(dx^1)^2 + (dx^2)^2 + (dx^3)^2\}, \qquad (8.901)$$

and let it correspond to n spherical bodies of masses $m_1, m_2, \ldots, m_n$, in an otherwise empty space-time. Then the results of Sec. 4.2 show that ψ must satisfy Laplace's equation

$$\nabla^2\psi = 0, \qquad (8.902)$$

and the appropriate solution must be

$$\psi = \sum_{i=1}^{n} \frac{m_i}{\{(x^1 - x_i^1)^2 + (x^2 - x_i^2)^2 + (x^3 - x_i^3)^2\}^{1/2}}, \qquad (8.903)$$

the ith condensation being located at (x_i^1, x_i^2, x_i^3). On the other hand, when there are no condensations, and a uniform perfect fluid is alone present, the space-time has the metric (8.213) with $(t, x, y, z) = (x^4, x^1, x^2, x^3)$. It therefore suggests itself that a combination of condensations with a distribution of perfect fluid would have a metric of form (4.401) wherein

$$D = 1 - \kappa\psi, \qquad A = B = C = \frac{R^2(x^4)}{c^2(1 + kr^2/4)^2}(1 + \kappa\omega), \qquad (8.904)$$

where ψ, ω are functions of all four coordinates and powers of κ higher than the first are to be neglected.

The first step in working out Einstein's equations may be made by taking B and C equal to A and denoting a partial derivative of A by a subscript. Thus Dingle's formulae are ($i, j = 1, 2, 3$)

$$8\pi G A T^{ii} = \tfrac{1}{2}\left(\frac{\nabla^2 A}{A^2} + \frac{\nabla^2 D}{AD} - \frac{\sum_{j=1}^{3} A_j^2}{A^3} - \tfrac{1}{2}\frac{\sum_{j=1}^{3} D_j^2}{AD^2}\right)$$
$$- \left(\frac{A_{44}}{AD} - \tfrac{1}{2}\frac{A_4 D_4}{AD^2} - \tfrac{1}{4}\frac{A_4^2}{A^2 D}\right) + \Lambda$$
$$- \left\{\tfrac{1}{2}\frac{A_{ii}}{A^2} + \tfrac{1}{2}\frac{D_{ii}}{AD} - \tfrac{3}{4}\frac{A_i^2}{A^3} - \tfrac{1}{4}\frac{D_i^2}{AD^2} - \tfrac{1}{2}\frac{A_i D_i}{A^2 D}\right\}, \qquad (8.905)$$

$$8\pi G A^2 T^{ij} = -\left\{\tfrac{1}{2}\frac{A_{ij}}{A} + \tfrac{1}{2}\frac{D_{ij}}{D} - \tfrac{3}{4}\frac{A_i A_j}{A^2} - \tfrac{1}{4}\frac{D_i D_j}{D^2}\right.$$
$$\left. - \tfrac{1}{4}\frac{A_i D_j + A_j D_i}{AD}\right\}, \qquad (i \neq j), \qquad (8.906)$$

$$- 8\pi GADT^{i4} = -\left(\frac{A_{i4}}{A} - \frac{A_i A_4}{A^2} - \tfrac{1}{2}\frac{D_i A_4}{AD}\right), \tag{8.907}$$

$$- 8\pi GDT^{44} = \frac{\nabla^2 A}{A^2} - \tfrac{3}{4}\frac{\sum\limits_{j=1}^{3} A_j^2}{A^3} - \tfrac{3}{4}\frac{A_4^2}{A^2 D} + \varLambda. \tag{8.908}$$

It will be assumed that, except in the (small) regions occupied by the condensations, the energy-tensor still has the form appropriate to a perfect fluid, viz.:

$$T^{\mu\nu} = \left(\rho + \frac{p}{c^2}\right)u^\mu u^\nu - g^{\mu\nu}\frac{p}{c^2}.$$

Suppose now that, for the space-time with coefficients (8.904), co-moving coordinates are possible; then $T^{i4} = 0$, $(i = 1, 2, 3)$ and, by integrating (8.907) once with respect to x^i,

$$\frac{\partial \log A}{\partial x^4} = FD^{1/2},$$

where F is an arbitrary function of x^4. Hence by (8.904), to the first power in κ,

$$2\frac{R'}{R} + \kappa\omega_4 = F(x^4)\left(1 - \frac{\kappa}{2}\psi\right),$$

and thus $F = 2R'/R$ and

$$\omega_4 = -\frac{R'}{R}\psi. \tag{8.909}$$

Also the velocity 4-vector for the perfect fluid becomes $(u^4, 0, 0, 0)$ and, since it is a unit vector, it satisfies

$$1 = (1 - \kappa\psi)(u^4)^2. \tag{8.910}$$

This form for the velocity 4-vector yields $T^{ij} = 0$, $(i \neq j)$, since the metric is orthogonal, and also $T^{ii} = p/(Ac^2)$, $(i = 1, 2, 3)$. Hence in (8.905), the term in the curly brackets must have the same value for each of the three values of i (the consistency relations for the problem) and in (8.906) the right-hand side must be zero for each pair of values ij, $(i \neq j)$. These conditions are satisfied if Z is a function symmetrical in (x^1, x^2, x^3) and

$$Z\delta_{ij} = -\left\{\tfrac{1}{2}\frac{A_{ij}}{A} + \tfrac{1}{2}\frac{D_{ij}}{D} - \tfrac{3}{4}\frac{A_i A_j}{A^2} - \tfrac{1}{4}\frac{D_i D_j}{D^2} - \tfrac{1}{4}\frac{A_i D_j + A_j D_i}{AD}\right\}.$$

Working out the expression on the right-hand side to the first order in κ with the aid of (8.904), we obtain

$$Z\delta_{ij} = \tfrac{1}{2}\frac{k\delta_{ij}}{1 + kr^2/4} - \frac{\kappa}{2}\left\{(\omega - \psi)_{ji} + \tfrac{1}{2}\frac{kx^i}{1 + kr^2/4}(\omega - \psi)_j + \tfrac{1}{2}\frac{kx^j}{1 + kr^2/4}(\omega - \psi)_i\right\}.$$

Hence symmetry with respect to i and j is secured if

$$\omega = \psi$$

and then

$$Z = \tfrac{1}{2}\frac{k}{1 + kr^2/4}.$$

The first of these equations, combined with (8.909), gives, after a partial integration with respect to x^4,

$$\psi = \omega = \Psi(x^1, x^2, x^3)R^{-1}, \qquad (8.911)$$

where Ψ is an arbitrary function of (x^1, x^2, x^3).

The considerations used so far involve, firstly, the introduction of co-moving coordinates and, secondly, the imposition of isotropy requirements on the coefficients of the metric which reduce the energy-tensor to a density and a pressure, at least at all points not occupied by condensations. These considerations do not suffice to determine the function ψ. However, the operator

$$\left(1 + \frac{kr^2}{4}\right)^2\left\{\nabla^2 - \tfrac{1}{2}\sum_{j=1}^{3}\frac{kx^j}{(1 + kr^2/4)}\frac{\partial}{\partial x^j}\right\},$$

is known to be the analogue[14] for the 3-space with metric

$$ds^2 = \frac{(dx^1)^2 + (dx^2)^2 + (dx^3)^2}{(1 + kr^2/4)^2}$$

of the operator ∇^2 in ordinary Euclidean 3-space whose metric is

$$ds^2 = (dx^1)^2 + (dx^2)^2 + (dx^3)^2.$$

Now (8.903) is a sum of the elementary solutions of Laplace's equation (8.902). Hence for the metric with coefficients (8.904) the function ψ, appropriate to an arbitrary number n of condensations, *will be defined* as a sum of elementary solutions[15] of the equation

$$\left\{\nabla^2 - \tfrac{1}{2}\sum_{j=1}^{3}\frac{kx^j}{1 + kr^2/4}\frac{\partial}{\partial xj}\right\}\Psi = 0,$$

where $\psi R = \Psi$ by (8.911). Converting the equation to spherical polars (r, θ, ϕ) by formulae of the form (8.212), it becomes, for $k \neq 0$,

$$\frac{\partial^2\Psi}{\partial r^2} + \frac{2}{r\left(1 + \dfrac{kr^2}{4}\right)}\frac{\partial\Psi}{\partial r} + \frac{1}{r^2\sin\theta}\frac{\partial}{\partial\theta}\left(\sin\theta\frac{\partial\Psi}{\partial\theta}\right) + \frac{1}{r^2\sin^2\theta}\frac{\partial^2\Psi}{\partial\phi^2} = 0, \qquad (8.912)$$

whilst, of course, for $k = 0$, it is simply $\nabla^2\Psi = 0$. The elementary solution[16] of (8.912) corresponding to a condensation of constant mass m_i located at $r = a_i$, $\theta = \theta_i$, $\phi = \phi_i$, is

$$\Psi_i = \left(\frac{1}{a_i'}\frac{z_i'}{z_i} - \frac{1}{a_i}\frac{z_i}{z_i'}\right)m_i,$$

where

$$z_i^2 = r^2 + a_i^2 - 2a_ir\{\cos\theta\cos\theta_i + \sin\theta\sin\theta_i\cos(\phi - \phi_i)\},$$
$$z_i'^2 = r^2 + a_i'^2 + 2a_i'r\{\cos\theta\cos\theta_i + \sin\theta\sin\theta_i\cos(\phi - \phi_i)\},$$

and a_i, a'_i are related by

$$a_i a'_i = \frac{4}{k}.$$

Thus for n condensations, the function ψ is

$$\left.\begin{aligned}
\psi = \frac{\Psi}{R} &= \frac{1}{R} \sum_{i=1}^{n} m_i \left(\frac{1}{a'_i} \frac{z'_i}{z_i} - \frac{1}{a_i} \frac{z_i}{z'_i} \right) \quad (k \neq 0), \\
&= \frac{1}{R} \sum_{i=1}^{n} \frac{m_i}{z_i} \quad (k = 0).
\end{aligned}\right\} \qquad (8.913)$$

Hence finally the space-time appropriate to n condensations immersed in a distribution of perfect fluid has the metric

$$ds^2 = (1 - \kappa\psi)(dx^4)^2 - \frac{R^2(1 + \kappa\psi)}{c^2(1 + kr^2/4)^2} \{(dx^1)^2 + (dx^2)^2 + (dx^3)^2\}, \qquad (8.914)$$

where ψ is given by one or other of the formulae (8.913) according to the value of k, and terms of order higher than the first in κ are neglected. The effect of ψ is to introduce small gravitational potentials analogous to those of mass-points in Newtonian theory, or, approximately, to those of the Schwarzschild space-time (5.119), in a space-time corresponding to a distribution of perfect fluid. So long as the masses m_i are small, therefore, it is evident that the results of Secs. 8.2 to 8.8 will not be greatly modified except, of course, in the immediate neighbourhood of a condensation where the terms in $\kappa\psi$ are no longer small and the approximation breaks down.

The condensations have fixed coordinates in the co-moving system and therefore move with the perfect fluid. If R is an increasing function of x^4, then at a point (r, θ, ϕ) which is remote from any condensation, the value of ψ continually decreases with the time. Hence the effect of the condensations is most conspicuous in the early stages and becomes increasingly unimportant as the expansion proceeds.

In the general case, when ψ is given by (8.913), the calculation of the components of the energy-tensor is laborious. But a simple illustration is obtained when k and R are assigned the values they possess in the de Sitter universe [model A2(vi–b)], viz.:

$$k = 0, \qquad R = R_0 e^{\sqrt{(\Lambda/3)}x^4}.$$

By (8.905) and (8.908) the components that do not vanish identically are given by

$$8\pi G A T^{ii} = \Lambda - 3\left(\frac{\Lambda}{3}\right) + \frac{\kappa}{R_0}\left(\frac{\Lambda}{3} - \frac{\Lambda}{3}\right)\Psi e^{-\sqrt{(\Lambda/3)}x^4} = 0, \qquad (i = 1, 2, 3)$$

$$-8\pi G D T^{44} = \Lambda - 3\left(\frac{\Lambda}{3}\right) + \frac{\kappa c^2}{R_0^3} e^{-3\sqrt{(\Lambda/3)}x^4} \nabla^2 \Psi = 0,$$

since, when $k = 0$, $\nabla^2 \Psi$ vanishes everywhere except at the condensations themselves. Thus the space-time (8.914) now represents an arbitrary distribution of gravitational condensations in otherwise empty space, all of which are receding from one another. This would seem to be a possible first approximation to the system of galaxies, regarded as spherical masses separated by empty regions.

CHAPTER 9

Observational Cosmology

It is often argued that some one of the uniform model universes already considered must necessarily represent the observed universe of galaxies. In spite of the heterogeneity that observation reveals, it is said that the universe must obey a cosmological principle which makes every part of it essentially similar to every other part. The principle is defended partly on the observational grounds described in Sec. 8.1. But obviously these can only refer to an undetermined fraction of the entire physical universe. The universal applicability of the cosmological principle is said to be necessary on other grounds, for example, because it is 'unthinkable' that there should be radical differences between different parts of the universe, or because it would be contrary to the spirit of the Copernican revolution if the terrestrial point of observation were to have a unique character. These arguments are largely illusory: it is quite easy to think of a universe containing one large region occupied by galaxies with empty space outside. All that need be assumed is that our Galaxy happens to lie near the centre of the region and that terrestrial telescopes are too weak to identify objects near the region's boundary. The Copernican objection to such an idea is also inapplicable. The transfer of the centre of the solar system from the Earth to the Sun is not dictated by a principle of modesty which debars the Earth from holding a special position in the system. The Copernican idea is accepted because it enormously simplifies and harmonizes all the observations of the motions of the bodies of the solar system. Without the idea, planetary motions would today be so complex in appearance as to be wellnigh unintelligible. But a similar confusion would be absent in cosmology[1] if our own Galaxy lay at or near the centre of a non-uniform distribution of galaxies. If therefore the uniform models described in the preceding chapter are employed in the interpretation of astronomical data, the reason lies not in necessity, but because these models appear to provide the simplest first step that can be taken. The models idealize, extend to the entire universe, and certainly exaggerate, the degree of uniformity which is observed in the accessible portion of the physical universe. Idealization of a physical situation, which means its replacement by a similar, but much simpler, one is a commonplace in mathematical physics. It is in this sense that the confrontation of the theory of the preceding chapter with the data of observation is to be understood.

A preliminary point concerns the physical counterpart of the perfect fluid of density ρ and pressure p which is described by the space-time (8.207). One interpretation is that the particles constituting this fluid are the galaxies themselves. The galaxies should therefore have world-lines represented by any time-like geodesic of (8.207). Nevertheless this identification of the fluid particles is always combined with the statement that the galaxies, regarded as sources of radiation, have special world-lines. This appears to be an arbitrary restriction imposed on the nature of the geodesics which represent the particles of the fluid.

An alternative interpretation of the perfect fluid is that it is the result of an imagined disintegration of all material bodies in the universe into their constituent atoms, the resulting stuff being imagined to be instantaneously and evenly spread out in space. This material may be called the *representative gas*; the density of this gas near the observer in Fig. 8 may be plausibly identified with the average density of matter in space computed by astronomers. The density will be determined in Sec. 9.2. The pressure of the representative gas may be taken to be the counterpart of all those forms of energy in the observed universe which are not described as mass. The internal energies of stars and interstellar gas clouds, their kinetic and gravitational energies, the pressure of radiation, and so on, are examples of these forms of non-material energy. All this energetic content of the observed universe is to be conceived of as distributed evenly among the products of the imagined disintegration. Such estimates[2] of this energy as have been made indicate that its density equivalent, p/c^2, is at the present moment, not larger than 10^{-6} times the density of matter. Hence zero-pressure models are likely to be sufficient for the elucidation of the data of observation.

This interpretation of the perfect fluid – which we shall adopt – is consistent with the postulate that galaxies, regarded as sources of radiation, have special world-lines. Clearly the imagined disintegration destroyed the galaxies as individual objects. They must be replaced in the model in some fashion and the special world-line postulate is the simplest definition of a source that can be made.

In the remainder of this chapter the terrestrial astronomer will be identified with the observer O of Fig. 8 and the instant t_0 with the present moment. The observer thus also has the special world-line $r = 0$.

9.1. Red-shift and Apparent Magnitude

The first kind of observational data which are interpretable by the formulae of the preceding chapter are the measurements of red-shifts and of the apparent magnitudes of galaxies. The relevant formulae are, firstly, (8.615) or

$$\mathscr{D} = \frac{R_0}{cT_0}(1 + z)\mathscr{S}_k\left\{\frac{cT_0}{R_0}I(z)\right\}, \qquad (9.101)$$

which gives $\mathscr{D}$ as a function of z, and either (8.813) or (8.814), namely

$$m = (5 \log cT_0 + M - 5) + K(t_0,z) + 5 \log \mathscr{D}, \qquad (9.102)$$

$$m_c = (5 \log cT_0 + M - 5) + 5 \log \mathscr{D}. \qquad (9.103)$$

Elimination of $\mathscr{D}$ between (9.101) and either (9.102) or (9.103) yields a relation between the observables m (or m_c) and z. We leave aside for the moment the exact relation between $\mathscr{D}$ and z and use instead the approximation (8.616) which gives

$$\log \mathscr{D} = \log z - \frac{1}{2E}(q_0 - 1)z,$$

correct to the order z^2. If also the first order approximation to the K-correction is employed, one finds by (8.816)

$$m = (5 \log cT_0 + M - 5) + 5 \log z + \left\{K_1 + W_1 - \frac{5}{2E}(q_0 - 1)\right\}z, \quad (9.104)$$

and, if $W_1 = 0$,

$$m_c = (5 \log cT_0 + M - 5) + 5 \log z - \frac{5}{2E}(q_0 - 1)z. \qquad (9.105)$$

These relations would determine T_0 (or H by (8.324)) and q_0 from pairs of measured values of (m, z) or of (m_c, z) provided that K_1 and W_1 were known and also provided that the observations referred to a set of galaxies whose absolute magnitudes were all equal. Clearly if the absolute magnitude of each galaxy was entirely arbitrary, or even if it varied in some unknown fashion with z, no conclusions could be drawn with regard to the values of the Hubble constant and the acceleration factor.

The objects which are most likely to fulfil the condition of the constancy of absolute magnitude are the brightest members of large clusters of galaxies. Sandage[3] has studied eighteen of these clusters, the average red-shifts for each cluster ranging from $z = 0.004$ to $z = 0.202$. The photographic magnitude of a 'composite' brightest cluster member was obtained by studying the relative apparent magnitudes of the first, third, fifth and tenth brightest galaxy in a cluster. The apparent magnitude of the brightest member computed in this way is given in the column headed m of Table VII. The red-shift of the cluster as a whole was the average of the red-shifts of as many members of each cluster as were measured. These red-shifts are given in the column headed z. The first order K-correction, $K_1 z$, for photographic magnitudes is not yet accurately known; if galaxies radiated like black-bodies[4] at some temperature between $5000°$ and $6000°$, K_1 would lie between 2 and 3. But galaxies do not radiate in this fashion and the value of K_1 calculated by Sandage from the spectral energy distribution of the galaxy M32 is 4.7. However, it is believed that even this value is an underestimate[5], though no specific numerical value has been stated. The corrected apparent magnitudes $m_c = m - 4.7z$ are shown in the column headed $m_c(S)$.

TABLE VII

Cluster	z	5 log z	m	y	$m_c(S)$	y_c	$m_c(B)$	m_c^*	y_c^*
Virgo	0·004	−12 + 0·0103	9·17	21·1597	9·16	21·1497	9·2	8·98	20·9697
Perseus 0316 + 4121	0·018	−9 + 0·2764	12·59	21·3136	12·51	21·2336		12·33	21·0536
Coma 1257 + 2812	0·022	−9 + 0·7121	12·94	21·2279	12·84	21·1279	12·8	12·66	20·9479
Hercules 1603 + 1755	0·036	−8 + 0·7815	14·28	21·4985	14·12	21·3385		13·94	21·1585
2308 + 0720	0·043	−7 + 0·1673	14·95	21·7827	14·78	21·6127		14·60	21·4327
2322 + 1425	0·044	−7 + 0·2173	15·25	22·0327	15·04	21·8227		14·86	21·6427
1145 + 5559	0·052	−7 + 0·5800	15·95	22·3700	15·71	22·1300		15·53	21·9500
0106 − 1536	0·053	−7 + 0·6214	15·46	21·8386	15·21	21·5886		15·03	21·4086
1024 + 1039	0·065	−6 + 0·0646	16·19	22·1254	15·88	21·8154		15·70	21·6354
1239 + 1852	0·072	−6 + 0·2867	15·55	21·2633	15·22	20·9333		15·04	20·7533
Cor. Bor. 1520 + 2754	0·072	−6 + 0·2867	16·26	21·9733	15·93	21·6433	15·6	15·75	21·4633
0705 + 3506	0·078	−6 + 0·4605	16·63	22·1695	16·26	21·7995		16·08	21·6195
Boötes 1431 + 3146	0·131	−5 + 0·5864	17·92	22·3336	17·31	21·7236		17·13	21·5436
1055 + 5702	0·134	−5 + 0·6355	17·94	22·3045	17·31	21·6745	16·9	17·13	21·4945
0025 + 2223	0·159	−4 + 0·0070	18·13	22·1230	17·39	21·3830		17·21	21·2030
0138 + 1840	0·173	−4 + 0·1902	17·97	21·7798	17·16	20·9698		16·98	20·7898
0925 + 2044	0·192	−4 + 0·4165	18·44	22·0235	17·54	21·1235	17·4	17·36	20·9435
Hydra 0855 + 0321	0·202	−4 + 0·5268	18·78	22·2532	17·84	21·3132		17·66	21·1332
0024 + 1654	0·290	−3 + 0·3120					18·7	18·70	21·3880
1448 + 2617	0·350	−3 + 0·7203					18·5	18·50	20·7797
1410 + 5224	0·460	−2 + 0·3138					19·3	19·30	20·9862

If

$$a = 5 \log cT_0 + M - 5,$$

$$b' = K_1 + W_1 - \frac{5}{2E}(q_0 - 1),$$

$$b = -\frac{5}{2E}(q_0 - 1), \tag{9.106}$$

$$y = m - 5 \log z,$$

$$y_c = m_c - 5 \log z,$$

then (9.104) and (9.105) become respectively

$$y = a + b'z, \tag{9.107}$$

$$y_c = a + bz. \tag{9.108}$$

The question of the so-called 'linearity of the red-shift versus apparent magnitude relation' is then resolved by deciding whether or not $y = a$ or $y_c = a$ represents the data. Fig. 10 shows a plot of y against z and an eye

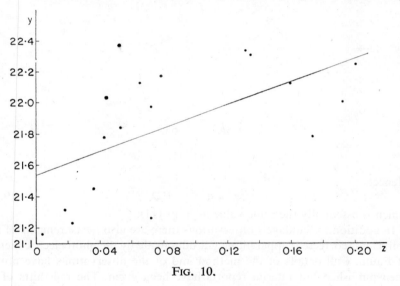

FIG. 10.

inspection suggests that y does vary with z. A least squares solution for y against z yields the straight line

$$y = (21 \cdot 54 \pm 0 \cdot 14) + (3 \cdot 74 \pm 1 \cdot 33)z. \tag{9.109}$$

The errors shown are the quadratic mean errors to be feared in the determination of the constants. The probable error in b' is $0 \cdot 89$ and the determination of this constant appears to be significant. The second equation of (9.106) yields

$$q_0 = 1 + (K_1 + W_1 - 3 \cdot 74) (0 \cdot 921). \tag{9.110}$$

Thus if $K_1 = 4\cdot7$ and $W_1 = 0$

$$q_0 = 1\cdot88 \pm 1\cdot22, \tag{9.111}$$

and, of course, if $K_1 > 4\cdot7$ with $W_1 = 0$ this positive value of q_0 is increased. On the other hand when the corrected apparent magnitudes are employed, the y_c entries of Table VII must be used and the result† is

$$y_c = (21\cdot55 \pm 0\cdot14) - (0\cdot973 \pm 1\cdot327)z, \tag{9.112}$$

the straight line in Fig. 11 corresponding to the mean values of the constants.

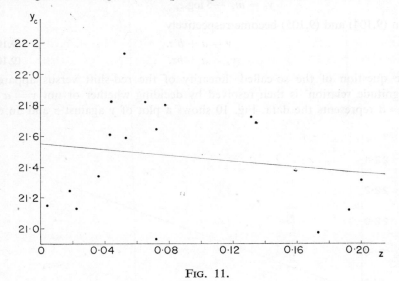

FIG. 11.

Hence

$$q_0 = 1\cdot90 \pm 1\cdot22, \tag{9.113}$$

which is essentially the same value as in (9.111).

In addition to Sandage's observations there are also measurements of red-shifts and (corrected) apparent magnitudes made by the photoelectric method of Baum. Full details of the method and of the observations have not yet been published but interim reports have been given. The red-shifts of the last three clusters in Table VII differ slightly from those published by Baum in 1962. They were obtained, together with the $m_c(B)$ entries, from a graph[6] of Baum's results which was exhibited at the American Astronomical Society meeting in the summer of 1960. The average difference between Sandage's and Baum's values of m_c for the five clusters observed by both investigators is $0^m\cdot18$. In the column headed m_c^*, Sandage's m_c have been reduced by $0^m\cdot18$ and Baum's values have been accepted for the last three clusters. Admittedly

† Sandage (1961 *Astrophys. J.* **133**, 355, Eqn. (26)) gives 21·58 for the constant term, the term in z being neglected.

this is a crude method of reducing one set of apparent magnitudes to another but it is nevertheless the case that the corresponding y_e^* are now related to z by

$$y_e^* = (21 \cdot 37 \pm 0 \cdot 11) - (0 \cdot 92 \pm 0 \cdot 61)z, \tag{9.114}$$

in which the quadratic mean errors are shown. Therefore the probable error in b is $\pm 0 \cdot 41$ and there is an improvement in the determination of b. It also follows that

$$q_0 = 1 \cdot 85 \pm 0 \cdot 57. \tag{9.115}$$

It will be remembered from equation (8.627) that a positive value of q_0 means that the rate of expansion of the model universe is decreasing at the present time. A simple exercise in speculation can reverse this conclusion by the assignment of an appropriate value to W_1. Suppose, for example, that an accelerated expansion is postulated a priori by asserting that the 'correct' model[†] is A2(vi-b) in which $q_0 = -1$. Then if $K_1 = 4 \cdot 7$, it follows that $W_1 = -3 \cdot 13$ and so, for the Hydra cluster, $W_1 z = -0 \cdot 63$. Thus by (8.819) the absolute magnitudes of the brightest members of this cluster are brighter by $0^m \cdot 63$ than those of supposedly similar nearby galaxies. Again by (8.502), the travel-time for the light from the Hydra cluster is, for the model in question,

$$t_0 - t = T_0 \ln (1 \cdot 202) = 0 \cdot 184 T_0.$$

A plausible value of T_0 is 10×10^9 years; therefore the rate of change of absolute magnitude amounts to $0^m \cdot 34$ per 10^9 years. Similar illustrative examples have been worked out by Sandage[7]. The real problem, however, is to produce observational evidence for a non-zero value of W_1. The change of intrinsic luminosity of spherical and elliptic galaxies is required because most of the bright galaxies in clusters are of these types. There seems to be no means of arriving at this change except by speculative assumptions regarding the stellar contents of such galaxies[7]. Tentative qualitative estimates of the evolutionary changes of colour for spiral galaxies lead to $0^m \cdot 03$ per 10^9 years and there is also some evidence for a residual Stebbins-Whitford effect that would make certain galaxies redder than they should be if the red-shift were due entirely to recession[8]. In theory, colour changes do lead, through (8.821), to the conclusion that the spectral energy distribution function, B, of galaxies varies with the departure-time. But it is unknown whether the observational indications do establish sufficiently rapid secular variations of B to produce, through (8.817) a value of W_1 which differs significantly from zero. Sandage's dictum[7] that 'the observational test of cosmology using the (m, z) data is intimately connected with the evolution of the stellar content of galaxies' must be treated only as a theoretical possibility until evolution can be shown to produce a significant non-zero value of W_1. A different kind of considera-tion amounts to the assertion that the observers pick clusters with intrinsically

† This model is also used in the steady-state theory.

brighter and brighter members as they seek to find larger and larger red-shifts[9]. A spurious value of W_1, due to selection, is thus introduced into the data. But no evidence is offered that the observers do, in fact, select clusters in this way; certainly the remotest cluster in Table VII, 1410 + 5224, was not picked out by any luminosity criterion but because it contained the radio source 3C295. At the moment therefore the reasons for believing that W_1 differs significantly from zero are unconvincing. The hypothesis that $W_1 = 0$ will therefore be accepted and used until solid evidence to the contrary is forthcoming.

Before turning to the computation of the Hubble constant, we shall discuss the effect of replacing the approximation (9.105) by the exact formula (9.103) because large red-shifts are to be anticipated in future observations, and it will therefore be eventually necessary to employ exact relations. The pairs of numbers (m_c^*, z) of Table VII will serve to illustrate a possible procedure. We write (9.103) in the form

$$m_c^* - 5 \log \mathscr{D} = a, \tag{9.116}$$

in which there are three parameters to be determined, namely, q_0 and σ_0, which occur in $\mathscr{D}$, and T_0 that is found in a. Suppose that a model of the universe is selected, which means that q_0 and σ_0 are assigned specific values, and $\mathscr{D}$ is therefore known as a specific function of z. Each pair of (m_c^*, z) values determines a residual

$$v_r = a + 5 \log \mathscr{D}(z_r) - (m_c^*)_r.$$

We would like to make $\sum_r v_r^2$ a minimum and, if there are n pairs of values (m_c^*, z), the usual least squares argument shows that the best-fitting value of a is

$$\bar{a} = \frac{1}{n} \sum_{r=1}^{n} \{(m_c^*)_r - 5 \log \mathscr{D}(z_r)\}.$$

It is then possible to recompute the sum of the squares of the residuals with $\bar{a}$ as the value of the constant in (9.116) and so

$$\Sigma = \Sigma(\bar{a} - w_r)^2,$$

where

$$w_r = (m_c^*)_r - 5 \log \mathscr{D}(z_r),$$

is the sum of the square of the residuals for the model in question. These operations may be repeated for a succession of models until a minimum value of Σ is obtained, say, Σ_m. Since there are three parameters to be found in each model, we shall accept as permissible ranges[10] in the values of the three parameters those models for which

$$\Sigma < \frac{n-2}{n-3} \Sigma_m.$$

The results of computations of this kind are listed in Table VIII. The model labelled 'approximate' has $5 \log \mathscr{D} = 5 \log z - 0.92z$; in this model $q_0 = 1.85$ but σ_0 is unspecified.

TABLE VIII

Model and Category		$\bar{a}$	Σ
'Approximate'	—	21·37	2·034
$q_0 = 2$, $\sigma_0 = 2$	A1(iv)	21·35	2·112
$q_0 = 4$, $\sigma_0 = 0$	A2(v)	21·43	2·255
$q_0 = 3$, $\sigma_0 = 0$	A3(v)	21·36	2·270
$q_0 = 1$, $\sigma_0 = 1$	A1(iv)	21·25	2·274
$q_0 = 2$, $\sigma_0 = 0.02$	A3	21·30	2·384
$q_0 = 0.5$, $\sigma_0 = 0.5$	A1(iii)	21·19	2·543
$q_0 = 0$, $\sigma_0 = 0$	A1(i)	21·12	2·902
$q_0 = -1$, $\sigma_0 = 0$	A2(vi–b)	21·00	4·139

If we adopt $\Sigma_m = 2.034$ then $\frac{19}{18}\Sigma_m = 2.147$ and the $q_0 = 2$, $\sigma_0 = 2$ model qualifies. One interpretation of the contents of Table VIII is that the data used are not accurate enough to define σ_0 and that is why the 'approximate' case gives the minimum Σ. But, of course, the list of models is clearly not exhaustive; there may be undetected models of categories A or B for which Σ is less than 2·034.

We now turn to the calculation of the Hubble constant H – or equivalently T_0 – from the value of the constant term in the red-shift versus apparent magnitude relation. Since cT_0 in (9.106) is in parsec we take $c = 0.3066$ pc/yr and then

$$T_0 = 3.261 \times 10^{0.2(a-M)} \text{ yr.}$$
$$H = 2.998 \times 10^{10} \times 10^{0.2(M-a)} \text{ km/sec/mpc.}$$

The apparent magnitudes in Table VII are corrected for absorption to the pole and so are $0^m{\cdot}25$ too faint. This can be allowed for by writing

$$M = M_A + 0.25$$

where M_A is the absolute magnitude corrected for absorption. The value $a = 21.55$ occurs in (9.112), whereas $a = 21.36$ is the mean of the $\bar{a}$ in the first two entries of Table VIII. It has been thought best to present the results in Table IX by assigning the same three values to H (or to T_0) for each a and calculating the M_A which would produce them.

TABLE IX

H (km/sec/mpc)	$T_0 \times 10^{-9}$ yr	M_A $a = 21.55$	M_A $a = 21.36$
150	6·52	−20·204	−20·934
100	9·78	−21·084	−21·275
75	13·04	−21·709	−21·899

The various values of H may also be interpreted as changes in the scale of distance. Since luminosity-distances are, in the first approximation, proportional to z/H, a change in the scale of distance by a factor $1/f$ for all objects whose red-shifts have been measured results in the multiplication of the original value of H by f. This would, of course, also alter the absolute magnitudes. Conversely if $H = 75f$ km/sec/mpc then all distances are multiplied by $1/f$ as compared with the distances corresponding to $H = 75$ km/sec/mpc.

There are alternative ways of estimating H by attempting to find directly the luminosity-distances of nearby galaxies, or of the Virgo cluster, for which the red-shifts are known. These red-shifts are necessarily small and do not exceed $z = 0·004$. Since by (8.615) and (8.616)

$$D = cT_0z,$$

for small z, an estimate of T_0 can thus be arrived at. An account of the available data is due to Sandage[11] who estimates that $H = (98 \pm 15)$ km/sec/mpc. If therefore a value of H of about 100 km/sec/mpc is accepted, the brightest galaxies in clusters have absolute photographic magnitudes of between -21 and $-21·28$ and the value of T_0 lies close to 10×10^9 yr.

The foregoing treatment shows that the observational data produce numerical values for the Hubble constant, H, and the acceleration factor, q_0. To this extent, therefore, a model universe has been specified. The reader can easily deduce from the various definitions of the velocity of recession found in equations (8.622) to (8.625), that the data are compatible with a number of velocity-distance relations within a given model. For example, when T_0 and q_0 are known, the equation (8.624) shows that $U = T_0U_0'$, correct to the order z^2. On the other hand, if luminosity-distance D is selected one finds that

$$D = cT_0z\{1 - \tfrac{1}{2}(q_0 - 1)z\}.$$

Inverting the series (8.622) for D'_0 it follows that

$$cz = D_0'\left\{1 - \tfrac{1}{2}(q_0 + 1)\frac{D_0'}{c}\right\}$$

and so

$$D = T_0D_0'\left\{1 - q_0\frac{D_0'}{c}\right\}.$$

Therefore the velocity-distance relation between U and U_0' is linear whereas, to the same order of approximation, it is non-linear between D and D_0' in the same model. The linearity of the velocity-distance relation is therefore a matter of definition and depends on the choice of 'distance'. Those readers who attach importance to the question of linearity will observe from equations (9.112) and (9.114) that the interesting observational point is the linearity or otherwise of the relation between corrected apparent magnitude m_c (or m_c^*) and log z. To the order z^2, linearity occurs if $q_0 = 1$ but not otherwise. Linearity is also present for all values of z in the particular model

A1(iv) which has $q_0 = 1$. There are many statements in the cosmological literature which seem to imply that an empirical linear relation between m_c and $\log z$ would tell us nothing about the model of the universe. This is clearly not the case: a well established empirical linear relation would prove that $q_0 = 1$ and this would be an item of great cosmological interest. It would in fact establish that the present rate of expansion of the universe was being slowed down.

One of the important purposes for which accurate values of H (or of T_0) and of q_0 are needed is the determination of the absolute radio magnitudes of extragalactic radio sources (radio galaxies). The only method at present available is to identify the radio source with the optical image of a galaxy and to measure the red-shift of the object in the visible spectrum. The red-shift then enables us to calculate $\mathscr{D}$ if q_0 is known. A measurement of the apparent radio magnitude of the source and a knowledge of its spectral index give m_r and K_r in (8.828). Thus M_r may be found. An alternative method is to measure m_r and also, for example, the apparent photographic magnitude m of the object. If the photographic K-correction is also known then T_0 and $\mathscr{D}$ may be eliminated from (8.813) and (8.828) to give.

$$M_r = m_r - m - (K_r - K) + M.$$

This formula would give M_r if an estimate of the absolute photographic magnitude of the optical object were known. On the assumption that $\mathscr{D}$ is accurately enough determined by the zero order approximation, $\mathscr{D} = z$, and with $H = 100$ km/sec/mpc, Maltby, Matthews and Moffet[12] have concluded that for 19 radio sources which they have studied, $M = -20 \cdot 5$ with a standard deviation of $0^{\mathrm{m}} \cdot 8$. Subsequent studies can alone show if this value, with its relatively small standard deviation, is generally applicable to radio galaxies.

9.2. Number counts

The interpretation of the red-shift data by means of uniform model universes is relatively simple because the theory gives directly an equation between the two observables, namely, the apparent magnitude and the red-shift of a source. Unfortunately this ceases to be the case for most of the other types of data; here the theoretical formulae express each observable in terms of a parameter. The parameter has to be eliminated before a direct equation between the two observables is attained. This type of investigation is well illustrated by the data on the numbers of sources of radiation.

(i) *Optical counts.* The work of E. Holmberg[13] shows that the average number, N, of galaxies, visible over the whole sky, which are brighter than apparent magnitude m follows the empirical relation†

$$0 \cdot 6m - \log N = +4 \cdot 25. \tag{9.201}$$

† Many writers prefer to use the average number, N_{sd}, of galaxies per square degree of the sky. Since there are 41,253 square degrees in the sky and $\log 41,253 \simeq 4 \cdot 62$ the relation between N and N_{sd} is $\log N_{sd} = \log N - 4 \cdot 62$.

o

A formula of this type may be interpreted in classical terms as follows: Suppose that every source of radiation has the same isotropic power output P. Suppose also that l is the distance from the observer to the source in Euclidean space and that source and observer are at mutual rest. The flux-density, S, of the source at the observer is proportional to P/l^2 so that its optical apparent magnitude, by (8.806) with $L \equiv S$, is

$$m = 5 \log l + constant.$$

Suppose finally that there is the same number of sources in each unit volume of Euclidean space, all sources being at rest relatively to the observer. The total number N within a sphere of radius l is proportional to l^3. Hence we have the two equivalent relationships

$$N = (constant)S^{-3/2}, \qquad \log N = 0 \cdot 6m + constant, \qquad (9.202)$$

for the dependence of N on flux-density or apparent magnitude respectively. These are two alternative forms of the 'minus three-halves' law for the distribution of sources of radiation in the Euclidean space of classical physics.

The equation (9.201) holds from $m = 9 \cdot 5$ to about $m = 11 \cdot 9$ and the data do not extend beyond $m = 12 \cdot 5$. Moreover there is an indication that between $m = 11 \cdot 9$ and $m = 12 \cdot 5$ there is a deficit in the number of observed galaxies as compared with the predictions of the formula (9.201). At $m = 12 \cdot 5$, the deficit in the observed, as compared with the theoretical, value of $\log N$ amounts to $0 \cdot 15$; it is attributed by Holmberg to his method of estimating magnitudes. Counts extending to greater depths of space were made by Hubble in the 1930's. This work, it is often said, is defective in that the successive apparent magnitudes to which the counts were made are inaccurate. But the amount of inaccuracy has never been measured and the observations have never been repeated. Until this is done, Hubble's work remains as the empirical evidence for the large scale uniformity of the observed universe. Table X contains, under m', the six limiting magnitudes to which Hubble

TABLE X

m'	18·20	18·47	19·00	19·40	20·00	21·03
$\log N$	6·328	6·502	6·777	6·955	7·301	7·777
y'	4·592	4·580	4·623	4·685	4·699	4·841
$10^{0 \cdot 2m' - 3 \cdot 87}$	0·589	0·669	0·851	1·02	1·35	2·17

believed he had counted galaxies, and under $\log N$ the number he found, extrapolated to the whole sky. The line headed y' contains the values of

$$y' = 0 \cdot 6m' - \log N,$$

and the last line, the values of $10^{0 \cdot 2m' - 3 \cdot 87}$ in which the constant factor is introduced for convenience only. Inspection of Fig. 12 suggests very strongly that a linear relationship exists between y' and $10^{0 \cdot 2m' - 3 \cdot 87}$. A least squares solution yields the linear empirical relation

$$0 \cdot 6m' - \log N = 4 \cdot 49 + 0 \cdot 16 \times 10^{0 \cdot 2m' - 3 \cdot 87}, \qquad (9.203)$$

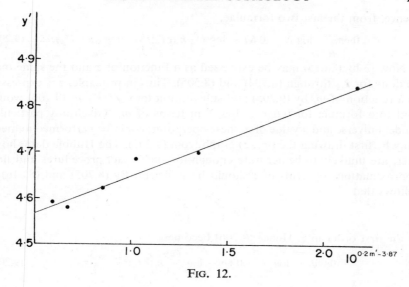

FIG. 12.

which is the straight line in Fig. 12. For values of m' that do not exceed 11, the second term on the right is negligibly small compared with the first term. Therefore if (9.201) and (9.203) are to give the same results for the numbers of bright galaxies, it is necessary to assume that m and m' are related by

$$0 \cdot 6(m' - m) = 0 \cdot 24,$$

or that

$$m' = m + 0 \cdot 4.$$

Thus (9.203) becomes

$$0 \cdot 6m - \log N = 4 \cdot 25 + 0 \cdot 16 \times 10^{0 \cdot 2m - 3 \cdot 79}. \tag{9.204}$$

It is perhaps worth noticing that this formula does give a slight deficit, amounting to 0·01, in $\log N$ at $m = 12 \cdot 5$ as compared with the prediction of (9.201).

We turn next to the theory and we have by (8.814)

$$m_c = a + 5 \log \mathscr{D}, \tag{9.205}$$

where a has the same meaning as in (9.106). We thus make the crude assumption that all galaxies have, on the average, the same absolute magnitude; more elaborate luminosity-functions are hardly justified at present in view of the uncertainties in the number-count data. If it be also assumed that galaxies do not form and do not disappear as time progresses, then the number within coordinate radius ω is by (8.703) and (8.714)

$$N = \frac{4\pi}{3} n_0 (cT_0)^3 \mathscr{V}_k(t_0, \omega).$$

Hence, from the last two formulae,

$$0.6m_c - \log N = 0.6a - \log\left\{\frac{4\pi}{3}n_0(cT_0)^3\right\} + \log(\mathscr{D}^3/\mathscr{V}_k). \qquad (9.206)$$

Now $\mathscr{D}$ by (8.615) may be expressed as a function of z and the same may be done for $\mathscr{V}_k$ through (8.704) and (8.505). Thus in principle, z is expressed as a function of m_c by (9.205) and substitution into $\mathscr{D}^3/\mathscr{V}_k$ in (9.206) would lead to a formula for $0.6m_c - \log N$ in terms of m_c. Given any particular model universe and a value of a, these operations could be performed numerically by first drawing the (m_c, z) graph from (9.205). The Hubble data, however, are unlikely to be accurate enough for such exact procedures and first approximations in terms of z should be sufficient. By (8.705) and (8.616) it follows that

$$\log\frac{\mathscr{D}^3}{\mathscr{V}_k} = \frac{3}{E}z,$$

to the first order in z. Hence (9.206) becomes

$$0.6m_c - \log N = 0.6a - \log\left\{\frac{4\pi}{3}n_0(cT_0)^3\right\} + \frac{3}{E}z, \qquad (9.207)$$

a formula which shows that, to the first order in z, the parameters q_0 and σ_0 are not explicitly present.

It is unlikely that Hubble applied to his magnitudes the large K-corrections that are nowadays in use. Suppose therefore for the moment that the m of (9.204) and the m_c of (9.207) are related by

$$m = m_c + k_1 z. \qquad (9.208)$$

This would turn (9.207) into

$$0.6m - \log N = 0.6a - \log\left\{\frac{4\pi}{3}n_0(cT_0)^3\right\} + \left(\frac{3}{E} - 0.6k_1\right)z. \qquad (9.209)$$

The z in the second term on the right may be replaced by m by combining the first approximations to (9.205) and (9.208), which yield

$$m = a + 5\log z. \qquad (9.210)$$

Hence the theoretical formula (9.209) now becomes

$$0.6m - \log N = 0.6a - \log\left\{\frac{4\pi}{3}n_0(cT_0)^3\right\} + \left(\frac{3}{E} - 0.6k_1\right)10^{0.2(m-a)}, \qquad (9.211)$$

which is identical in form with the empirical formula (9.204). Therefore equating coefficients we have

$$\left.\begin{aligned}0.6a - \log\left\{\frac{4\pi}{3}n_0(cT_0)^3\right\} &= 4.25, \\ \left(\frac{3}{E} - 0.6k_1\right)10^{-0.2a} &= 0.16 \times 10^{-3.79}.\end{aligned}\right\} \qquad (9.212)$$

With $a = 21.55$ it follows that $k_1 = 1.28$ and therefore by (9.208)

$$m_c = m - 1.3z. \qquad (9.213)$$

Hence if $m < 11$, m_c differs from m by less than $0^{\text{m}}\cdot01$ and such a small change is unlikely to alter Holmberg's formula (9.201). We may therefore accept (9.211) as valid both for Holmberg's data and for Hubble's.

The important number for cosmology is n_0, the number of galaxies per unit volume in the observer's neighbourhood. If $H = 75f$ km/sec/mpc then (8.324) shows that

$$cT_0 = \frac{3\cdot997 \times 10^3}{f} \text{ mpc.}$$

Hence by (9.212)

$$n_0 = 10^{0\cdot6a - 15\cdot6775} f^3 \text{ gal (mpc)}^{-3},$$

or with $a = 21.55$

$$n_0 = 1\cdot79 \times 10^{-3} f^3 \text{ gal (mpc)}^{-3}. \tag{9.214}$$

Before the implications of this number are considered, we discuss briefly Bondi's interpretation of Hubble's counts in the steady-state theory. For the present purpose, the method is equivalent to the use of the model A2(vi–b) and to the identification of the empirical N of (9.204) with the $\bar{N}$ obtained from (8.715) and (8.709). Bondi works to the second approximation in z but this seems to be hardly justified by the accuracy of the data. In this model, to the first order in z,

$$\bar{N} = n_0 \frac{4\pi}{3} (cT_0)^3 z^3 \left(1 - \frac{9}{4}z\right),$$

$$\mathscr{D}^3 = z^3(1 + 3z).$$

Thus in (9.211) N is replaced by $\bar{N}$ and the factor $\dfrac{3}{E}$ becomes $\dfrac{21}{4E}$. Hence if again $a = 21\cdot55$, it follows that $k_1 = 2\cdot9$. Therefore the data can be interpreted in this fashion also, provided that a larger correction to the apparent magnitudes is made than was required by (9.213).

The number n_0 provides an estimate of the average density of matter in space if the average mass of a galaxy is known and if, of course, the main part of the material in the universe is indeed concentrated in the galaxies. With a distance scale corresponding to $H = 75$ km/sec/mpc Thornton Page[14] and his co-workers give the following data on masses, which are expressed in units of $10^{10} \mathscr{M}_\odot$: 16 single spiral and irregular galaxies have a mean mass of 8·6; 14 pairs of spiral and irregular galaxies, a mean of $3\cdot8 \pm 1\cdot3$; 4 single elliptical galaxies, a mean of 30, but one galaxy (M87) is estimated to have a mass of 100; and 14 pairs of elliptical galaxies, a mean of 80 ± 13. Thus, though many objects in this list have masses near $10^{10} \mathscr{M}_\odot$, it is possible for the mass of a galaxy to range up to $10^{12} \mathscr{M}_\odot$. In order not to underestimate the average density we shall assume that the mass $\mathscr{M}$ of an average galaxy lies in the range

$$2\cdot56 \times 10^{13} \mathscr{M}_\odot \geq \mathscr{M} \geq 2\cdot56 \times 10^{12} \mathscr{M}_\odot. \tag{9.215}$$

The present average density, ρ_0, of the representative gas in the model universe, which occurs in (8.402), is then defined to be

$$\rho_0 = n_0 \mathcal{M}. \qquad (9.216)$$

With $f = 1$ in (9.214) and, of course, $\mathcal{M}_\odot = 1\cdot99 \times 10^{33}$ gr., the range in which ρ_0 lies is

$$3\cdot1 \times 10^{-30} \text{ gr.cm}^{-3} \geq \rho_0 \geq 3\cdot1 \times 10^{-31} \text{ gr.cm}^{-3}. \qquad (9.217)$$

Essentially the same range has been found by Oort[15] who used an alternative method in which the mass to light ratio of galaxies played an important role. He also employed, for the constant term in the empirical relation corresponding to (9.201), Hubble's original value which is $9\cdot05 - 4\cdot62 = 4\cdot43$. Hence it appears that Oort's method makes as ample an allowance as does ours for the possibility that the masses of galaxies may have been underestimated. Reference should also be made to the work of Kiang[16] on the luminosity-function of galaxies whose apparent photographic magnitudes are not fainter than 15. He finds

$$n_0 = 0\cdot46 \left(\frac{H}{100} \right)^3 = 1\cdot94 \times 10^{-1} f^3 \text{ gal (mpc)}^{-3},$$

which is about 100 times the value given by (9.214). But all except two or three per cent of the galaxies in each unit volume have absolute magnitudes in the range $- 19\cdot5$ to -14. These galaxies are therefore of relatively low mass and the average would be expected to lie in the range $10^{10 \pm 1} \mathcal{M}_\odot$. Therefore the upper limit of the average density of matter will not exceed about 10^{-30} gr.cm^{-3}.

It is often argued that the average density of matter in space computed in this way refers to luminous matter only and that there is a great deal of additional 'non-luminous' matter present. It is certainly true that galaxies contain non-luminous material in the form of interstellar gas-clouds. Estimates of the amount of non-luminous material give a fraction of a few per cent of the total mass of a galaxy for this type of constituent[17]. Perhaps in irregular galaxies the fraction may sometimes be as high as thirty per cent. Thus the bulk of the mass of a galaxy is found in the luminous stars and these occupy a minute fraction of the entire volume of a galaxy. This is true even if stars, the Sun for example, have no definite boundaries but shade away gradually into the intervening space. Direct and positive evidence would be needed to show that there was any significant amount of matter between galaxies. At any rate, the choice of a very high value for the mass of a galaxy, made in (9.215), should allow for the non-luminous material observed to be associated with galaxies. The proponents of high densities[18], of between 10^{-29} gr.cm^{-3} and 10^{-25} gr.cm^{-3}, support their view by an appeal to the 'planet round Arcturus' type of contention which was discussed at the end of Chapter 1. The additional material is said to be present because, if it were there, it would produce no observable effects. An example of the application of this method is found in the statement[19] that an attempt to measure the amount of hydrogen in the regions between galaxies by radio astronomical means leads to an upper limit for its density of 3×10^{-29} gr.cm^{-3}. But examination of what actually happened when the observations were made reveals that nothing was observed; the upper limit was based solely on the fact that the observing apparatus did not measure with infinite accuracy. The experiment did nothing to establish the presence of inter-galactic hydrogen: it merely answered the hypothetical question: 'If it is assumed that the hydrogen is there, how much might there be in order that it should remain undetectable?' It therefore seems preferable to await the production of positive evidence in favour of the presence of significant amounts of inter-galactic material before any cosmological conclusions are based on substantially higher values of ρ_0 than those given in (9.217).

The parameter which enters into the specification of a model universe, and which is determined by ρ_0, is σ_0 given by (8.402). The values (9.217) depend on taking $H = 75$ km/sec/mpc. But if $H = 75 \, f$ km/sec/mpc then all volumes are multiplied by $1/f^3$ and all densities by f^3. However, the methods by which the masses of galaxies are obtained make these masses proportional to the distances employed. Thus the density (9.216) must be multiplied by f^2. Again H and h_1 are proportional to one another; therefore, in the formula for σ_0, namely

$$\sigma_0 = \frac{4\pi G}{3} \frac{\rho_0}{h_1^2},$$

it is clear that σ_0 is *independent of the distance scale* and its value may thus be obtained by using (9.217) together with $H = 75$ km/sec/mpc or $h_1 = 2\cdot43 \times 10^{-18}$ sec^{-1}. Thus σ_0 lies in the range

$$0\cdot147 \geq \sigma_0 \geq 0\cdot015. \qquad (9.218)$$

This is a conclusion not without cosmological interest; if it is combined with the values of q_0 given by (9.113), (9.115) or even with $q_0 = 1$ the definitions (8.404) show that in a zero-pressure model the *cosmical constant Λ and the space-curvature constant k are both negative*. These conclusions thus depend in part on galaxy counts, but they utilize only the constant terms in the empirical relations between $\log N$ and m_c and between m_c and z. The pessimistic view expressed by Sandage[20] with regard to counts of galaxies must be understood in terms of his preliminary assumption that $\Lambda = 0$ and that therefore $q_0 = \sigma_0$ in all his models. He is in fact trying to choose between one or another of the models of class A1 directly from the observations. This is indeed an impossible task at present as it would require the empirical determination of the *second order* terms in z in (9.102) as well as in (9.206). It is also possible that much of the belief that the average density of matter in space is higher than that given by (9.217) is founded on the assumption that the cosmical constant 'ought' to be zero. This means that $q_0 = \sigma_0$ and therefore, if q_0 lies between 1 and 3, ρ_0 must be at least ten times larger than the upper limit in (9.217). It must then be supposed that the mass of an average galaxy is at least $2\cdot56 \times 10^{14} \mathcal{M}_\odot$ or, alternatively, that there is a very great deal of unobservable matter in the universe.

The conclusions so far reached suggest that q_0 lies between 1 and 3 and that σ_0 is considerably smaller than q_0, as indicated by (9.218). The positive value of q_0 means that the expansion of the universe is subject, at the present moment, to a retardation. The obvious physical cause of a retardation would be the gravitational self-attraction of the representative gas. But the low value of σ_0 implies that there is insufficient material present to account for the relatively large retardation. Einstein's equations however indicate that the additional 'force' impeding the motion is traceable to a negative value of the cosmical constant. Indeed, it has been shown in Sec. 6.5 that a negative cosmical constant has the same effect as the gravitational self-attraction of additional matter.

It is also clear that there are two classes of model universe, whose properties are expressible in terms of elementary functions, which can be regarded as extreme cases. The models A1(ii), (iii) and (iv) form one extreme and contain a high-density representative gas. At the other extreme lie the models of category A2 in which the density is zero. The model that best fits the observed universe lies somewhere between these two extremes and requires elliptic functions for its specification. Until higher accuracy in the values of q_0 and σ_0 is attained, it is probably preferable to interpret any data of observation in terms of models of the two extreme cases in turn rather than to embark on the use of a model involving elliptic functions.

(ii) *Counts of radio galaxies.* The statistics of the numbers of radio galaxies, N, counted to successive limits of the flux-density, S, have so far usually been represented by empirical relations of the form

$$N = C_1 S^{-0\cdot5(3+\mu)}, \tag{9.219}$$

where $\mu \geq 0$ and C_1 is a constant. The numerical values of μ have ranged[21] from a little larger than zero to about 1. None of the counts contain enough radio galaxies with very large values of S to inspire confidence in the validity of (9.219) for the neighbourhood of the observer. We shall therefore assume that the formula holds only outside a 'standard' region, centred at the observer, whose boundary corresponds to a small value, z_s, of the red-shift. The question then arises whether or not an equation like (9.219) is compatible with the theory of uniform model universes.

We assume for simplicity that, at each instant t, all radio galaxies have the same absolute radio magnitude $M_r(t)$. As was pointed out in Sec. 8.8 this is equivalent to asserting that the absolute radio magnitudes of all radio galaxies with the same red-shift are equal. We also suppose that the spectral index has the same constant value in all sources and that the observed flux-densities have been converted to apparent radio magnitudes by (8.829). Under these assumptions it will now be shown that there must be a secular change either in the number-density of radio galaxies, or in their absolute radio magnitudes, or in both at once, if the empirical formula (9.219) is to be recovered, approximately at least, from the theory of zero-pressure uniform model universes. The proof of this statement is based on the theoretical formula (8.716) which may be written, with the aid of (8.503) with $\varepsilon_0 = 0$ and (8.512), as

$$\frac{dN}{dz} = 4\pi n_0 R_0^2 c T_0 \alpha(z) \mathscr{S}_k^2(\omega) \frac{Z(z)}{1+z}$$

$$\simeq 4\pi n_0 (cT_0)^3 \alpha(z) z^2 \{1 - 2(q_0 + 1)z + \ldots\}. \qquad (9.220)$$

Here, of course, n_0 is the number-density of radio galaxies alone and not of all galaxies as in (9.214). This theoretical formula is to be compared with the corresponding empirical one (9.219) which must therefore be transformed. To do this we first combine it with (8.829) which leads to

$$\log N = 0{\cdot}2(3 + \mu)m_r + C_2, \qquad (9.221)$$

where C_2 is a constant independent of z. Thus differentiating with respect to z

$$\frac{dN}{dz} = 0{\cdot}2E(3 + \mu)N\frac{dm_r}{dz}.$$

But by (8.827) and (8.828)

$$\frac{dm_r}{dz} = \frac{dM_r}{dz} + \frac{5}{E}\left(\frac{1}{\mathscr{D}}\frac{d\mathscr{D}}{dz} - \frac{1+x}{2} \cdot \frac{1}{1+z}\right),$$

and, with the same two formulae and (9.221),

$$N = C_3 10^{0{\cdot}2(3+\mu)M_r} \mathscr{D}^{(3+\mu)}(1 + z)^{-0{\cdot}5(1+x)(3+\mu)},$$

where C_3 is a constant independent of z. Hence the empirical formula corresponding to the exact form of (9.220) is

$$\frac{dN}{dz} = (3 + \mu)C_3 10^{0{\cdot}2(3+\mu)M_r} \mathscr{D}^{(2+\mu)}$$

$$\times (1 + z)^{-0{\cdot}5(1+x)(3+\mu)}\left\{\frac{E}{5}\mathscr{D}\frac{dM_r}{dz} + \frac{d\mathscr{D}}{dz} - \frac{1+x}{2}\frac{\mathscr{D}}{1+z}\right\}. \qquad (9.222)$$

In principle, therefore, the identification of (9.222) with the exact form of (9.220) in any particular model of the universe would give $\alpha(z)$ as a function of z and of $M_r(z)$. However, it is more illuminating to consider approximations in terms of z. To this end we assume that

$$M_r(z) = M_0 - \frac{5}{E}w_r z,$$

where M_0 and w_r are constants. After some calculation in which (8.616) is employed, the approximate form of (9.222) is found to be

$$\frac{dN}{dz} = C_4 z^{2+\mu}\left\{1 - \frac{4+\mu}{2}(2w_r + q_0 + x)z\right\}, \qquad (9.223)$$

where C_4 is a constant. Hence equating this expression for dN/dz to that given by (9.220) it follows that the approximate form of $\alpha(z)$ is

$$\alpha(z) = C_5 z^{\mu}[1 + 2\{1 - x - 2w_r - (q_0 + x + 2w_r)\mu/4\}z], \qquad (9.224)$$

where C_5 is a constant that may be normalized so that $\alpha(z_s) = 1$. If $\mu > 0$, it must be assumed that $\alpha = 1$ for all $z \leq z_s$; but for $\mu = 0$ it is mathematically possible to take $z_s = 0$ and then to normalize C_5 so that $C_5 = 1$. Clearly, if $\mu > 0$, there is no possibility of α being constant whatever the values of x, w_r and q_0 may be. However, if $\mu = 0$ it follows that

$$\alpha(z) = 1 + 2(1 - x - 2w_r)z, \qquad (9.225)$$

so that α may be constant to this order of approximation if

$$w_r = \tfrac{1}{2}(1 - x). \qquad (9.226)$$

This is a positive number because $-1 \cdot 1 \leq x \leq -0 \cdot 2$ for radio galaxies[22]. Hence when $\mu = 0$, the number-density of radio galaxies changes only because of the expansion if their absolute radio magnitudes become more negative (i.e. their intrinsic power output *increases*) on the average with increasing z. This is another way of saying that radio galaxies were radiating more strongly in the past than they are now doing. Alternatively, if $w_r = 0$, so that there is no secular change in radiative power, it follows that α must increase with z. There must therefore have been intrinsically more radio galaxies per unit volume in the past than there are now. The case $\mu = 0$ corresponds to the 'minus three-halves' law (9.202) connecting N and S. The empirical establishment of such a law would therefore solve the problem of the distribution of radio galaxies in space without an appeal to secular changes only if it could also be demonstrated that the red-shifts of these galaxies were negligibly small compared with unity. But this would contradict the observed fact that a considerable number of them have moderately large red-shifts and a few of them, very large ones.

Corresponding results follow for the steady-state theory interpretation in which

$$q_0 = -1, \qquad \alpha = (1 + z)^{-3} \simeq 1 - 3z.$$

Thus, if $\mu > 0$, (9.224) cannot be recovered; but if $\mu = 0$, agreement could be attained provided that in (9.225)

$$w_r = (5 - 2x)/4.$$

This requires greater secular changes of power output in the past than does (9.226). In any case, secular changes of radiative power are forbidden by the strict uniformity postulate of the steady-state theory. For if they existed, an observer could use them to 'locate' himself in time.

The reason why the optical counts are interpretable in terms of a constant α whereas the counts of radio galaxies are not, is easily seen. The theoretical formula (9.206) has been derived for a constant α and it is, to the first approximation in z, of the form

$$\log N = 0.6m_c - \frac{3}{E}z + constant. \qquad (9.227)$$

Thus there is a deficit in N at each value of m_c as compared with the predictions of the 'minus three-halves' law (9.202). The optical counts led to the empirical relation (9.204) or

$$\log N = 0.6m - 0.16 \times 10^{0.2m-3.79} + constant,$$

and so again a deficit in N is predicted. But the radio counts led to (9.221) or

$$\log N = 0.6m_r + 0.2\mu m_r + constant.$$

Therefore, if $\mu > 0$, there is an excess of N at each m_r as compared with (9.202) whereas, of course, if $\mu = 0$ the predictions are identical. In neither case is a formula of type (9.227) obtained unless, as has been said, the red-shifts of most radio galaxies are negligibly small.

The formula (9.224) and its consequences depend on the assumption that radio galaxies are all instantaneously of the same intrinsic power output, in other words, all have the same absolute radio magnitude at each instant t. This can hardly be expected to correspond to the facts and therefore a luminosity-function must be introduced. It allows for a spread of absolute radio magnitude among the radio sources in each unit volume of space. The luminosity-function may be derived in the following way: Let it be supposed that an observer has studied an area of Q steradians of his celestial sphere, which is a large enough area to be representative of the entire sky. In this region he has discovered all the radio sources it contains whose apparent radio magnitudes do not exceed m_{r1}, say. He has also been able to calculate the absolute radio magnitudes of these sources and has found that they lie in the range of (negative) values

$$-j_1 \geq M_r \geq -j_2. \qquad (9.228)$$

Let the number-density of sources with absolute radio magnitudes in the interval $M_r \pm dM_r/2$ in Shell r of Fig. 8 be

$$n(t, M_r)dM_r,$$

where t is the departure-time. The corresponding number-density in a nearby shell for which the departure-time is effectively t_0 is

$$n(t_0, M_r)dM_r \equiv n_0(M_r)dM_r.$$

If the sources are permanent, so that none appears or disappears with the passage of time, then by (8.711)

$$n(t, M_r)dM_r = \left(\frac{R_0}{R}\right)^3 n_0(M_r)dM_r.$$

The luminosity-function† is therefore determined, in a given model of the universe, when $n_0(M_r)$ has been found. It gives the number per unit volume of all sources having absolute radio magnitude M_r per unit interval of M_r. Consider next the total numbers of sources within coordinate radius ω that are observed in the portion of area Q steradians of the observer's celestial sphere. Let the number of sources having absolute radio magnitudes lying in the range $M_r \pm dM_r/2$ be (by (8.713) with $\alpha = 1$ and 4π replaced by Q),

$$N(M_r)dM_r = QR_0^3 n_0(M_r)dM_r \int_0^\omega \mathscr{S}_k^2(\omega)d\omega,$$

or, by (8.702) and (8.703)

$$N(M_r)dM_r = \frac{Q}{3}(cT_0)^3 n_0(M_r)dM_r \mathscr{V}_k(t_0, z),$$

where, by (8.506), ω has been replaced by z. Hence

$$n_0(M_r) = \frac{3N(M_r)dM_r}{Q(cT_0)^3 dM_r \mathscr{V}_k(t_0, z)}, \tag{9.229}$$

which gives the luminosity-function from the data of observation. For definiteness let dM_r be 2 magnitudes. Then the observed numbers, $N(M_r)$, of sources in the ranges $M_r \pm 1$ at the absolute radio magnitudes M_r, $M_r + 2$, $M_r + 4$, etc., of the range (9.228) can be counted. But each pair of values (M_r, m_{r1}), $(M_r + 2, m_{r1})$, etc., corresponds to a different value of $\mathscr{V}_k(t_0, z)$ because each pair gives rise to its own value of z. When the model of the universe is given and M_r is assumed to be independent of the departure-time, equations (8.828) and (8.615) determine the required sequence of red-shifts z and therefore also the sequence of $\mathscr{V}_k(t_0, z)$. Hence the function $n_0(M_r)$ may be evaluated numerically from (9.229) at each of the absolute radio magnitudes M_r, $M_r + 2$, etc. The results may be represented by some empirical formula between n_0 and M_r. Henceforward $n_0(M_r)$ will stand for this formula.

The final step is to calculate the relation between N and S, analogous to (9.219), which is to be anticipated from the luminosity-function. A particular flux-density, S_g, say, produces by (8.829) a corresponding m_{rg}. Combined with some value $-j$ of M_r, lying in the range (9.228), this m_{rg} will produce a specific value of the red-shift, say, z_j. The total number of sources over the whole sky that lie within the distance corresponding to z_j and have absolute

---

† The term is sometimes used more loosely in the radio astronomical literature in the following way: Let N be the total number of sources that have been counted in some experiment and let it be the case that their absolute radio magnitudes have also been found. Then a function $\phi(M_r)$ can be determined which gives the fractional numbers, out of the total of N, of sources in each unit range of M_r. This is called the 'luminosity-function'. When the total volume V in which the N sources lie has also been estimated, then ϕ and V could be employed to give n_0 provided *that all sources within V had been counted in the experiment*.

radio magnitudes in the interval dM_r at $M_r = -j$ is, by (8.716) with $\alpha = 1$,

$$\Delta N(z_j, -j) = 4\pi n_0(-j)dM_r R_0^2 cT_0 \int_{0_j}^{z_j} \mathscr{S}_k^2(\omega) \frac{Z(z)}{1+z} dz. \qquad (9\cdot230)$$

For a given model of the universe the integral can be evaluated. The interval dM_r of (9.229) need not be identical with the dM_r of (9.230), but the two intervals should not differ greatly from one another. For example, if the first interval is 2 magnitudes, the second might be 1 magnitude. With this in mind, $\Delta N(z_j, -j)$ is computed for each integral value of M_r in the range (9.228), keeping S_g fixed. The total number of sources with flux-densities not less than S_g is therefore

$$N_g = \sum_{j=j_1}^{j_2} \Delta N(z_j, -j).$$

Thus one point, (N_g, S_g), has been computed numerically on the graph of the N–S relation derived from the given model of the universe combined with the luminosity-function $n_0(M_r)$. Repetition of the foregoing procedure for different S_g, yields the N–S relation in numerical form. It can then be compared with the observed relation (9.219). In practice, it turns out that the necessary numerical computations are rather intricate; the details can be found in an investigation by McVittie and Roeder[23]. The models A1 were examined but the theory again predicted too small a value of N at small flux-densities as compared with (9.219). Therefore the introduction of a luminosity-function failed to account for the excess in the number of remote sources. The conclusion that no luminosity-function can solve the problem is, of course, illegitimate. The $n_0(M_r)$ derived by McVittie and Roeder will undoubtedly be improved upon as more data accumulate; and other models of the universe than the models A1 have still to be examined.

A different line of attack is due to Hoyle and Narlikar[24] who use the model of the steady-state theory. They postulate statistical fluctuations in the spatial distribution of radio galaxies and show that (9.219) may be reproduced by this device. But such a postulate again seems to contradict the basic assumption of the steady-state theory, namely, that all positions in space are at all times indistinguishable from one another. It is this strict uniformity hypothesis, applied to all regions of space, however small, which leads to the model A2(vi – b) and to its properties that are essential features of Hoyle and Narlikar's theory. Indeed, as was pointed out in Sec. 8.7 spatial fluctuations, on a cosmological scale, in the number of sources of radiation are incompatible with the uniformity assumption on which *any* uniform model of the universe is based. It is therefore evident that Hoyle and Narlikar's treatment has still to be supplemented by the discovery of the metric of a space-time in which the material is distributed irregularly in space.

A more general method of treating counts of radio galaxies will now be developed which is suggested by the ideas of Ryle[25]. The procedure is easily applicable to the case of spectral indices which vary with frequency. Instead of starting from (9.219) as the given empirical formula, the argument runs as follows: Let $N_R = N/4\pi$ be the number of radio galaxies per steradian with flux-densities not less than $S(\nu)$, where ν is the frequency at which the observations are made. Consider then the value of the function†

$$\alpha_R = N_R S^{3/2}(\nu).$$

By (8.830) and (8.615) we have

$$S(\nu) = \frac{P\{\nu(1 + z), t\}}{R_0^2(1 + z)\mathscr{S}_k^2(\omega)},$$

and by (8.713)

$$N_R = n_0 R_0^3 \int_0^\omega \alpha(Y)\mathscr{S}_k^2(\omega)d\omega,$$

where $Y = (1 + z)^{-1}$ and may thus be expressed in terms of ω by (8.505). Therefore combining the last two formulae,

$$\alpha_R = \frac{n_0 P^{3/2}\{\nu(1 + z), t\} \int_0^\omega \alpha(Y)\mathscr{S}_k^2(\omega)d\omega}{(1 + z)^{3/2}\mathscr{S}_k^3(\omega)}. \qquad (9.231)$$

It is again more illuminating to express this as a series in z and it is sufficient to calculate the first two terms of the series. Define the constants α_1, π_ν, π_t by

$$\left.\begin{array}{l}\alpha(Y) = 1 + 2\alpha_1 z, \\[2mm] \pi_\nu = \nu\dfrac{\partial}{\partial \nu}\{\ln P(\nu, t_0)\}, \\[2mm] \pi_t = -T_0\left[\dfrac{\partial}{\partial t}\{\ln P(\nu, t)\}\right]_0,\end{array}\right\} \qquad (9.232)$$

and use also the approximations for a zero-pressure model,

$$\omega = \frac{cT_0}{R_0}z\{1 - \tfrac{1}{2}(q_0 + 1)z\},$$

$$\mathscr{S}_k = \omega,$$

$$t = t_0 - T_0 z.$$

It then follows, after some calculation, that

$$\alpha_R = \tfrac{1}{3}n_0 P^{3/2}(\nu, t_0)\{1 + \tfrac{3}{2}(\alpha_1 + \pi_\nu + \pi_t - 1)z\}, \qquad (9.233)$$

and therefore α_R has the same form, to this order of approximation, in all models. The relation between z and S is, in the first approximation,

$$S(\nu) = \frac{P(\nu, t_0)}{c^2 T_0^2}\frac{1}{z^2},$$

which again follows from (8.830) and (8.615). Therefore (9.233) is also

$$\alpha_R = \tfrac{1}{3}n_0 P^{3/2}(\nu, t_0)\left\{1 + \tfrac{3}{2}(\alpha_1 + \pi_\nu + \pi_t - 1)\frac{P^{1/2}(\nu, t_0)}{cT_0}S^{-1/2}\right\}, \qquad (9.234)$$

† We have denoted Ryle's 'α' by α_R in order to avoid confusion with the α of Sec. 8.7.

and so the predicted formula between N_R and S is

$$N_R = \tfrac{1}{3}n_0 P^{3/2}(\nu, t_0)S^{-3/2}\left\{1 + \tfrac{3}{2}(\alpha_1 + \pi_\nu + \pi_t - 1)\frac{P^{1/2}(\nu, t_0)}{cT_0}S^{-1/2}\right\}. \qquad (9.235)$$

This formula shows that (9.219) is a very awkward representation of the data when a comparison between theory and observation is desired. In fact α_R is a power series in z which may in turn be converted into a series of powers of $S^{-1/2}$ of which the first two terms occur in (9.235). In (9.219) the series is represented in a roundabout way as $S^{-\mu/2}$. It would seem to be preferable to interpret future counts of radio galaxies by a formula of type (9.235) rather than by (9.219).

The results already deduced from (9.224) and (9.225) also follow from (9.233). It is clear from the exact formula (9.231) for α_R that, short of some mathematical miracle, this quantity must vary with z, and therefore with S, as more and more remote sources are included in the counts. The variability of α_R is confirmed by (9.233) unless indeed all the sources counted are so close to the observer that their red-shifts are entirely negligible compared with unity. It is also found empirically[25] that α_R *increases* with decreasing limits of flux-density and therefore with increasing z. But if P is proportional to ν^x, where x is a constant independent of ν, it follows that $\pi_\nu = x$ and so π_ν is a negative number lying in the range $-1\cdot1 \leq \pi_\nu \leq -0\cdot2$. Thus α_R increases with z if the coefficient of z in (9.233) is positive which means that

$$\alpha_1 + \pi_t > 1 - \pi_\nu > 0.$$

Hence it must be assumed that radio galaxies were either more numerous in the past than they are now $(\alpha_1 > 0)$ or that they were intrinsically more luminous $(\pi_t > 0$, i.e. $\partial P/\partial t < 0)$ or that some combination of these effects was present. In the steady-state theory interpretation (model A2(vi–b)) α should be $(1 + z)^{-3}$. Ryle and Clarke's conclusion[26] that the Cambridge counts cannot be interpreted in terms of this expression for α may be demonstrated by writing $\alpha = (1 + z)^{-3 + 2\alpha_s} \simeq 1 - (3 - 2\alpha_s)z$, where α_s is a constant. Then $\alpha_1 = -0\cdot5(3 - 2\alpha_s)$ and the coefficient of z in (9.233) would be positive if

$$\alpha_s + \pi_t > 2\cdot5 - \pi_\nu > 0.$$

If there are no secular changes of intrinsic radiative power $(\pi_t = 0)$, then α_s is certainly not zero and the steady-state expression for $\alpha(z)$ is violated. If $\alpha_s = 0$, so that $\alpha(z)$ has the correct value, then π_t must be different from zero. This implies secular changes in radiative power, a result which has also been deduced from (9.225).

Finally we consider the case of a spectral index which varies with frequency and, for simplicity, we shall assume that the function P is independent of the departure-time so that there are no secular changes of power output. Since

$P(\nu)$ is then proportional to $\nu^{x(\nu)}$ it follows that $\pi_t = 0$ and that

$$\pi_\nu = x + (\nu \ln \nu)\frac{dx}{d\nu}.$$

For most sources, this is a negative number because x and $dx/d\nu$ are both negative. Nevertheless a number of cases exist in which $dx/d\nu$ is positive and even a few in which x itself is positive. Suppose that for illustrative purposes, a very simple luminosity-function is introduced as follows: Let the fraction $(1 - \chi)n_0$ of the sources each have a constant spectral index equal to x_1, while the remainder, χn_0, have a variable index $x_2(\nu)$. Let the first group of sources have a power output function $P_1(\nu)$ proportional to ν^{x_1}, while the second group have $P_2(\nu)$ proportional to $\nu^{x_2}(\nu)$. Let the function $\alpha(Y)$ that occurs in (9.228) be $(1 + 2\alpha_1 z)$ for the first group and $(1 + 2\alpha_2 z)$ for the second, both to the first approximation in z. Then the total number of sources per steradian counted down to flux-density S is

$$N_R = CS^{-3/2}\{1 + C'S^{-1/2}\},$$

where C, C' are the functions of ν given by

$$C = \tfrac{1}{3}n_0\{(1 - \chi)P_1^{3/2} + \chi P_2^{3/2}\},$$

$$C' = \frac{3}{2cT_0}\frac{1}{(1 - \chi)P_1^{3/2} + \chi P_2^{3/2}}$$

$$\times \left\{ (1 - \chi)(\alpha_1 + x_1 - 1)P_1^2 + \chi\left(\alpha_2 + x_2 + (\nu \ln \nu)\frac{dx_2}{d\nu} - 1\right)P_2^2\right\}.$$

If the counts are repeated using the observations made at some other frequency, ν' say, the quantities n_0, χ, α_1, α_2 and x_1 will not change. But this is insufficient to keep C and C' fixed because P_1, P_2 and x_2 will have new values at ν'. The term $1 + C'S^{-1/2}$ is a representation of the $S^{-\mu/2}$ of the empirical formula (9.219). Hence it is to be anticipated that the value of μ will change with the frequency at which the counts on the population of radio sources are made.

9.3. Angular diameters

It was explained in Sec. 8.6 that the angular diameters of extended sources of radiation, all of the same local size, had a law of variation with red-shift different from that of luminosity-distance. Therefore a sufficiently large number of sources with measured diameters and red-shifts could give, through (8.609) for example, a new determination of q_0. Similarly, counts of radio galaxies of measured diameters would also, in principle, yield new information about the parameters of the model universe through a combination of (8.608) and (8.713). The obstacle to progress along these lines lies in the difficulty of hitting upon some feature of an extended source of radiation which is, firstly, recognizable at all distances and secondly, can be assumed to have the same value in terms of local distance whatever the red-shift of the source may be. In other words, the feature must be such that there is some degree of certainty and uniqueness in the definition of l in (8.608). In this section therefore we content ourselves with developing certain formulae that might be useful in practice though we have no data to offer by which these formulae might be checked.

Hubble[27] has shown that the surface brightness of elliptical galaxies is proportional to

$$\left(1 + \frac{a}{a_0}\right)^{-2},$$

where a is the angular distance from the centre of the image to the point in question, and a_0 is a constant that varies from one galaxy to another. It will be assumed for simplicity that a_0 has the same value in a set of idealized galaxies and that a measures the angular radius from the central point A to P of Fig. 9. Thus in (8.832)

$$\gamma(P, A) = \left(1 + \frac{a}{a_0}\right)^{-2},$$

$$\gamma(P_s, A_s) = \left(1 + \frac{a_s}{a_0}\right)^{-2}.$$

Again, let m'', m''_s be the apparent magnitudes per square second of arc at points P, P_s which lie on the circles defined by a, a_s, respectively. Then (8.832) may be written

$$m'' - K(z) = m_s - 5 \log\left\{\frac{(1 + a_s/a_0)}{(1 + a/a_0)} \frac{1}{(1 + z)^2}\right\}. \tag{9.301}$$

Points lying on the same *isophotal diameters* in the given, and the standard, galaxy are defined by the condition that $m'' = m''_s$. By (9.301), the angular distances of the isophotes from the centres of the images are related by

$$1 + \frac{a}{a_0} = \left(1 + \frac{a_s}{a_0}\right)(1 + z)^{-2}10^{-0\cdot2K(z)}, \tag{9.302}$$

or, to the first order in z,

$$\frac{a}{a_0} = \frac{a_s}{a_0} - \left(1 + \frac{a_s}{a_0}\right)(2 + 0\cdot2EK_1)z, \tag{9.303}$$

where K_1 is a constant. Hence when the standard galaxy is unchanged and a sequence of similar galaxies of successively greater red-shifts is considered, a given isophotal diameter contracts in accordance with the exact formula (9.302) or the approximate formula (9.303). It has been emphasized by Sandage[20] that the change in the angular size of an isophotal diameter depends, not only on the red-shift, but also on the K-correction.

The radio galaxies present even greater complexity than do galaxies optically observed. It appears that a large percentage of them are double[12] in the sense that there are two centres of radio emission with the optical image of the associated galaxy lying between them. It is not yet known whether the separation between the two centres can be regarded as statistically constant in terms of local distance. As to the angular diameters of individual sources of radio emission, another difficulty arises. The observations are normally interferometric and yield the so-called fringe visibilities. From these the angular diameters must be deduced using some model of the surface emission of the source. The cosmological results so far obtained are inconclusive[28] and it is best to await further observational work before theoretical interpretations are attempted. The march of a against S, deducible from (8.608) and (8.824) or of a against N from (8.608) and (8.713), would, when the necessary observational data are available, throw additional light on the best-fitting model of the universe.

The property of distance by apparent size, by which it passes through a maximum value before the observer's horizon is reached, re-appears indirectly in the radio astronomical literature[29]. For example, the brightness temperature of sources of the same flux-density and the same emitting area varies as ξ^2 (see Eqn. (8.835)). Therefore in a model universe in which ξ possesses a maximum value, there will be two sources with the same brightness temperature, one with a small and the other with a large red-shift. The former lies closer to the observer than the maximum of ξ, the latter lies beyond it.

It has also been argued that an observational detection of a minimum value of the angular diameter of a source before the observer's horizon is reached would provide a means of discriminating between general relativity and the steady-state theory. The discovery of such an effect would certainly rule out all the models of category A2, including that of the steady-state theory A2(vi–b). Conversely, if it could be proved that the effect were absent in the observed universe, the models would be restricted to *any one* of the class A2, and not necessarily to the steady-state model A2(vi–b). Indeed, the absence of the effect would merely show that σ_0 was small compared with ρ_0 and that, if the minimum of a existed at all, it would be found close to the observer's horizon. It must also be remarked that there is no special significance about the value $z = 1 \cdot 25$ for the red-shift at which the minimum of the angular diameter occurs. The results on the minima in models A1(ii), (iii) and (iv) demonstrate that the corresponding red-shifts vary with q_0. If q_0 is large enough, the minimum occurs at a value of z considerably smaller than $1 \cdot 25$; as q_0 tends to zero, the minimum lies closer and closer to the observer's horizon where z is infinite.

9.4. Total Background Radiation

It is often of interest to evaluate the total amount of radiation of some particular frequency which an observer might expect to receive from all sources in the universe. The radiation may be in the radio part of the spectrum, in the optical, or even in the form of gamma rays. Calculations of this kind also serve to resolve Olbers' paradox because they show that the total background radiation has a small finite value. Therefore the sky is dark at night which it would not be if the sources were at rest in the Euclidean space of classical physics and were uniformly distributed throughout it.

We begin with the case of radio sources because the mathematics involved are relatively simple. Let us assume that the emission by a source is given, in watts, by (8.822), namely,

$$B_0 \left(\frac{\nu_e}{\nu_0} \right)^x d\nu_e, \tag{9.401}$$

where B_0 is assumed to be independent of the departure-time, x is a constant, and ν_0 is now the frequency at which the observer carries out his observations. By (8.317) an emitted frequency ν_e becomes ν at the observer, where $\nu(1 + z) = \nu_e$. Therefore a given frequency ν could correspond to any ν_e, however large, provided that the red-shift of the source were itself large enough. But there is no reason to suppose that (9.401) is valid for high frequencies, for example, in the optical domain. Therefore it is necessary to impose limits on the range of validity of (9.401) and to say that it holds good only between frequencies ν_a and ν_b, say. We assume that these limits are common to all sources in the universe so that

$$\nu_a \leq \nu_0 \leq \nu_e \leq \nu_b, \tag{9.402}$$

and that B_0 and x also have the same values in all sources. The limitation (9.402) means that only those sources whose red-shifts satisfy

$$1 + z \leq 1 + z_b = \frac{\nu_b}{\nu_0}, \tag{9.403}$$

will contribute to the radiation of frequency ν_0 at the observer.

The total emission in watts by a source is

$$L_0 = \frac{B_0}{\nu_0^x} \int_{\nu_a}^{\nu_b} \nu_e^x d\nu_e = \frac{B_0}{\nu_0^x} \frac{\nu_b^{1+x} - \nu_a^{1+x}}{1 + x},$$

provided that $x \neq -1$. If $x = -1$, then the factor $\dfrac{\nu_b^{1+x} - \nu_a^{1+x}}{1+x}$ in this and all following formulae must be replaced by $\ln(\nu_b/\nu_a)$. We therefore have

$$\frac{B_0}{\nu_0^x} = \frac{(1 + x)L_0}{\nu_b^{1+x} - \nu_a^{1+x}}. \tag{9.404}$$

Now for a nearby source $\nu_e \simeq \nu_0$; hence if P_0 is the power output in watts per cycle per second at frequency ν_0 we have, by (9.401) with $\nu_e = \nu_0$ and (9.404),

$$P_0 d\nu_0 = \frac{(1 + x)L_0}{\nu_b^{1+x} - \nu_a^{1+x}} \nu_0^x d\nu_0.$$

Hence for a source in Shell r of Fig. 8 which has an appreciable red-shift,

$$B_0 \left(\frac{\nu_e}{\nu_0} \right)^x d\nu_e = \frac{P_0}{\nu_0^x} \nu_e^x d\nu_e = P_0 (1 + z)^{1+x} d\nu_0. \tag{9.405}$$

Consider the portion of the surface of Shell r defined by points having coordinates

$$(\theta + \varepsilon_\theta, \phi + \varepsilon_\phi) \quad \text{where} \quad 0 \le \varepsilon_\theta \le d\theta, \quad 0 \le \varepsilon_\phi \le d\phi.$$

The number of sources lying in this portion of the shell is, by the differential form of (8.713) with $\alpha = 1$,

$$n_0 R_0^3 \mathscr{S}_k^2(\omega)d\omega \, (\sin\theta d\theta d\phi) = n_0 R_0^3 \mathscr{S}_k^2(\omega)d\omega d\Omega,$$

where $d\Omega$ is the solid angle subtended by the portion of Shell r, according to the observer. If D (metres) is the luminosity-distance of Shell r, then the rate of arrival of radiative energy from the sources, per unit area at the observer, is

$$\frac{n_0 R_0^3 \mathscr{S}_k^2 d\omega d\Omega}{4\pi D^2} P_0 (1+z)^{1+x} dv_0 \quad \text{W.m}^{-2}.$$

Substitution for D from (8.615) and for $d\omega$ from the differential form of (8.505) reduces this to

$$\frac{n_0 c T_0}{4\pi} P_0 \{Y^{-x} Z(Y)dY\} dv_0 d\Omega.$$

The contributions of all shells from the observer ($Y = 1$) outwards must now be summed, taking due account of (9.403). This means that the lower limit for Y is $Y_b = \dfrac{v_0}{v_b}$. The total is therefore

$$\frac{n_0 c T_0}{4\pi} P_0 \left\{ \int_{Y_b}^{1} Y^{-x} Z(Y)dY \right\} dv_0 d\Omega \quad \text{W.m}^{-2}.$$

The radio brightness of the observer's sky is this quantity divided by dv_0 and by $d\Omega$. It is therefore, using the expression (8.408) for Z in a zero-pressure model,

$$b = \frac{n_0 c T_0}{4\pi} P_0 \int_{Y_b}^{1} \frac{Y^{-x+\frac{1}{2}}dY}{\{2\sigma_0 + (q_0 + 1 - 3\sigma_0)Y - (q_0 - \sigma_0)Y^3\}^{1/2}}, \qquad (9.406)$$

where b is in W.m^{-2} (c/s)$^{-1}$ sterad^{-1}. The lower limit Y_b is necessarily greater than zero and therefore the integration does not extend to the observer's horizon which is given by $Y = 0$. The spectral index x is a negative number; thus for all likely models of the universe, the integrand in (9.406) is continuous and finite everywhere in $1 \le Y \le Y_b$. The brightness b of the observer's sky is therefore also finite. The resolution of Olbers' paradox thus depends on the motion of the sources with respect to the observer.

The observed background radiation of the sky at 100 Mcs has a brightness temperature of 500°K. If it is assumed[30] that 35 per cent of this radiation originates outside the halo of our Galaxy, it follows that b in (9.406) is $5 \cdot 2 \times 10^{-22}$ W.m^{-2} (c/s)$^{-1}$ sterad^{-1}. For illustrative purposes, the model A1(i) may be chosen which gives $(1 - x)^{-1}$ for the integral in (9.406) if $Y_b \simeq 0$. With $x = -0 \cdot 8$, $H = 100$ km/sec/mpc and all sources assumed to be normal spiral galaxies, for which P_0 is equal to about 10^{22} W.(c/s)$^{-1}$, it is found that n_0 cannot exceed 3 sources per (mpc)^3. But if all sources are similar to Cygnus A for which $P_0 = 4 \times 10^{28}$ W.(c/s)$^{-1}$, then n_0 is reduced to 10^{-7} sources per (mpc)^3. Alternatively, when every galaxy is regarded as a radio source and the number-density of galaxies is given by (9.214), the foregoing value of b leads to $P_0 = 8\cdot8 \times 10^{23}$ W.(c/s)$^{-1}$, for a distance scale in which $H = 100$ km/sec/mpc. This is about the power output per cycle per second of NGC 5128 at 100 Mc/s.

Additional calculations of this kind are given by McVittie and Wyatt[30] who have also estimated the contribution to the radio brightness to be expected from extremely remote sources whose optical radiation reaches the observer at radio frequencies. At any rate, a measurement of the radio brightness of the sky combined with an estimate of the reciprocal of the Hubble constant provides a value of the product n_0P_0 in each model of the universe; it cannot, of course, give n_0 and P_0 separately.

A second problem of this general type is that of the expected density of photons of some given frequency near the observer due to all sources in the universe. Let us assume that photons of a frequency v_0 in the optical range are in question. The emission of a source in watts will be written

$$dL_e = \beta B(v_e)dv_e,$$

where β is a constant common to all sources and the spectral energy distribution function B is independent of the departure-time and is also the same for all sources. For a nearby source, the total power output in watts in the range v_1 to v_1' of observed frequency is

$$L_0 = \beta \int_{v_1}^{v_1'} B(v)dv = \beta I_0, \qquad (9.407)$$

where I_0 stands, of course, for the definite integral. Thus the power output of a source with appreciable red-shift in the observed bandwidth dv_0 centred on v_0 is

$$dL_e = \frac{L_0}{I_0}B(v_0/Y)\frac{dv_0}{Y}, \qquad (9.408)$$

where $Y = (1 + z)^{-1}$.

Consider again the sources which lie in the whole of Shell r of Fig. 8. By the differential form of (8.713) with $\alpha = 1$, their number is

$$dN = 4\pi n_0 R_0^3 \mathscr{S}_k^2(\omega)d\omega.$$

Thus, if D (cm) is the luminosity-distance of Shell r, the quantity

$$\frac{1}{c}\frac{dNdL_e}{4\pi D^2},$$

is the energy density in joule per cm^3 of the radiation of frequency v_0 in the bandwidth dv_0 at the observer due to all sources in Shell r. This is the density produced by photons of energy $h\nu_0$ where h is Planck's constant. Therefore the number of these photons per cm³ and per unit frequency interval is

$$Q_0 = \frac{1}{c}\left(\frac{dNdL_e}{4\pi D^2}\right)\frac{1}{d\nu_0}\frac{1}{h\nu_0}.$$

Proceeding as in the derivation of (9.406), we find for a zero-pressure model, that

$$Q_0 = \frac{n_0 L_0}{I_0 h\nu_0}T_0\int_0^1 \frac{B(\nu_0/Y)Y^{1/2}dY}{\{2\sigma_0 + (q_0 + 1 - 3\sigma_0)Y - (q_0 - \sigma_0)Y^3\}^{1/2}}. \qquad (9.409)$$

The integration has been pushed to the horizon $Y = 0$ which implies that B is applicable to all frequencies from 0 to ∞. Clearly Q_0 must still be multiplied by some appropriate bandwidth before the density of photons of frequency ν_0 is attained.

The quantity $n_0 L_0$ may be estimated if the sources are identified with galaxies. Let L_0 be the average power output of a galaxy in the optical range and let $\mathscr{M}$ be its mass. The corresponding quantities for the Sun are $L_\odot$ and $\mathscr{M}_\odot$. The mass to light ratio for the galaxy is then

$$\mu = \frac{\mathscr{M}}{\mathscr{M}_\odot}\frac{L_\odot}{L_0}.$$

Hence

$$n_0 L_0 = \frac{n_0 \mathscr{M}}{\mu}\frac{L_\odot}{\mathscr{M}_\odot} = \frac{\rho_0}{\mu}\frac{L_\odot}{\mathscr{M}_\odot}, \qquad (9.410)$$

where $\rho_0 = n_0\mathscr{M}$ is the average density of matter in space.

Numerical computations have been carried out by the author[31] on the assumption that galaxies radiate like black bodies at a temperature of 5000°K and that the range of optical frequencies, ν_1 to ν_1', corresponds to the wavelengths 10,000 Å to 3200 Å. The frequency ν_0 was $2\cdot418 \times 10^{14}$ c/s which is that of 1 electron-volt photons. The results quoted below refer to a distance scale in which $H = 75$ km/sec/mpc and Oort's value $\mu = 21$ was adopted. A model universe in which $q_0 = 1\cdot02$, $\sigma_0 = 0\cdot02$ and $\rho_0 = 4\cdot2 \times 10^{-31}$ gr.cm⁻³ gave

$$Q_0 = 9\cdot38 \times 10^{-18} \quad \text{1-eV. photons cm}^{-3}(\text{c/s})^{-1}. \qquad (9.411)$$

On the other hand, the model with $q_0 = \sigma_0 = 0\cdot79$ and $\rho_0 = 1\cdot67 \times 10^{-29}$ gr.cm⁻³, gave

$$Q_0 = 3\cdot44 \times 10^{-16} \quad \text{1-eV. photons cm}^{-3}(\text{c/s})^{-1}. \qquad (9.412)$$

Thus wide fluctuations in Q_0 are to be anticipated according to the model chosen and to the average density of matter it implies. For a bandwidth equal to 5 per cent of ν_0, the density of 1-eV. photons is $1\cdot1 \times 10^{-4}$ cm⁻³ for (9.411) and $4\cdot2 \times 10^{-3}$ cm⁻³ for (9.412).

Corresponding computations may be carried out for the gamma-ray flux, or for any other form of radiation whose spectral energy distribution is known[31].

9.5. Miscellaneous questions

The models of the universe that have a negative cosmical constant and in which the acceleration factor exceeds the density parameter in value, have ages shorter than T_0 ($\simeq 10 \times 10^9$ years) as may be seen by inspecting Table VI. The ages of the models are therefore shorter than those computed[32] for stars, globular and galactic clusters, the Galaxy, etc. The age of the oldest galactic cluster, NGC 188, is thought to be $11\cdot2 \times 10^9$ years, it having been reduced from a previous estimate of 16×10^9 years. An old globular cluster like M3 is unlikely to be much older than 10×10^9 years. An age of this order of magnitude seems reasonable from the point of view of the internal constitution and nuclear evolution of individual stars, in contrast to the great ages, of up to 24×10^9 years, which were regarded as possible some years ago. The age of the Galaxy is estimated to be $(13\cdot2 \pm 1\cdot0) \times 10^9$ years. Clearly the ages of the models in Table VI, except for the last one, are shorter than these time-intervals deduced from the extrapolated life-times of individual stars or of stellar aggregates. However the ages of model universes represent extrapolations from the motion of expansion observed at present in the universe of galaxies. Thus they give the time-intervals during which conditions similar to those now prevailing can be supposed to have existed in the past. These time-intervals are therefore minimum ages and so may well be shorter than the life-times of individual astronomical objects.

In Chapters 8 and 9, the material content of a model universe has been interpreted as a representative gas, in other words, as an idealized representation of the universe of galaxies. However, an alternative point of view is possible: the gas may be regarded as physically real and as the material out of which the galaxies are to be formed. Their formation depends on the occurrence of irregularities in an initially uniform gas. This type of investigation lies outside the scope of the present volume because observational checks of the theories that have been propounded are clearly unavailable. A considerable literature on the subject[33] does, however, exist to which the interested reader is referred.

In conclusion it is worth examining the statement that the point-source zero-pressure models are 'evolutionary', a description often applied to them. Evolution is legitimately attributed to individual objects in the observed universe. Thus a star may be said to evolve, because, in the course of time its chemical composition alters, or it loses or acquires mass, or its luminosity changes. An interstellar gas cloud may go through a sequence of states that ultimately transform it into a star; and so on. Such developments are comparable to those that have occurred in the forms of animal life on this Earth during the lapse of geological time. But they are connected with the discreteness of astronomical objects in the observed universe, a discreteness which is abolished for the representative gas that fills a model universe. With this idealization, the concept of evolution goes by the board also. In fact, what is meant by an 'evolutionary' model universe is simply one in which the density and pressure of the representative gas vary with the time. That this situation carries with it no implication of evolution is self-evident; it merely implies that, in the observed universe, the mutual distances apart of the galaxies are increasing. The treatment of an evolving universe in general relativity must await the solution of the formidable mathematical problems that arise when the discreteness of astronomical objects is taken into account.

Appendix

The models of the universe whose scale-factor R is expressible as an elementary function of t are listed below. Only models in which the density and pressure are either positive or zero are included. The relevant theory, and the explanation of the notation, will be found in Sec. 8.4. The definition of the ω-coordinate of a source is contained in equations (8.505) to (8.510) and that of the horizon value, ω_m, in (8.514). The dimensionless factor $\mathscr{D}$ which occurs in the expression for the luminosity-distance of a source is defined in (8.615). Throughout the calculations frequent use must be made of (8.405).

Given the specification of the model and the explicit expressions for ω and $\mathscr{D}$ in terms of z, the remaining functions of interest to observational cosmology are calculable either analytically or numerically. Examples of such functions are: the angular diameter of a source (Sec. 8.6); the volume of space (Sec. 8.7); the flux-density of a radio source (Eqns. (8.824) or (8.830)); and the various other functions discussed in Chapters 8 and 9.

CATEGORY A1

Definition of the category: $q_0 = \sigma_0 \geq 0$.

$$Z(z) = (1 + z)\{1 + 2(q_0 + 1)z + (4q_0 + 1)z^2 + 2q_0z^3\}^{-1/2}.$$

A1(i). $q_0 = \sigma_0 = 0$; $\quad k = -1$, $\quad \Lambda = 0$ (Milne's model).

$$R = ct; \, R_i = 0 \text{ at } t_i = 0.$$
$$A = 1.$$
$$\omega = \ln(1 + z), \qquad \omega_m = \infty.$$
$$\mathscr{S}_{-1}(\omega) = \sinh \omega.$$
$$\mathscr{D} = z(1 + \tfrac{1}{2}z).$$

Minimum of a occurs at $z = \infty$ (the horizon) and is $2l/(cT_0)$.

The coordinate transformation

$$\bar{t} = t \cosh \omega, \qquad u = ct \sinh \omega,$$

turns the metric of this model into

$$ds^2 = d\bar{t}^2 - \frac{1}{c^2}(du^2 + u^2d\theta^2 + u^2 \sin^2\theta d\phi^2),$$

which is the metric of the Minkowski space-time expressed in terms of spatial spherical polar coordinates.

221

A1(ii). $q_0 = \sigma_0 < 0.5;$ $\quad k = -1,$ $\quad \Lambda = 0.$

$$R = \frac{cT_0 q_0}{(1 - 2q_0)^{3/2}} (\cosh 2\psi - 1),$$

$$t = \frac{q_0 T_0}{(1 - 2q_0)^{3/2}} (\sinh 2\psi - 2\psi).$$

$R_i = 0$ at $t_i = 0.$

$$A = \frac{q_0}{(1 - 2q_0)^{3/2}} (\sinh 2\psi_0 - 2\psi_0),$$

$$\cosh 2\psi_0 = \frac{1 - q_0}{q_0}.$$

$$\omega = 2 \sinh^{-1}\left(\frac{1 - 2q_0}{2q_0}\right)^{1/2} - 2 \sinh^{-1}\left\{\frac{1 - 2q_0}{2q_0(1 + z)}\right\}^{1/2},$$

$$\omega_m = 2 \sinh^{-1}\left(\frac{1 - 2q_0}{2q_0}\right)^{1/2}.$$

$$\mathscr{S}_{-1}(\omega) = \sinh \omega.$$

$$\mathscr{D} = \frac{1}{q_0^2}[q_0 z + (q_0 - 1)\{(1 + 2q_0 z)^{1/2} - 1\}].$$

For the minimum of a see after A1(iv).

A1(iii). $q_0 = \sigma_0 = 0.5;$ $\quad k = 0, \Lambda = 0$ (Einstein-de Sitter universe).

$$R = (\tfrac{9}{2})^{1/3} C t^{2/3}; \quad R_i = 0 \text{ at } t_i = 0.$$

$$A = \tfrac{2}{3}.$$

$$\omega = \frac{6^{1/3}c}{C} t_0^{1/3}\{1 - (1 + z)^{-1/2}\},$$

$$\omega_m = \frac{6^{1/3}c}{C} t_0^{1/3}.$$

$$\mathscr{S}_0(\omega) = \omega.$$

$$\mathscr{D} = 2\{(1 + z) - (1 + z)^{1/2}\}.$$

For minimum of a see after A1(iv).

A1(iv). $q_0 = \sigma_0 > 0.5;$ $\quad k = +1, \Lambda = 0.$

$$R = \frac{cT_0 q_0}{(2q_0 - 1)^{3/2}} (1 - \cos 2\psi),$$

$$t = \frac{q_0 T_0}{(2q_0 - 1)^{3/2}} (2\psi - \sin 2\psi).$$

$R_i = 0$ at $t_i = 0$

and $R = 0$ again when $t = \dfrac{2\pi q_0 T_0}{(2q_0 - 1)^{3/2}}.$

$$A = \frac{q_0}{(2q_0 - 1)^{3/2}} (2\psi_0 - \sin 2\psi_0),$$

$$\cos 2\psi_0 = \frac{1 - q_0}{q_0}.$$

$$\omega = 2\sin^{-1}\left(\frac{2q_0 - 1}{2q_0}\right)^{1/2} - 2\sin^{-1}\left\{\frac{2q_0 - 1}{2q_0(1 + z)}\right\}^{1/2},$$

$$\omega_m = 2\sin^{-1}\left(\frac{2q_0 - 1}{2q_0}\right)^{1/2}.$$

$$\mathscr{S}_{+1}(\omega) = \sin\omega.$$

$$\mathscr{D} = \frac{1}{q_0^2}[q_0 z + (q_0 - 1)\{(1 + 2q_0 z)^{1/2} - 1\}].$$

The minimum of a in models A1(ii), A1(iii) and A1(iv) occurs at the value of z given by that positive real root of

$$2z^3 + 3(2 - 3q_0)z^2 + 6(q_0 - 1)z - \frac{q_0^2 - 6q_0 + 4}{q_0} = 0,$$

which also satisfies

$$(1 + 2q_0 z)^{1/2}(q_0 z + 2 - 3q_0) = (q_0 - 1)(q_0 - 2 - 3q_0 z),$$

the square root factor being positive. The minimum of a occurs at:

$z = 1 \cdot 5$ for $q_0 = 0 \cdot 30$;

$z = 1 \cdot 25$ for $q_0 = 0 \cdot 5$;
$z = \frac{3}{4}(7 - 3\sqrt{(5)}) + \frac{1}{4}\{30(25 - 11\sqrt{(5)})\}^{1/2} \simeq 1 \cdot 03$ for $q_0 = 3 - \sqrt{(5)} \simeq 0 \cdot 76$;

$z = 1$ for $q_0 = 1$;
$z = \frac{3}{4}(7 + 3\sqrt{(5)}) - \frac{1}{4}\{30(25 + 11\sqrt{(5)})\}^{1/2} \simeq 0 \cdot 64$ for $q_0 = 3 + \sqrt{(5)} \simeq 5 \cdot 24$.

Any value of a, including the minimum, may be calculated from

$$a = \frac{l}{cT_0} \frac{q_0^2(1 + z)^2}{q_0 z + (q_0 - 1)\{(1 + 2q_0 z)^{1/2} - 1\}}.$$

CATEGORY A2

Definition of the category: $\sigma_0 = 0$.

$$Z(z) = (1 + z)\{1 + 2(q_0 + 1)z + (q_0 + 1)z^2\}^{-1/2}.$$

The model A1(i) also belongs to this category.

A2(v). $q_0 > 0$, $\sigma_0 = 0$; $k = -1$, $\Lambda < 0$.

$$R = \frac{cT_0}{(q_0 + 1)^{1/2}}\left[\cos\left\{\frac{q_0^{1/2}(t_0 - t)}{T_0}\right\} - \frac{1}{q_0^{1/2}}\sin\left\{\frac{q_0^{1/2}(t_0 - t)}{T_0}\right\}\right],$$

$R_i = 0$ at $t_i = 0$ and $R = 0$ again at $t = \pi q_0^{-1/2}T_0$.

$$A = \frac{1}{q_0^{1/2}}\tan^{-1}q_0^{1/2}.$$

$$\omega = \cosh^{-1}\left\{\left(\frac{1 + q_0}{q_0}\right)^{1/2}(1 + z)\right\} - \cosh^{-1}\left(\frac{1 + q_0}{q_0}\right)^{1/2},$$

$$\omega_m = \infty.$$

$\mathcal{S}_{-1}(\omega) = \sinh \omega.$

$$\mathcal{D} = \frac{1+z}{q_0}[\{(1 + q_0)(1 + z)^2 - q_0\}^{1/2} - (1 + z)].$$

The minimum of a is $\dfrac{l}{cT_0}\dfrac{q_0}{(1 + q_0)^{1/2} - 1}$ and it occurs at $z = \infty$ (the horizon).

A2(vi). $q_0 < 0$, $\sigma_0 = 0$.

There are three sub-cases. Write $q_0' = -q_0 > 0$.

A2(vi–a). $q_0' > 1$; $k = +1$, $\Lambda > 0$.

$$R = \frac{cT_0}{(q_0' - 1)^{1/2}}\left\{\cosh\left(\frac{q_0'^{1/2}(t_0 - t)}{T_0}\right) - \frac{1}{q_0'^{1/2}}\sinh\left(\frac{q_0'^{1/2}(t_0 - t)}{T_0}\right)\right\}.$$

The minimum of R is $R_i = cT_0/q_0'^{1/2}$; let this occur at $t_i = 0$. Then R tends to infinity as t tends to $-\infty$ and also as t tends to $+\infty$. The maximum of z is $\left(\dfrac{q_0'}{q_0'-1}\right)^{1/2} - 1$ and it occurs for a source with departure-time $t = 0$. The minimum of z is -1 and it occurs for a source with departure-time $t = -\infty$.

$$A = \frac{1}{q_0'^{1/2}}\tanh^{-1}\frac{1}{q_0'^{1/2}} \qquad \text{(for age to minimum of } R\text{)}.$$

$$\omega = \sin^{-1}\left\{\left(\frac{q_0' - 1}{q_0'}\right)^{1/2}(1 + z)\right\} - \sin^{-1}\left(\frac{q_0' - 1}{q_0'}\right)^{1/2}.$$

ω increases up to the value of $\dfrac{\pi}{2} - \sin^{-1}\left(\dfrac{q_0' - 1}{q_0'}\right)^{1/2}$ corresponding to the minimum of R.

$\mathcal{S}_{+1}(\omega) = \sin \omega.$

$$\mathcal{D} = \frac{1+z}{q_0'}[1 + z - \{q_0' - (q_0' - 1)(1 + z)^2\}^{1/2}].$$

The $\mathcal{D}$ of a source with departure-time $t = 0$ is $(q_0' - 1)^{-1}$. The value of a for a source with departure-time $t = 0$ is $lq_0'/(cT_0)$.

A2(vi–b). $q_0' = +1$; $k = 0$, $\Lambda > 0$ (de Sitter universe).

$$R = R_0e^{(t-t_0)/T_0}, \qquad R_i = 0 \text{ at } t_i = -\infty.$$
$$T_0 = (3/\Lambda)^{1/2}.$$
$$A \text{ is infinite.}$$
$$\omega = \frac{cT_0}{R_0}z, \qquad \omega_m = \infty.$$
$$\mathcal{S}_0(\omega) = \omega.$$
$$\mathcal{D} = z(1 + z).$$

The minimum of a is $l/(cT_0)$ and occurs at $z = \infty$ (the horizon).

$$V = \frac{4\pi}{3}(cT_0)^3 z^3,$$

$$\bar{V} = 4\pi(cT_0)^3\left\{\ln(1 + z) - \frac{z(2 + 3z)}{2(1 + z)^2}\right\}.$$

The conditions $k = 0$ and T_0 equal to a constant independent of t_0 are sufficient to determine the metric of this space-time. The properties $\sigma_0 = 0$ and $T_0 = (3/\Lambda)^{1/2}$ of the de Sitter universe are derived from Einstein's gravitational equations. These facts are made use of in the steady-state theory which accepts the metric of the model A2(vi–b) but rejects Einstein's equations. The relations given above, apart from $\sigma_0 = 0$ and $T_0 = (3/\Lambda)^{1/2}$, are also valid in the steady-state theory. In counting sources of radiation the volume $\bar{V}$ is employed.

A2(vi–c). $0 < q_0' < 1$; $k = -1, \Lambda > 0$.

$$R = \frac{cT_0}{(1 - q_0')^{1/2}}\left[\cosh\left\{\frac{q_0'^{1/2}(t_0 - t)}{T_0}\right\} - \frac{1}{q_0'^{1/2}}\sinh\left\{\frac{q_0'^{1/2}(t_0 - t)}{T_0}\right\}\right],$$

$R_t = 0$ at $t_t = 0$.

$$A = \frac{1}{q_0'^{1/2}}\tanh^{-1}q_0'^{1/2}.$$

$$\omega = \sinh^{-1}\left\{\left(\frac{1 - q_0'}{q_0'}\right)^{1/2}(1 + z)\right\} - \sinh^{-1}\left(\frac{1 - q_0'}{q_0'}\right)^{1/2},$$

$\omega_m = \infty$.

$\mathscr{S}_{-1}(\omega) = \sinh \omega$.

$$\mathscr{D} = \frac{1 + z}{q_0'}[1 + z - \{q_0' + (1 - q_0')(1 + z)^2\}^{1/2}].$$

The minimum of a is $\dfrac{l}{cT_0}\dfrac{q_0'}{1 - (1 - q_0')^{1/2}}$ and occurs at $z = \infty$ (the horizon).

CATEGORY A3

Certain models of this category are expressible in terms of elementary functions.

A3(vii). $\zeta = 0$ models with $q_0 \neq \sigma_0, \sigma_0 > 0$.

In such models

$$\sigma_0 = \frac{\eta^3}{2(\eta - 1)(\eta + 2)^2}, \qquad q_0 = \frac{\eta^2 - 2\eta + 4}{2(\eta + 2)(\eta - 1)},$$

$$\frac{\Lambda T_0^2}{3} = -(q_0 - \sigma_0) = -\frac{4}{(\eta - 1)(\eta + 2)^2},$$

$$k\left(\frac{cT_0}{R_0}\right)^2 = -(q_0 + 1 - 3\sigma_0) = -\frac{3\eta^2}{(\eta - 1)(\eta + 2)^2},$$

$$\eta_1 = \eta_2 = \tfrac{1}{2}\eta.$$

There are two sub-cases.

A3(vii–a). $q_0 > \sigma_0 > 0$.

Hence $\eta > 1$, $k = -1$, $\Lambda < 0$.

$$R = cT_0\left(\frac{\eta-1}{3}\right)^{1/2}(\eta+2)\sin^2\psi,$$

$$t_0 - t = T_0\left(\frac{\eta-1}{3}\right)^{1/2}(\eta+2)\{\sqrt{(3)}(\psi_0 - \psi) - \tan^{-1}(\sqrt{(3)}\tan\psi_0)$$
$$+ \tan^{-1}(\sqrt{(3)}\tan\psi)\},$$

$$\sin\psi_0 = \frac{1}{\eta^{1/2}},$$

$R_t = 0$ at $t_t = 0$ and $R = 0$ again at $t = (\eta-1)^{1/2}(\eta+2)\pi T_0$.

$$A = \left(\frac{\eta-1}{3}\right)^{1/2}(\eta+2)\{\sqrt{(3)}\psi_0 - \tan^{-1}(\sqrt{(3)}\tan\psi_0)\}.$$

$$\omega = 2\tan^{-1}\left(\frac{\eta-1+\eta z}{3}\right)^{1/2} - 2\tan^{-1}\left(\frac{\eta-1}{3}\right)^{1/2},$$

$$\omega_m = \pi - 2\tan^{-1}\left(\frac{\eta-1}{3}\right)^{1/2}.$$

$$\mathscr{S}_{-1}(\omega) = \sinh\omega.$$

$$\mathscr{D} = \frac{1}{\eta}\left(\frac{\eta-1}{3}\right)^{1/2}(\eta+2)(1+z)\sinh\omega.$$

A3(vii–b). $q_0 < \sigma_0$, $\sigma_0 > 0$.

Hence $\eta < 0$, $k = +1$, $\Lambda > 0$.

Write $\eta = -\eta'$, $\eta' > 0$. Since σ_0 and q_0 must be finite, $\eta' \neq 2$.

$$R = cT_0\left(\frac{\eta'+1}{3}\right)^{1/2}(\eta'-2)\sinh^2\psi,$$

$$t_0 - t = T_0\left(\frac{\eta'+1}{3}\right)^{1/2}(\eta'-2)\{\tanh^{-1}(\sqrt{(3)}\tanh\psi_0) - \sqrt{(3)}\psi_0$$
$$+ \sqrt{(3)}\psi - \tanh^{-1}(\sqrt{(3)}\tanh\psi)\},$$

$R_t = 0$ at $t_t = 0$,

$$\sinh\psi_0 = \frac{1}{\eta'^{1/2}}.$$

Since $t_0 - t$ is real, $\sqrt{(3)}\tanh\psi_0 \leq 1$ or $\eta' > 2$.

$$A = \left(\frac{\eta'+1}{3}\right)^{1/2}(\eta'-2)\{\tanh^{-1}(\sqrt{(3)}\tanh\psi_0) - \sqrt{(3)}\psi_0\}.$$

$$\omega = \ln\left\{\frac{(\eta'+1)^{1/2}+\sqrt{(3)}}{(\eta'+1)^{1/2}-\sqrt{(3)}}\frac{\{1+\eta'(1+z)\}^{1/2}-\sqrt{(3)}}{\{1+\eta'(1+z)\}^{1/2}+\sqrt{(3)}}\right\},$$

$$\omega_m = \ln\left\{\frac{(\eta'+1)^{1/2}+\sqrt{(3)}}{(\eta'+1)^{1/2}-\sqrt{(3)}}\right\}.$$

$$V = \frac{4\pi}{3}(cT_0)^3 z^3,$$

$$\bar{V} = 4\pi(cT_0)^3 \left\{ \ln(1 + z) - \frac{z(2 + 3z)}{2(1 + z)^2} \right\}.$$

The conditions $k = 0$ and T_0 equal to a constant independent of t_0 are sufficient to determine the metric of this space-time. The properties $\sigma_0 = 0$ and $T_0 = (3/\Lambda)^{1/2}$ of the de Sitter universe are derived from Einstein's gravitational equations. These facts are made use of in the steady-state theory which accepts the metric of the model A2(vi–b) but rejects Einstein's equations. The relations given above, apart from $\sigma_0 = 0$ and $T_0 = (3/\Lambda)^{1/2}$, are also valid in the steady-state theory. In counting sources of radiation the volume $\bar{V}$ is employed.

A2(vi–c). $0 < q_0' < 1; \quad k = -1, \Lambda > 0.$

$$R = \frac{cT_0}{(1 - q_0')^{1/2}} \left[\cosh \left\{ \frac{q_0'^{1/2}(t_0 - t)}{T_0} \right\} - \frac{1}{q_0'^{1/2}} \sinh \left\{ \frac{q_0'^{1/2}(t_0 - t)}{T_0} \right\} \right],$$

$R_t = 0$ at $t_t = 0$.

$$A = \frac{1}{q_0'^{1/2}} \tanh^{-1} q_0'^{1/2}.$$

$$\omega = \sinh^{-1}\left\{ \left(\frac{1 - q_0'}{q_0'}\right)^{1/2} (1 + z) \right\} - \sinh^{-1}\left(\frac{1 - q_0'}{q_0'}\right)^{1/2},$$

$\omega_m = \infty.$

$\mathscr{S}_{-1}(\omega) = \sinh \omega.$

$$\mathscr{D} = \frac{1 + z}{q_0'}[1 + z - \{q_0' + (1 - q_0')(1 + z)^2\}^{1/2}].$$

The minimum of a is $\dfrac{l}{cT_0} \dfrac{q_0'}{1 - (1 - q_0')^{1/2}}$ and occurs at $z = \infty$ (the horizon).

CATEGORY A3

Certain models of this category are expressible in terms of elementary functions.

A3(vii). $\zeta = 0$ models with $q_0 \neq \sigma_0, \sigma_0 > 0.$

In such models

$$\sigma_0 = \frac{\eta^3}{2(\eta - 1)(\eta + 2)^2}, \qquad q_0 = \frac{\eta^2 - 2\eta + 4}{2(\eta + 2)(\eta - 1)},$$

$$\frac{\Lambda T_0^2}{3} = -(q_0 - \sigma_0) = -\frac{4}{(\eta - 1)(\eta + 2)^2},$$

$$k\left(\frac{cT_0}{R_0}\right)^2 = -(q_0 + 1 - 3\sigma_0) = -\frac{3\eta^2}{(\eta - 1)(\eta + 2)^2},$$

$$\eta_1 = \eta_2 = \tfrac{1}{2}\eta.$$

There are two sub-cases.

A3(vii–a). $q_0 > \sigma_0 > 0$.

Hence $\eta > 1$, $k = -1$, $\Lambda < 0$.

$$R = cT_0\left(\frac{\eta - 1}{3}\right)^{1/2}(\eta + 2)\sin^2\psi,$$

$$t_0 - t = T_0\left(\frac{\eta - 1}{3}\right)^{1/2}(\eta + 2)\{\sqrt{(3)}(\psi_0 - \psi) - \tan^{-1}(\sqrt{(3)}\tan\psi_0)$$
$$+ \tan^{-1}(\sqrt{(3)}\tan\psi)\},$$

$$\sin\psi_0 = \frac{1}{\eta^{1/2}},$$

$R_i = 0$ at $t_i = 0$ and $R = 0$ again at $t = (\eta - 1)^{1/2}(\eta + 2)\pi T_0$.

$$A = \left(\frac{\eta - 1}{3}\right)^{1/2}(\eta + 2)\{\sqrt{(3)}\psi_0 - \tan^{-1}(\sqrt{(3)}\tan\psi_0)\}.$$

$$\omega = 2\tan^{-1}\left(\frac{\eta - 1 + \eta z}{3}\right)^{1/2} - 2\tan^{-1}\left(\frac{\eta - 1}{3}\right)^{1/2},$$

$$\omega_m = \pi - 2\tan^{-1}\left(\frac{\eta - 1}{3}\right)^{1/2}.$$

$$\mathscr{S}_{-1}(\omega) = \sinh\omega.$$

$$\mathscr{D} = \frac{1}{\eta}\left(\frac{\eta - 1}{3}\right)^{1/2}(\eta + 2)(1 + z)\sinh\omega.$$

A3(vii–b). $q_0 < \sigma_0$, $\sigma_0 > 0$.

Hence $\eta < 0$, $k = +1$, $\Lambda > 0$.

Write $\eta = -\eta'$, $\eta' > 0$. Since σ_0 and q_0 must be finite, $\eta' \neq 2$.

$$R = cT_0\left(\frac{\eta' + 1}{3}\right)^{1/2}(\eta' - 2)\sinh^2\psi,$$

$$t_0 - t = T_0\left(\frac{\eta' + 1}{3}\right)^{1/2}(\eta' - 2)\{\tanh^{-1}(\sqrt{(3)}\tanh\psi_0) - \sqrt{(3)}\psi_0$$
$$+ \sqrt{(3)}\psi - \tanh^{-1}(\sqrt{(3)}\tanh\psi)\},$$

$R_i = 0$ at $t_i = 0$,

$$\sinh\psi_0 = \frac{1}{\eta'^{1/2}}.$$

Since $t_0 - t$ is real, $\sqrt{(3)}\tanh\psi_0 \leq 1$ or $\eta' > 2$.

$$A = \left(\frac{\eta' + 1}{3}\right)^{1/2}(\eta' - 2)\{\tanh^{-1}(\sqrt{(3)}\tanh\psi_0) - \sqrt{(3)}\psi_0\}.$$

$$\omega = \ln\left\{\frac{(\eta' + 1)^{1/2} + \sqrt{(3)}}{(\eta' + 1)^{1/2} - \sqrt{(3)}}\frac{\{1 + \eta'(1 + z)\}^{1/2} - \sqrt{(3)}}{\{1 + \eta'(1 + z)\}^{1/2} + \sqrt{(3)}}\right\},$$

$$\omega_m = \ln\left\{\frac{(\eta' + 1)^{1/2} + \sqrt{(3)}}{(\eta' + 1)^{1/2} - \sqrt{(3)}}\right\}.$$

$$\mathscr{S}_{+1}(\omega) = \sin \omega.$$

$$\mathscr{D} = \frac{1}{\eta'}\left(\frac{\eta'+1}{3}\right)^{1/2}(\eta'-2)(1+z)\sin\omega.$$

EINSTEIN UNIVERSE

Definition: $R = constant = R_e,\ p = 0.$

Hence $k = +1,\ \Lambda = c^2/R_e^2 > 0.$

The red-shift of every source is zero. The density of the representative gas is

$$\rho_e = \frac{\Lambda}{4\pi G},$$

and its total mass is

$$M_e = \frac{\pi}{2G}\frac{c^3}{\Lambda^{1/2}}.$$

CATEGORY B

The two models B(viii–a) and B(viii–b) are analogues with pressure of the zero-pressure model A1(iii).

B(viii–a). $n = 2,\ k = 0,\ \Lambda = 0.$

Hence $\sigma_0 = \frac{1}{2},\ q_0 = \frac{1}{2}(1 + 3\varepsilon_0).$

$$t_0 - t = \frac{2}{3}(1 + \varepsilon_0)T_0\left\{1 - \left(\frac{R}{R_0}\right)^{3/2} + \frac{3}{2}\frac{\varepsilon_0}{1+\varepsilon_0}\ln\frac{R}{R_0}\right\}.$$

The initial instant $t_i = 0$ is defined as that instant at which the density and pressure are infinite. At this instant, $R = R_i$, where by (8.421) and (8.422),

$$R_i = \frac{\varepsilon_0{}^{2/3}}{(1+\varepsilon_0)^{2/3}}R_0.$$

The introduction of the pressure has thus removed the initial condition $R_i = 0$ of model A1(iii). The age factor A is now defined as the lapse of time from $R = R_i$ to $R = R_0$. It is

$$A = \frac{2}{3}\left\{1 + \varepsilon_0\ln\frac{\varepsilon_0}{1+\varepsilon_0}\right\}.$$

If ε_0 is small, say $\varepsilon_0 = e^{-y},\ (y \geq 11)$, then

$$A \simeq \frac{2}{3}(1 - ye^{-y}) < \frac{2}{3}.$$

The introduction of a pressure has reduced the age of the model as compared with that of model A1(iii).

B(viii–b). $n = 3$, $k = 0$, $\Lambda = 0$.

Hence $\sigma_0 = \frac{1}{2}$, $q_0 = \frac{1}{2}(1 + 3\varepsilon_0)$.

$$R = \frac{\varepsilon_0}{1 + \varepsilon_0} R_0 \cosh^2 \psi,$$

$$t_0 - t = \frac{\varepsilon_0^{3/2}}{6} T_0 \{\sinh 3\psi_0 - \sinh 3\psi - 15 (\sinh \psi_0 - \sinh \psi)$$
$$+ 24(\tan^{-1} e^{\psi_0} - \tan^{-1} e^{\psi})\},$$

$$\cosh \psi_0 = \left(1 + \frac{1}{\varepsilon_0}\right)^{1/2}.$$

The initial instant $t_i = 0$ is defined as that instant at which the density and pressure are infinite. The initial value of R deduced from (8.421) and (8.422) is

$$R_i = \frac{\varepsilon_0}{1 + \varepsilon_0} R_0.$$

The age factor for the lapse of time from $R = R_i$ to $R = R_0$ is

$$A = \frac{\varepsilon_0^{3/2}}{6} (\sinh 3\psi_0 - 15 \sinh \psi_0 + 24 \tan^{-1} e^{\psi_0}).$$

If ε_0 is small compared with unity $e^{\psi_0} \simeq 2\varepsilon_0^{-1/2}$ and

$$A \simeq \frac{2}{3}\left(1 - \frac{15}{4}\varepsilon_0\right) < \frac{2}{3}.$$

References and Notes

The following bibliography does not claim to be exhaustive but is intended as a guide to readers who would like additional information on points raised in the text. An historical account of relativity theory and its precursors will be found in Sir Edmund T. Whittaker's *History of the Theories of the Aether and Electricity* (1954; New York: Philosophical Library), particularly in Chapters 2 and 5 of Volume II, where copious references are also given. Extensive treatments of relativity will be found in the treatises listed below under Refs. 2 and 4 of Chapter 1 and Ref. 2 of Chapter 3.

CHAPTER 1

1. EINSTEIN, A. 1905 *Ann. Phys.*, **17**, 891.
   EINSTEIN, A. 1916 *Ann. Phys.*, **49**, 769.
2. Some examples of theories of this type will be found in:
   WEYL, H. 1918 *Space-Time-Matter*. New York: Dover Publications, Inc. (1951 printing). §§ 35–36.
   EDDINGTON, A. S. 1924 *Mathematical Theory of Relativity*. Cambridge: University Press. Chap. VII.
   BERGMAN, P. G. 1942 *Introduction to Relativity*. New York: Prentice-Hall. Chap. XVII.
   EINSTEIN, A. 1950 *The Meaning of Relativity*. Princeton: University Press. App. II.
3. DINGLE, H. 1937 *Through Science to Philosophy*. Oxford: Clarendon Press.
4. TOLMAN, R. C. 1934 *Relativity, Thermodynamics and Cosmology*. Oxford: University Press. § 8.1.
5. JEFFREYS, H. 1941 *Phil. Mag.*, **32**, 177.
6. MILNE, E. A. 1935 *Relativity, Gravitation and World-Structure*. Oxford: University Press; and 1948 *Kinematic Relativity*. Oxford: University Press.
   BONDI, H. 1960 *Cosmology*. Cambridge: University Press.
   JORDAN, P. 1952 *Schwerkraft und Weltall*. Braunschweig: Fr. Vieweg und Sohn.

CHAPTER 2

1. For more detailed treatments, consult:
   SYNGE, J. L., and SCHILD, A. 1949 *Tensor Calculus*. Toronto: University Press.
   EISENHART, L. P. 1949 *Riemannian Geometry*. Princeton: University Press.
2. SYNGE, J. L., and SCHILD, A., *loc. cit.* § 3.1.

3. The usual notation for R^2_{λ} is R; it has been modified to prevent confusion with the R of Chaps. 8 and 9.
4. SYNGE, J. L., and SCHILD, A., *loc. cit.* § 3.4.
5. The reduction of one form of the metric to another and the consequent equivalence of geometries, referred to in Sec. 2, depend on the Riemann-Christoffel tensor. See Eisenhart, L. P., *loc cit.* § 10.

CHAPTER 3

1. A different solution of the indeterminacy problem is given in:
ECKART, C. 1940 *Phys. Rev.*, **58**, 919.
TAUB, A. H. 1948 *Phys. Rev.*, **74**, 328.
An alternative interpretation of the proper-density defined in Sec. 3.8 is also proposed.
2. For more detailed treatments consult:
DINGLE, H. 1940 *The Special Theory of Relativity*. London: Methuen & Co. New York: John Wiley & Sons.
McCREA, W. H. 1949 *Relativity Physics*. London: Methuen & Co.
MØLLER, C. 1952 *The Theory of Relativity*. Oxford: Clarendon Press.
3. The question of rotation and of the motion of a system of particles or of a rigid body are the subjects of the papers listed below:
VAN STOCKUM, W. J. 1937 *Proc. Roy. Soc. Edinb.*, **57**, 135, and 1938 *Proc. R. Irish Acad.*, **44**, 109.
CLARK, G. L. 1947–49 *Proc. Roy. Soc. Edinb.*, **62**, 412 and 434.
HOGARTH, J. E., and McCREA, W. H. 1952 *Proc. Camb. Phil. Soc.*, **48**, 616.
SALZMAN, G., and TAUB, A. H. 1954 *Phys. Rev.*, **95**, 1659.
4. McCREA, W. H. 1951 *Proc. Roy. Soc. A*, **206**, 562.
McVITTIE, G. C. 1952 *Proc. Roy. Soc. A*, **211**, 295.

CHAPTER 4

1. PAPAPETROU, A. 1951 *Proc. Roy. Soc. A*, **209**, 248, and 1951 *Proc. Phys. Soc. Lond.*, **64**, 57. The references given in these papers should also be consulted.
2. DINGLE, H. 1933 *Proc. Nat. Acad. Sci. Wash.*, **19**, 559.
3. TAUB, A. H. 1951 *Ann. Math. Princeton*, **53**, 472.
4. KUSTAANHEIMO, P. 1953 *Proc. Edinb. Math. Soc.*, Ser. 2, **9**, 17.
5. The general case, in which orthogonality is dispensed with, is considered by VAN STOCKUM, W. J. 1937 *Proc. Roy. Soc. Edinb.*, **57**, 135.
6. OZSVÁTH, I., and SCHÜCKING, E. 1962 *Recent Developments in General Relativity*. London: Pergamon Press. p. 339.

CHAPTER 5

1. DARWIN, C. G. 1958 *Proc. Roy. Soc. A*, **249**, 180.
2. CLEMENCE, G. M. 1947 *Rev. Mod. Phys.*, **19**, 361 and 1949 *Proc. Am. Phil. Soc.*, **93**, 532.
3. DUNCOMBE, R. L. 1956 *Astron. J.*, **61**, 174.

4. Table II adopts the lay-out used by OVENDEN, M. W. 1952 *Sci. Progr.*, **40**, 645, and the individual references are as follows:
   a. 1919 *Phil. Trans. A*, **220**, 291.—*b.* 1924 *Pub. Dom. Astrophys. Obs.*, **2**, 275.—*c.* 1923 *Lick Obs. Bull.*, **11**, 41, and 1928, **13**, 130.—*d.* 1924 *Mon. Not. R. Astr. Soc.*, **84**, 150.—*e.* 1931 *Abh. Preuss. Akad. Berlin*, No. 1, and 1933 *Lembang Ann.*, **5**, II.—*f.* 1940 *C.R. Acad. Sci. U.R.S.S.*, **29**, 189, and 1941 *Phys. Ber.*, **22**, 934.—*g.* 1940 *Jap. J. Astr. Geo.*, **18**, 51.—*h.* 1950 *Astron. J.*, **55**, 49.—*i.* 1953 *Astron. J.*, **58**, 87.—*j.* 1932 *J. Phys. Radium, Ser.* 7, **3**, 281.—*k.* 1923 *Phys. Z.*, **24**, 476.—*l.* 1932 *Z. Astrophys.*, **4**, 221.—*m.* 1931 *Observatory*, **54**, 292.—*n.* 1932 *Z. Astrophys.*, **4**, 208.

5. MITCHELL, S. A. 1951 *Eclipses of the Sun*. New York: Columbia Univ. Press. Chap. XVIII.

6. McVITTIE, G. C. 1932 *Mon. Not. R. Astr. Soc.*, **92**, 868.

7. MØLLER, G. 1952 *The Theory of Relativity*. Oxford: Clarendon Press. pp. 247 and 346–47.

8. HECKMANN, O. 1942 *Theorien der Kosmologie*. Berlin: Springer-Verlag. § 16.

9. WHITROW, G. J. 1961 *The Natural Philosophy of Time*. London and Edinburgh: Nelson. p. 212.

10. POUND, R. V., and REBKA, G. A. 1960 *Phys. Rev. Letters*, **4**, 337.

11. ADAM, M. G. 1958 *Mon. Not. R. Astr. Soc.*, **118**, 106. 1959 *Mon. Not. R. Astr. Soc.*, **119**, 460.
    HIGGS, L. A. 1962 *Mon. Not. R. Astr. Soc.*, **124**, 51.

12. BLAMONT, J. E., and RODDIER, F. 1961 *Phys. Rev. Letters*, **7**, 437.

13. POPPER, D. M. 1954 *Astrophys. J.*, **120**, 316.

14. FINDLAY-FREUNDLICH, E. 1954 *Phil. Mag.*, **45**, 303.

CHAPTER 6

1. BLANKFIELD, J., and McVITTIE, G. C. 1959 *Arch. Rat. Mechs. and Anal.*, **2**, 337.

2. The contents of Sec. 6.5 follow SCHLÜTER, A. 1955 *Astron. J.*, **60**, 141.

3. There is a considerable literature on the subject of gravitational waves. An introduction to the subject is WEBBER, J. 1961 *General Relativity and Gravitational Waves*. New York: Interscience. Investigations of particular topics will be found in the following papers, which also contain many references: TAKENO, H. 1959 *Tensor*, **11**, 23; SACHS, R. 1961 *Proc. Roy. Soc. A*, **264**, 309; BONDI, H., VAN DER BURG, M. G. J., and METZNER, A. W. K. 1962 *Proc. Roy. Soc. A*, **269**, 21.

CHAPTER 7

1. BURGERS, J. M. 1946 *Proc. Acad. Sci. Amst.*, **49**, 2.
   McVITTIE, G. C. 1950 *Mon. Not. R. Astr. Soc.*, **110**, 224.

2. McVITTIE, G. C. 1954 *Astrophys. J.*, **119**, 352.

3. See also McVITTIE, G. C. 1953 *Proc. Roy. Soc. A*, **220**, 339.

4. CHAPMAN, S., and COWLING, T. G. 1953 *The Mathematical Theory of Nonuniform Gases*. Cambridge: University Press. Chap. 11.

5. There is therefore no preferred direction for the gravitational force in the gas taken as a whole, any more than there is for the velocity. This point is overlooked by LAYZER, D. 1954 *Astron. J.*, **59**, 268, who argues in effect that the equations (7.402) and (7.403) are not deducible from Newtonian gravitational theory. It appears to be undoubtedly true, however, that they follow from Newtonian gravitational theory combined with Newtonian hydrodynamics as originally argued by MILNE, E. A., and McCREA, W. H. 1934 *Quart. J. Math.*, **5**, 73.

CHAPTER 8

1. For a general account of galaxies see PAYNE-GAPOSCHKIN, C. 1954 *Introduction to Astronomy*. New York: Prentice-Hall, Inc. Chaps. XVI and XVII. The clustering effect is described by SHANE, C. D., and WIRTANEN, C. A. 1954 *Astron. J.*, **59**, 285.

The following theoretical papers bear on the subject matter of Chap. 8:

DAVIDSON, W. 1959 *Mon. Not. R. Astr. Soc.*, **119**, 665. 1960 *ibid.*, **120**, 271. 1962 *ibid.*, **124**, 79.

LAMLA, E. 1959–60 *Astron. Nach.*, **285**, 49.

MATTIG, W. 1959–60 *Astron. Nach.*. **285**, 1.

McCREA, W. H. 1934–35 *Z. Astrophys.*, **9**, 290.

METZNER, A. W. K., and MORRISON, P. 1959 *Mon. Not. R. Astr. Soc.*, **119**, 657.

MAST, C. B., and STRATHDEE, J. 1959 *Proc. Roy. Soc. A*, **252**, 476.

ROBERTSON, H. P. 1933 *Rev. Mod. Phys.*, **5**, 62.

SANDAGE, A. 1962 *Astrophys. J.*, **136**, 319.

VAN DER BORGHT, R. 1961 *Aust. J. Phys.*, **14**, 295.

2. RUSSELL-DUGAN-STEWART. 1938 *Astronomy*. New York: Ginn & Co. Vol. II, § 689 and § 716.

3. McVITTIE, G. C. 1959 *Encycl. Physics*. Berlin: Springer, **59**, 445.

4. PAGE, T., DAHN, C. C., and MORRISON, E. F. 1961 *Astron. J.*, **66**, 614.

5. See ROBERTSON, H. P. 1929 *Proc. Nat. Acad. Sci. Wash.*, **15**, 822, and references there given.

6. JEFFREYS, H. and B. S. 1946 *Methods of Mathematical Physics*. Cambridge: University Press. Chap. 25.

7. McVITTIE, G. C. 1963 *H. P. Robertson: In Memoriam*. Philadelphia: Soc. Ind. and Appl. Math. p. 18.

8. RINDLER, W. 1956 *Mon. Not. R. Astr. Soc.*, **116**, 662.

9. CONWAY, R. G., KELLERMANN, K. I., and LONG, R. J. 1963 *Mon. Not. R. Astr. Soc.*, **125**, 261.

KELLERMANN, K. I. 1963 *Astron. J.*, **68**, 539.

10. BROWN, R. HANBURY, and HAZARD, C. 1952 *Phil. Mag.*, **43**, 137.

11. See KALITZIN, N. ST., 1961 *Mon. Not. R. Astr. Soc.*, **122**, 41; also JUST, K., and KRAUS, K. 1962 *Z. Astrophys.* **55**, 127, for lists of references.

12. McVITTIE, G. C. 1933 *Mon. Not. R. Astr. Soc.*, **93**, 325.

13. The method is adapted from McVITTIE, G. C. 1931 *Mon. Not. R. Astr. Soc.*, **91**, 274.

14. EISENHART, L. P. 1949 *Riemannian Geometry*. Princeton: University Press. § 14.
15. HADAMARD, J. 1923 *Lectures on Cauchy's Problem in Linear Partial Differential Equations*. Yale: University Press. pp. 75 *et seq*.
16. WHITTAKER, J. M. 1928 *Proc. Camb. Phil. Soc.*, **24**, 414.

CHAPTER 9

1. OMER, G. C. 1949 *Astrophys. J.*, **109**, 164.
2. DE SITTER, W. 1930 *Bull. Astr. Insts. Netherlds.*, **5**, 211.
   McVITTIE, G. C. 1961 *Fact and Theory in Cosmology*. London: Eyre and Spottiswoode. p. 144.
3. HUMASON, M. L., MAYALL, N. U., and SANDAGE, A. 1956 *Astron. J.*, **61**, 97.
4. DE SITTER, W. 1934 *Bull. Astr. Insts. Netherlds.*, **7**, 210.
5. WHITFORD, A. E. 1956 *Astron. J.*, **61**, 352.
6. The graph was similar to that published by W. A. BAUM on p. 397 of 1962 *Problems of Extra-galactic Research*. Ed. G. C. McVITTIE. New York: Macmillan.
7. SANDAGE, A. 1961 *Astrophys. J.*, **134**, 916.
8. SCHMIDT, M. 1962 *Problems of Extra-galactic Research*. Ed. G. C. McVITTIE. New York: Macmillan. p. 170.—OKE, J. B. *ibid.*, p. 34.
9. SCOTT, E. L. 1957 *Astron. J.*, **62**, 248. NEYMAN, J., and SCOTT, E. L. 1959 *Encycl. Physics*. Berlin: Springer, **53**, 416.
10. PANNEKOEK, A., and VAN DIEM, E. 1937 *Bull. Astr. Insts. Netherlds.*, **8**, 297.
11. SANDAGE, A. 1962 *Problems of Extra-galactic Research*. Ed. G. C. McVITTIE. New York: Macmillan. p. 359.
12. MALTBY, P., MATTHEWS, T.A., and MOFFET, A. T. 1963 *Astrophys. J.*, **137**, 153.
13. HOLMBERG, E. 1958 *Medd. Lund Obs. Ser. II, No. 136*. Eqn. (12).
14. Ref. 4, Chap. 8 above.
15. OORT, J. H. 1958 *La Structure et l'Evolution de l'Univers*. Brussels: Stoops. p. 163.
16. KIANG, T. 1961 *Mon. Not. R. Astr. Soc.*, **122**, 263.
17. WESTERHOUT, G. 1962 *Problems of Extra-galactic Research*. Ed. G. C. McVITTIE. New York: Macmillan. p. 170.
18. BONDI, H. 1960 *Cosmology*. Cambridge: University Press. 2nd Ed. pp. 45–47.
19. 1963 *Radio Astronomy Today*. Eds. PALMER, H. P., DAVIES, D. R., and LARGE, M. I. Manchester: University Press. p. 230. Also private correspondence with Dr. D. R. Davies.
20. SANDAGE, A. 1961 *Astrophys. J.*, **133**, 355.
21. MILLS, B. Y., SLEE, O. B., and HILL, E. R. 1958 *Aust. J. Phys.*, **11**, 360. 1960 *ibid.*, **13**, 676.
    SCOTT, P. F., and RYLE, M. 1961 *Mon. Not. R. Astr. Soc.*, **122**, 389.
    BENNETT, A. S. 1962 *Mon. Not. R. Astr. Soc.*, **125**, 75.
22. Ref. 9, Chap. 8 above.
23. McVITTIE, G. C., and ROEDER, R. C. 1963 *Astrophys. J.*, **138**, 899.

24. HOYLE, F., and NARLIKAR, J. V. 1961 *Mon. Not. R. Astr. Soc.*, **123,** 133. 1962 *ibid.*, **125,** 13.
25. RYLE, M. 1958 *Proc. Roy. Soc. A*, **248,** 289.
26. RYLE, M., and CLARKE, R. W. 1961 *Mon. Not. R. Astr. Soc.*, **122,** 349.
27. HUBBLE, E. P. 1930 *Astrophys. J.*, **71,** 231.
28. ALLEN, L. R., BROWN, HANBURY R., and PALMER, H. P. 1962 *Mon. Not. R. Astr. Soc.*, **125,** 57.
29. CLARKE, R. W. 1962 *Nature*, **194,** 171.
30. McVITTIE, G. C., and WYATT, S. P. 1959 *Astrophys. J.*, **130,** 1.
31. McVITTIE, G. C. 1962 *Phys. Rev.*, **128,** 2871.
32. WOOLF, N. J. 1962 *Astron. J.*, **67,** 286.
    SCHMIDT-KALER, TH. 1961 *Observatory*, **81,** 226.
33. See, for example, BONNER, W. B. 1957 *Ann. Inst. H. Poincare*, **15,** 133. VAN ALBADA, G.B. 1960 *Bull. Astr. Insts. Netherlds.*, **15,** 165. LAYZER, D. 1962 *Astrophys. J.*, **136,** 138.

Index